001.422
W179e

D1180153

CHRISTIAN
HERITAGE
COLLEGE
LIBRARY

PRESENTED BY

Andrew L. Wade

STATISTICAL METHODS

I like to think of the constant presence in any sound Republic of two guardian angels: the Statistician and the Historian of Science. The Statistician keeps his finger on the pulse of Humanity, and gives the necessary warning when things are not as they should be. The Historian . . . will not allow Humanity to forget its noblest traditions or to be ungrateful to its greatest benefactors. If the Statistician is like a physician, the Historian is like a priest—the guardian of man's most precious heritage. . . . Humanity must be protected by the watchful Statistician, and it must be sustained in its newer and bolder efforts by the consciousness of every antecedent effort, to which it owes its culture, its dignity, and its excellence.   George Sarton

The struggle for life compels us to consult the oracles. But the modern oracles must be scientific.   Thiele

Elementary
Statistical
Methods

HELEN M. WALKER
PROFESSOR OF EDUCATION, TEACHERS
COLLEGE, COLUMBIA UNIVERSITY

43-8152

New York
HENRY HOLT
AND COMPANY

CIPW

COPYRIGHT, 1943

BY

HENRY HOLT AND COMPANY, INC.

September, 1948

PRINTED IN THE UNITED STATES OF AMERICA

PREFACE

The general purposes and methods of the text and the most efficient ways of using it are discussed in the short introductory chapter. The standards set for the book are: (1) complete clarity for the beginner and such simplicity of exposition as will make the text practically self-teaching, (2) more than ordinary attention to the development of underlying concepts and to interpretation, (3) such harmony with recent developments in the mathematical theory of statistics as will insure a satisfactory foundation for more advanced study, (4) the presentation of a fundamental core of introductory material which can be covered by an average class in one semester, and (5) the inclusion of other material to serve as reference and as invitation to further study.

Writing this book has not been a matter of months, but of years, during which time a continuing conscious effort has been made to discover the nature and causes of student difficulties. Probing students' thinking has led to the conviction that (1) certain common deficiencies in their background exist and make trouble, (2) certain erroneous concepts are too widespread to be disregarded. This conviction caused me to write for my own students expositions of a number of matters usually not treated in statistics texts (see, for example, Chapter VI and sections on pages 106, 122, and 217), and to devise developmental exercises in which the student would be required to assume an active role in the discovery of ideas and relationships (see, for example, Exercise 23, page 214). Such material proved so valuable an aid to the students' understanding of the rest of the text that it has been retained in the published form. While such material increases the bulk of this text, it does not increase—on the contrary, it appears to decrease—the time needed for studying the text.

For nearly a decade the mimeographed notes used by my classes have been undergoing a continual process of revision. In 1939, with the help of Dr. B. A. Liu, these notes were completely rewritten and bound together in a multilithed edition, which was used as a class text by myself and by three colleagues. Utilizing the suggestions which came from students and teachers, I rewrote certain sections of the material and put out a new multilithed edition in 1941, from which I have since taught three classes. The students in these classes have been active collaborators, suggesting numerous small changes in wording by which clarity might be improved. Throughout the academic year of 1941–42,

45201

Miss Emma Spaney was studying with me various methods of instruction in elementary statistics, and met regularly with groups of students in two classes, analyzing their questions and difficulties. On the basis of her notes and my own, I once more revised the entire book, making changes where such seemed indicated, and Miss Spaney read this final version. Dr. Liu and Miss Spaney read proof and worked through the numerical material after it was set up in proof.

Certain special features which the student needs to know are discussed in the introductory chapter. The points to be mentioned now relate more particularly to the teacher's use of the text.

Treatment of Symbolism. Symbolism is the language in which statistical laws can be expressed most economically and with the least ambiguity. To pretend that this is not so and to rely almost entirely on words for the expression of statistical relations does not really simplify the presentation; it only appears to simplify, and betrays the student because what looks simple turns out to be obscure.

I have found that a relatively small amount of time and energy applied directly to learning to use symbolic language makes all the rest of the course clearer and easier. The explanation of the rules for the use of symbolic language and exercises for translating symbols into words and words into symbols in Chapter VI are one of the unusual features of this text. After studying this chapter, even the student who has a strong initial prejudice against mathematical symbolism usually finds himself reading and writing formulas without strain.

Experience convinces me that the difficulties of symbolism for the beginner are like the nettle—painful when touched gingerly and harmless when grasped boldly. While some of the pages in this text may at first sight look alarming to the non-mathematical student, the care which is here devoted to helping the student translate the symbols into words and understand their meaning soon gives that student mastery over a device that is valuable not only in the study of this text but also in reading periodicals which carry statistical articles.

The variety of symbols used in different texts is another source of difficulty for the beginner. A glossary of symbols has been placed in Appendix E in response to the oft-expressed wish of students that an author would indicate whether he is using a standard symbol, a symbol of his own invention which he intends to use throughout the text with the same meaning, or a more or less casual, *ad hoc* symbol employed for convenience in a particular connection and not used again. This glossary not only presents a systematic listing of the symbols employed in this text, but also shows their relationship to some of the other common symbols which the student may encounter in other books and technical papers.

Nature of Exercises Provided. The exercises in this text are intended to serve two distinct purposes. Some are the usual type of practice exercise, presenting applications of the methods under discussion. Exercises of this kind can be readily supplied by any teacher. Real data providing applications of procedures are easily obtained. Therefore, only a minimum number of such exercises has been given here.

A second type of exercise is designed to clarify meanings, to encourage the student in an active search for relationships, to stimulate his abstract imagination in respect to statistical ideas. Such exercises have been marked with an asterisk, to warn student and teacher that these should not be omitted, even for a minimum course. These starred exercises constitute one of the most helpful features of the book, because developmental exercises of this type cannot be quickly constructed, as can exercises of a drill nature.

Because each of these developmental exercises is timed to come at a particular stage in the expository treatment, it seems desirable to place them in the text itself and not in a separate manual. The use of a separate manual has advantages and disadvantages, and one of the latter is that too many students do not use text and manual together in the way the author intended. When the exercises are in the text itself, they are less easily disregarded.

Historical notes have been introduced not for their own sake, but to illuminate the meaning of some idea or procedure.

Preparation for Study of Statistical Inference. The traditional custom of treating in one chapter of an elementary text the normal curve and the standard error of a difference has serious disadvantages. If the student is able to understand the chapter, he is likely to be left with several erroneous notions which he must later discard when he studies a more adequate treatment. The student usually finds this chapter excessively difficult because he is asked to consider the final step in a logical process without sufficient help on the intermediate phases. He needs to build up the concept of a sampling distribution, he needs to visualize the standard deviation of that distribution, and he needs to become familiar with the relationship between abscissa, proportion of area in a given segment of the curve, and proportion of samples having a statistic within a specified size range. Developing these ideas requires time. In this text the chapter on the normal curve contains no applications to tests of significance, but merely a statement that the most important applications are to problems of sampling, plus a forward reference to Chapter XV. Scattered throughout the text are paragraphs inviting the student's attention to the idea of the fluctuation of a statistic from sample to sample, but giving him no procedures, no formulas. The concluding chapter, XV, gives a general introduction to problems of sampling, with far more than ordinary emphasis upon methods of selecting samples, and far more than ordinary attention to the underlying concept of the sampling distribution. This chapter may be considered as a bridge between descriptive statistics and statistical inference.

Flexibility. For a very short course, Chapters IV, X, and XV may be omitted without affecting the understanding of the rest of the text. For a richer course, these chapters may be included and the mathematical notes in Appendix B and the supplementary procedures in Appendix C studied. Footnotes and special bibliographies at the ends of certain chapters suggest other material valuable to the student able to pursue the subject more thoroughly.

Reference Material. The reference features of this text have been segregated so that they will not interfere with the teaching function of other sections. These reference features include a glossary of symbols, list of formulas, mathematical notes, and supplementary procedures in the appendix and bibliographies on special topics at the ends of chapters.

H. M. W.

February 1, 1943

ACKNOWLEDGMENTS

A teacher owes more to his students than to anyone else. Those who have helped me by an enlightening question revealing the ambiguity in material which I had fondly hoped was crystal clear, those who have offered stimulating and candid comment on the exposition of some particular point, those who have exerted a persistent pressure for the publication of my class notes, are too numerous to acknowledge by name, but a warm sense of gratitude to them is in my mind.

Next to his students, a teacher is chiefly indebted to his own teachers. To Henry Alford Ruger, my first teacher of statistics, friend, mentor, and colleague over many years, I owe a stimulation and a profound dissatisfaction with results achieved which only those who also have studied with him can appreciate. More recently, and for shorter periods, I have enjoyed the privilege of attending the classes of R. A. Fisher, Harold Hotelling, Jerzy Neyman, Egon Pearson, and Abraham Wald, and am debtor to each for some measure of additional insight into the meaning of statistical theory and method.

From a succession of able assistants I have received much help in the clarification of the mimeographed notes which my classes have studied. Singly and sometimes in groups, in conversation and in correspondence, they have berated me for failing to publish these. Among recent assistants, Mr. Sherman Tinkelman, Dr. Bangnee A. Liu, and Miss Emma Spaney deserve special thanks. Dr. Liu and Miss Spaney helped with the preparation of this manuscript and read proof. Three other teachers, Prof. Irving Lorge and Prof. Robert Thorndike of Teachers College, and Prof. C. C. Ross of the University of Kentucky, used the text in its first multilithed form and made valuable suggestions for changes and additions.

H. M. W.

CONTENTS

xi

CONTENTS xvii

TABLES

CHARTS AND DIAGRAMS

CHAPTER I

ORIENTATION *

A science of the individual is a contradiction in terms.

Schopenhauer

The object of statistical knowledge is not the single event and not the invariant law, but is the relatively uniform behavior of some aggregate constitution, belonging to an aggregate of things and events, and the probability that this average behavior will remain, within limits, approximately, although always imperfectly, uniform.   Josiah Royce

The Nature of Statistical Thinking. Statistical method is one of the devices by which men try to understand the generality of life. Out of the welter of single events, human beings seek endlessly for general trends; out of the vast and confusing variety of individual characters, they continually search for underlying group characters, for some picture of the group to which the individual belongs. This group picture is not merely a summary of the individuals which form the group. It transcends the individuals. It has meaning of its own not to be discovered through the most intense contemplation of any single individual. Such group trends are sometimes apprehended subjectively and almost intuitively by a person of penetrating insight, who observes, without the aid of numerical computations, that "this group is more variable than that" or "these two characteristics are not likely to occur in the same individual," or the like. Such statements are fundamentally statistical in nature, because they relate to tendencies which are true of a group as a whole but which either have no meaning with reference to a single individual, or may not be true of a particular selected individual. That these statements are vague, subjective, debatable, quite possibly false, and inefficiently arrived at does not keep them from being statistical in nature.

Controlled, objective methods by which group trends are abstracted from observations on many separate individuals are called *statistical methods*. If his conclusions are to be objective and verifiable and his procedures efficient, the statistician has no choice but to use numerical methods. As Adolphe Quetelet once observed in the first lecture of a

---

* This chapter is addressed in part to teachers and in part to students. The students in this case being adults, no very clear distinction need be made. The entire chapter had best be read by both.

1

course on the history of science, "The more advanced the sciences have become, the more they have tended to enter the domain of mathematics, which is a sort of center toward which they converge. We can judge of the perfection to which a science has come by the facility, more or less great, with which it may be approached by calculation." *

The nature of statistical thinking can be clarified more satisfactorily by experience with statistical material than by verbal definition; however, a contrast originally suggested by the British physicist, James Clerke Maxwell, and later elaborated by the American philosopher, Josiah Royce, provides help for the beginner. Search for knowledge of the world leads to three kinds of thinking which they called the historical, the mechanical, and the statistical. "Historical thinking" deals with a single event, its causes and its consequences, or with a series of events in the order of their occurrence; "statistical thinking" deals with a *set* of similar events or observations, and its conclusions apply to the set as a whole rather than to individual members of that set. "Statistical thinking" deals not with individual, but with mass phenomena. In this terminology, the case study would be "historical" in nature, and is properly contrasted with the statistical study, whose conclusions apply to the group as a whole, and not necessarily to some selected member of that group. In "mechanical thinking," the conclusions follow inexorably from the premises, and apply universally whenever the premises hold. In "statistical thinking," on the other hand, conclusions are not inescapable, but only probable; when the premises hold, the conclusions are *usually* true, but not *always*, or *necessarily*, true. The essential characteristic of a statistical study is therefore not that it employs numerical computation—though that is inevitable in any large study—but that it deals with a *group*. In this terminology, formal logic and most pure mathematics would be classed as "mechanical." Probably many persons would think of the physical sciences as coming in the same category, because the precision of observation is great and the conclusions highly dependable. However, Maxwell held that molecular physics is essentially statistical in nature, and most modern scientists are vividly aware of the element of uncertainty in their generalizations and predictions.

Statistical Method and Statistical Theory. Statistical method might conceivably have an intuitive base, as, in fact, was the case for certain formulas once popular and now obsolete. In order, however, that the meaning of a particular measure shall be clear and unequivocal, it must be part of a logical structure, and formulas which cannot be related to

* Quoted by Mailly on p. 159 of "Essai sur la vie et les ouvrages de Quetelet," *Annuaire de L'Académie Royale des Sciences, des Lettres et des Beaux-Arts de Belgique*, 41 (Brussels, 1875).

such a logical structure are of little value and soon disappear from use. This underlying logical pattern is the mathematical theory of statistics. It is distinct from statistical method inasmuch as it could be studied as a branch of pure mathematics without any recourse to concrete data, but it is a kind of mathematical model so organized that a close parallelism exists between the abstract relationships of statistical theory and the concrete data of statistical method. At the present time, through the efforts of a growing number of accomplished mathematicians, statistical theory is expanding with very great rapidity. As a consequence, statistical method is undergoing changes, new and improved methods being continually reported in the periodical literature.

To be a creative participant in the development of statistical theory, one must have a very thorough foundation in advanced mathematics; to keep abreast of the newer developments of statistical method by reading the increasingly voluminous periodical literature, one must have a very fair knowledge of college mathematics including advanced calculus, theory of probability, and matrix theory. Most textbooks, including this one, are an attempt to select certain portions of this rich treasury and to simplify them so that they can be grasped by an intelligent reader whose mathematical preparation does not extend beyond elementary algebra. It must be admitted, however, that the research worker who has to depend exclusively on textbooks because he cannot read the original papers will always be considerably hampered by such dependence.

Descriptive Statistics and Statistical Inference. Statistical studies may be separated into two easily differentiated classes: those whose purpose is to describe the group characteristics of the particular data observed, and those which use the observed data as a basis for generalizing to a larger, unknown, population which has not been observed. The first class of studies may be called *descriptive statistics;* the type of generalization employed in the second is *statistical inference.* Of the two, statistical inference is much more fascinating, has greater appeal to the imagination, calls for a keener sense of logic, and makes a greater contribution toward an understanding of the statistical nature of the universe. However, statistical inference cannot be taught without teaching descriptive statistics, and the choice lies between attempting to present them simultaneously or delaying the discussion of inference until the student is well grounded in the computational devices for describing groups. In the writer's experience, beginning students are always confused by too early a discussion of sampling distribution and testing of hypotheses. These are abstract concepts of a fairly difficult nature, which, for the average person, need to be most carefully developed. It is therefore the writer's conviction that the most satisfactory first-year course consists of a semester's work in descriptive statistics followed by one in statistical inference, with certain more advanced topics in correlation taught in a third term if possible, or included at the end of the second term if a third term is out of the question. The chief objection to this division is the fact that some students do not take a second semester's work, and thus miss the part of the course which is most stimulating and which has the most to contribute to an understanding of research. On the other hand, it is unrealistic to suppose that one semester's study of statistical method could possibly prepare even a brilliant student to carry on statistical research. In fact, the brilliant student would be likely to recognize his need of further study.

The present text has therefore been prepared as an introductory first-semester course. The concluding chapter on *Sampling* has been inserted as a link with the study of *statistical inference*, and need not be included in the work of the first semester if most of the students expect to take a second semester's work.

Character of the Presentation in This Text. Certain inescapable difficulties beset the path of the student beginning to study statistics. If he is warned about these in advance, he can be spared a certain amount of annoyance. The teacher of statistics and the writer of a textbook must face these difficulties and make a choice between possible alternatives. These choices define one's philosophy of teaching the subject.

1. Emphasis. The person who is to carry out a large-scale statistical study needs, either in his own person or in that of an assistant, at least five distinct kinds of training. (1) He needs to be well versed in the subject-matter of the field in which his research is conducted, to know the sources of data available and the approved devices of measurement in that field. No amount of statistical training will enable a man to do competent research in a content field he does not know thoroughly. A text in statistical method, however, can take no responsibility for this aspect of the research worker's training. (2) He needs to know how to organize masses of data for efficient tabulation, and how to lay out economical routines for handling data and for computation. (3) He needs to know effective means of presenting data in tabular and graphic form. (4) He needs to know the mathematical theory of statistics in order to have assurance that there is a fair correspondence between his data and the assumptions underlying the formulas he uses. (5) He needs to be acquainted with a variety of statistical techniques, the limitations and relative advantages of each, the assumptions on which it is based, the place it occupies in a logical analysis of the data, and the interpretations which can be made from it. Obviously not all of these can be crowded into one introductory course. With no intent to minimize the importance of the others, the major emphasis in this text will be placed on the fifth of these needs.

2. Order of Topics. One of the peculiar difficulties in any presentation of statistical method is that there appears to be no sequence of material in which every topic can be fully developed as it comes without borrowing from the future. The student quite naturally but quite erroneously imputes this difficulty to careless organization on the part of the expositor. The wise instructor takes the student into his confidence, telling him occasionally that complete clarification of the topic in hand depends upon the development of some other topic not yet reached. This will be a source of mild annoyance when the reference is forward, but a source of distinct satisfaction when the other topic is reached and a backward reference brings out new meanings in the topic previously studied. A spiral organization is necessary, and, in the end, satisfying.

3. Mathematical Preparation. The extreme diversity of mathematical background usually found in a beginning class creates problems for both teacher and student. To meet this heterogeneity, several devices have been employed here. The body of the text has been written for the student whose study of mathematics ended when he left high school, but who understood and remembers his elementary algebra. At certain points where students of this type ordinarily experience difficulty, as for example with statistical symbolism, special explanations are provided which the student with mathematical training is told he can safely omit. For the student who has trouble with more elementary mathematics, the author's *Mathematics Essential for Elementary Statistics* * was prepared some years ago.

The student with mathematical training often fares badly in an elementary course in statistics. He wants to be assured that there is some mathematical justification for the formulas he uses, that they are not mere rules-of-thumb. He can proceed faster than other students and he would like to know what supplementary materials to read to enlarge his understanding. For him, and for him only, occasional *Mathematical*

---

* Henry Holt and Co., 1935. In my own classes, I require each student to take the self-scoring tests with which most of the chapters begin. Those who make no errors on a test do nothing further with that chapter. Those who make errors, study the explanatory material and the practice exercises, then take a second self-scoring test parallel to the first one. Each student goes through the book at his own speed, reporting each week on a 3 × 5 card the chapters he has studied and the number of errors made on each test. A student with good mathematical background can finish the book in a few hours, while the student who cannot do that needs the help he secures from it. By this method, practically no class time is taken up with difficulties that relate to the simpler aspects of mathematics.

Notes have been provided in the Appendix. It is hoped that the vistas thus opened up may beguile a few well-trained persons into advanced study. To those for whom a particular mathematical note is not clear, there is one uniform piece of advice—"Skip it!" The entire plan of the book would be thwarted if some student should insist upon a public explanation of that which is not intended as part of the basic course.

4. Flexibility. A textbook is a compromise between a set of teaching materials appropriate for study in a prescribed period and a reference work from which help on a specific problem can be sought. To permit some flexibility, certain topics have been marked as appropriate to omit in a minimum course. The special bibliographies at the end of certain chapters are intended to supplement the material in those chapters and are furnished only when there is an intentional omission of some topic which it is thought either a teacher or an inquiring student may wish to pursue further.

Footnotes often contain collateral material which is interesting but not essential.

5. Abstract Imagination. The purpose of statistical method is to abstract from a mass of discrete facts certain information which will enable one to comprehend the whole. Therefore statistical measures are essentially *abstractions*. Such abstract concepts have to be built up by experience, just as one builds up the concepts suggested by the words "quaint," "patriotism," "irresponsibility," "nevertheless," "implication," for which no photograph or diagram can suffice. These concepts must grow in the imagination. To stimulate such imagination is the purpose of certain sets of artificial data used throughout the text and of certain developmental exercises, both verbal and numerical. The building of concepts is a more important undertaking than any other aspect of the course, because without clear concepts, all skills will come to naught.

6. Extent of Data Provided. Some teachers prefer to use a new set of data for every problem, thus demonstrating to their classes the wide variety of situations in which statistical methods may be applied and the richness of material available for illustrative purposes. Others prefer to use the same set of data over and over in order to economize the mental energy of the class, which focuses its attention at once upon the new method without having also to adjust to a new content. Each plan has its advantages and its disadvantages. In this text, the second method has been followed. Statistical compilations are now so easy to obtain that any teacher who prefers the first method can with very little effort bring in additional data for practice exercises.

Some teachers prefer to use, as practice material, data in which the arithmetic has been made relatively easy. Others prefer to use more realistic and therefore more arithmetically difficult problems. Again, each practice has its disadvantages. There is danger that the student may become so absorbed in the arithmetic complexities of a very long problem that he fails to think about the relationships the problem is designed to clarify. The short problem with easy arithmetic may be so planned that it effectively contributes to the building of concepts. On the other hand, if too many short problems are used, the student may develop false notions of what a real study should involve and may never learn to handle competently life-sized sets of data. Because the emphasis in this text is on the development of meanings rather than on computational skill, the bias is probably in the direction of too many short problems rather than too many long ones. Making up sets of artificial data to illustrate a particular relationship is not always easy; if made on the spur of the moment, they sometimes backfire. It is, however, always easy for a teacher to supplement the text with data from genuine studies which he or some colleague may have in progress, or which can be obtained from published research studies.

Reading Habits. Some students who have consciously trained themselves in habits of very rapid reading and who are not accustomed to the study of scientific or mathematical material, may find it necessary to revise their patterns of study. Until they come to understand that in work of this nature one does not read a page at a gulp, they may feel a sense of frustration, may feel that progress is slow because the number of pages covered in a given period of time is far below their average. The student must learn to change gear, some material being appropriately covered at high speed, and other material calling for thoughtful perusal— for continual comparison of the section under consideration and earlier sections. As Chrystal, a great English teacher of algebra in the nineteenth century, once said, "Every mathematical book that is worth anything must be read 'backwards and forwards,'" and then he quoted the advice of a French mathematician, "Allez en avant, et la foi vous viendra." The advice is still good.

The following pattern of study is suggested as likely to produce the clearest understanding for a given expenditure of time. (1) Read rapidly through a chapter to get a general impression of the material contained and the purpose of the discussion. In this rapid preliminary reading, try to keep a chapter or two ahead of the class discussion. (2) Just before a section is taken up in class, go over it in detail, comparing, rereading, solving problems, verifying numerical statements, making note of all points which are not fully clear. At this stage, it may be helpful to consult other texts treating the same topics. Questions may then be raised in class as to points which need further clarification. (3) As soon as possible after a section has been discussed in class, read it once more to consolidate the understandings gained from the class discussion. (4) Several weeks later, reread once more. The habit of rereading chapters studied some weeks earlier not only clarifies one's understanding, it tends to improve morale. Points that seemed completely obscure on a first reading now seem so obvious that you wonder why you put a question mark in the margin there. On the other hand, some points which seemed quite simple on a first reading now, in the light of further knowledge, have new implications which raise new queries in your mind.

Students of literature and the social studies, unaccustomed to scientific and mathematical work, are sometimes discouraged by their need to read statistical material many times. They should be told that this is a characteristic of the type of material. It is a fairly safe guess that most persons who have achieved distinction in a technical field would usually feel that a technical book which can be read straight through without ever rereading a page is hardly worth reading at all.

Misuses of Statistics. Fundamental and pervasive as statistical thinking is in the modern world, it must not be supposed to be an end in itself. Statistical method is a tool for organizing facts so as to render them available for study. A statistical study can only describe what is; it cannot determine what ought to be except insofar as it may throw light upon the probable concomitants and consequences of certain situations. It is fatuous to suppose that statistical method can provide mechanical substitutes for thinking, although it is often an indispensable aid to thinking. Men see the increasing prevalence of statistical method in scientific studies and sometimes, failing to grasp the underlying reasons for this development, assume that the use of tables, formulas, and numerical summaries is a badge of respectability. As a result studies which are truly subjective in nature are invested with a false show of objectivity, and a vast superstructure of computation is raised upon a foundation inappropriate to such treatment. This is neither good statistics nor good philosophy. Not all writers are clear in their own minds as to when they are assembling and organizing facts and when they are making philosophical interpretations of facts. Both are important and neither is furthered by an attempt to make philosophy wear the accoutrements of statistics.

Asking Questions of Data. Confronted with a set of raw data, the novice is tempted to ask himself, "What measures have I learned to compute which I might make use of in respect to these data?" This is exactly the wrong way around. He ought to say, "For what questions would I like to have these data provide the answers? Do I know how to organize the data so that they can throw light on these problems?" It would be still better to set up the questions before the data are gathered, and to ask, "What data are needed to provide the answers to these questions?"

Appendix A contains the scores of 109 fourth-grade children on a group of tests. The data are in about the form in which raw data are often presented for analysis. Imagine yourself connected in some way with the school from which these children come, and try to formulate a list of questions to which you think these figures might provide the answer. After you have written down a list of such questions, classify them, grouping together all those which are similar as to general type even though different as to subject matter.

Your list of questions probably contains the following types:

1a	Average status:	On the average, how old were these children? What was their average IQ? What was the most typical score in each test?
1b	Comparison of averages:	Were these boys older on the average than these girls? On which tests did these boys exceed the girls? How do these scores compare with the published norms of the tests?
1c	Generalization:	What is the average age of fourth-grade children? On which test may boys in the fourth grade be expected to exceed girls and vice versa? In a fourth-grade class, what score may the upper quarter of the class be expected to exceed in a certain one of the tests?
2a	Variability:	What was the range of scores in arithmetic computation? How old was the oldest pupil? The youngest? How much variation was there among the scores on a certain one of the tests? What range of scores included the middle half of the group? The middle 90% of the group?
2b	Comparison of variability:	Were these boys more or less homogeneous in score on a certain one of the tests than these girls? Were these pupils more or less variable than those for whom the test was standardized?
2c	Generalization:	In general, how wide an age-range is to be expected in the fourth grade? In general, are boys at the fourth-grade level more or less uniform than girls in regard to scores on a certain one of the tests?

3a	Relationship:	Were the oldest children the fastest readers? Was there a tendency for children who scored above average on one test to score above average on another?
3b	Comparison of relationship:	Which of these tests yielded scores most closely related to intelligence? Is the relationship between intelligence quotient and scores on a certain one of the tests more or less close than has usually been found in other similar studies?
3c	Generalization:	What is the nature of the relationship between any two of these measures for fourth-grade children in general? If the intelligence quotients are known for another set of fourth-grade children, can we use these as a basis for estimating their scores on a certain one of the tests?
4	Application of group data to study of a single individual:	Is Pupil X above or below the average of this group in a certain one of the tests? On which test does he stand highest in respect to the average of this group? What proportion of the group has higher scores on a certain one of the tests? In the light of the known relationship between intelligence quotient and a certain one of the tests, does his test score appear to be higher or lower than one might have expected it to be? On the basis of the intelligence quotient of one of these children, what is the best estimate that can be made of his score on a certain one of the tests?

Questions 1c, 2c, and 3c are questions in the area of statistical inference. The remaining questions are of the sort upon which the main emphasis of this first course is placed.

CHAPTER II

THE NATURE OF MEASUREMENT

The direct measurement of a magnitude, by superposition or any similar process, is most frequently an operation quite impossible for us to perform; so that if we had no other means for determining magnitudes than direct comparisons, we should be obliged to renounce the knowledge of most of those which interest us . . . for the human mind has been compelled to renounce, in almost all cases, the direct measurement of magnitudes, and to seek to determine them indirectly, and it is thus that it has been led to the creation of mathematics.　　　　Auguste Comte

Measurement and Counting. Civilization depends in very large part upon counting, measurement, and computation. The necessary basis for scientific work is a precision in observation and in thinking which would be impossible without counting. Without counting, measurement would be impossible, because the essence of measurement is the comparison of that which is measured to a unit or to a counted set of units. Measurement, however, does not possess the absolute precision of counting. No matter what kind of instrument is used to measure a quantity, it is theoretically possible to devise another instrument capable of measuring that quantity to a greater degree of precision than that effected by the first instrument; that is, measurement is precise only to a degree which varies from one situation to another, from one instrument to another. To utilize numerical data wisely, it is essential to recognize and understand certain inescapable limitations as to their precision.

Numbers obtained by counting indivisible units are *exact*, and a succession of such numbers is a *discrete series*. A count of the number of persons in a room may yield, let us say, 48. If one more person enters, the count leaps from 48 to 49 without passing through any intermediate fractional values. At no time is it "slightly under 49," or "a little more than 48." The count is exact, and proceeds by a series of leaps from integer to integer. Numbers obtained by measurement are *approximate* and belong to a *continuous series*. If a man says he has driven 48 miles, we understand that the distance is approximately 48 miles, perhaps a little more and perhaps a little less. In order to increase his mileage from 48 to 49 miles he must pass through all the infinitely many gradations of distance between the two. Distance cannot increase at a leap by a whole

11

unit, discretely, but must increase continuously. Nor can distance ever be measured with complete precision. Measured on the speedometer of an automobile, it can be easily measured within a tenth of a mile, or perhaps estimated within a third of that error. A micrometer will measure the thickness of a hair and distinguish between 0.001 and 0.002 of an inch. A base line for surveying purposes can be laid off so as to have an error of not more than an inch in 10 miles. The wave length of light has been measured at the Mt. Wilson Observatory to such accuracy that a variation of one part in 100,000,000 can be detected. Yet even this high degree of precision is not the absolute precision of counting; even the wave length of light is an approximate number. (Note the root of the word approximate, to "come near to." Popular usage imputes a certain opprobrium to this word, which may or may not be merited, depending upon the situation in which the approximation occurs.)

Parallel Continuous and Discrete Series. Time is obviously a continuum, but its passage may be marked off in various ways by periodically occurring events which form a discrete series. Thus the number of birthdays a man has lived through is a discrete variable behind which lies the parallel continuous variable of his age. Or the number of times a clock has struck the hour since midnight is a measure of the continuous variable, time elapsed since midnight. The discrete variable increases by jerks, but periodically, at the instant the observation is taken; it matches the underlying continuous variable of which it forms a measure. The smaller the gaps in the discrete variable, the more precise is the measurement of the continuous. The interval between two such adjacent observations determines the precision of measurement.

Other illustrations of parallel continuous and discrete series are these: (1) A ten-mile speedway has a marker at each mile. The number of markers passed is the measure of distance traveled. (2) In the gasoline pump in a filling station a bell rings as each full gallon of gas is drawn out. The number of times the bell has rung is a measure of gasoline drawn.

It is often desirable to treat discrete data as though they are continuous. For example, reports often contain such statements as "The number of children per family in the cases studied was 1.8." Clearly 1.8 children has meaning only if the discrete data, which can have no values between 1 and 2, are referred to a parallel, underlying, continuum, which in this case is an abstraction.

Imagine a line segment, as OA, laid off, and numbered in intervals of one inch, and imagine a point moving continuously from O toward A. At any given instant, the distance from O to the moving point will be named by the number nearest to that point. For example, when the

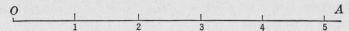

point is nearer to 3 than it is to 2 or to 4, the distance from O to it will be named 3. The number 3 will thus represent any position of the point in the interval beginning at $2\frac{1}{2}$ and extending to $3\frac{1}{2}$, an interval 1 inch wide. This *is measurement to the nearest inch.* What range of points does the number 2 represent? The number 5?

Now imagine a line segment, OB, laid off and numbered in quarter-inches, so that measurement can be made "to the nearest quarter-inch." As the point moves from O toward B, its distance from O is named 3 only

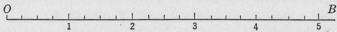

when the point is nearer to 3 than to either of the adjacent subdivisions $2\frac{3}{4}$ or $3\frac{1}{4}$, and that will be when the point is in the interval from $2\frac{7}{8}$ to $3\frac{1}{8}$, an interval which is $\frac{1}{4}$ inch wide. *Note that a single entry in the discrete series is matched with an interval in the continuous series.*

Exercise* 1

1. Which of the following is an observation of a discrete variable and which of a continuous variable?

    a. Weight at birth for a given individual

    b. Number of dependents of a factory worker

    c. Number of men employed in a factory

    d. Average daily gain in weight of rats in a nutrition experiment

    e. Mental age of a child in an orphanage

    f. Intelligence quotient of a subnormal child

    g. Time in seconds required for a hundred-yard dash

2. Give two additional illustrations of a continuous variable.

3. Give two additional illustrations of a discrete variable.

4. Give two illustrations of a discrete variable used as the measure of a continuous variable.

5. If measurement is recorded to the nearest inch only, how would you name each of the points A, B, C, D, E, and F in the adjacent diagram?

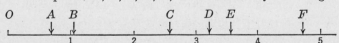

6. If measurement is recorded to the nearest half-inch, how would you name the same points?

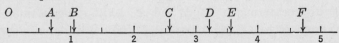

---

* Exercises or problems marked with an asterisk contain developmental material which should not be omitted even for a minimum course.

7. If measurement is recorded to the nearest quarter-inch, how would you name the same points?

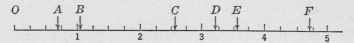

8. If distance is measured to the nearest inch, what interval is represented by the number 43? What interval if measurement is to the nearest half-inch? The nearest quarter-inch?

9. If weight is reported to the nearest half-pound, what interval is represented by each of these numbers: 137, $102\frac{1}{2}$, $163\frac{1}{2}$?

10. If a speedometer registers tenths of a mile, what interval is represented by each of these readings: 2372.6, 1460.3, 4700.0, 5203.9?

11. The only numbers marked on the scale in the adjacent sketch are five units apart. How would you name each of the indicated points, P, Q, R, S, and T if it must be named by one of the indicated numbers?

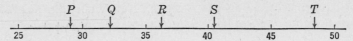

What interval is represented by the number 35 here? How wide is this interval?

12. If the only numbers marked on the scale in the adjacent sketch are 7 units apart, how would you name each of the points, H, J, K, L, M, and N?

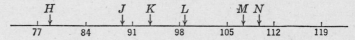

What interval is represented by the number 91? The number 112? How wide are these intervals?

Confusion in Practice. Everyone is familiar with the confusion in age data due to the fact that some observers record "age to nearest birthday" and some record "age to last birthday." In terms of a linear diagram, this means that the persons in the first group designate a score-interval by the number at its midpoint, as in A, while those in the second group

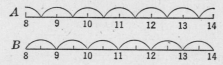

designate the score-interval by the number at its beginning point, as in B. In the first case, the number 10 designates an interval extending from $9\frac{1}{2}$ to $10\frac{1}{2}$ and centering at 10; in the second it designates an interval extending from 10 to 11 and centering at $10\frac{1}{2}$. With equal appropriateness the interval might be named by the number corresponding to its end-point, but in practice that is seldom done. One familiar illustration of this rather uncommon practice is provided by the calendar. The twentieth century precedes rather than follows the year 2000.

In the relatively simple, practical matter of recording and tabulating scores of all kinds, a similar diversity of practice is apparent. The student who reads widely in many texts must become adjusted to the fact that some writers use the first method and some the second method of defining a score-interval. Since it is manifestly impossible to agree with all those writers who might be considered authorities, we are free to make our own definition of a score-interval, and we will choose the practice which is the simpler, which is unambiguous, which is in accord with standard practice in the physical sciences, and which is now showing strong ascendency even in elementary texts in statistics. In this text, *every score will be treated as if located at the middle of a unit score-interval*. The unit, of course, may be $\frac{1}{8}$ of an inch, or $\frac{1}{4}$ of a mile, or 5 pounds or 0.1 of a degree, or any other fraction which happens to be convenient.

In all published data, the writer should state what unit has been employed and what a score means. It is very misleading to label a column of figures merely "age" or "weight." Even "age in years" is not enough, but "age to nearest year" or "age in years to last birthday" would be quite clear. If children are asked to give their ages, they will usually report age to last birthday. It is then a good practice either to insert a footnote explaining that age is given to last birthday or, still better, to change the figures so that ages reported as 4, 5, 6 are published as $4\frac{1}{2}$, $5\frac{1}{2}$, $6\frac{1}{2}$. Because practice is not yet fully standardized, a writer should consistently tell his readers what his scores mean. If there is any reasonable doubt about the definition of scores occurring in a table, a footnote should be attached to the table telling what interval a score covers.

Significant Digits. If you should say that a line you have measured is 40.35 meters long, you would be saying that the unit in which you are reporting your measurement is $\frac{1}{100}$ of a meter, and that the line contains 4035 such units. If you should describe the same line as 4035 centimeters, you would be saying that a centimeter is the unit and that the line contains 4035 such units. If, having measured the line in centimeters (or hundredths of a meter), you decide to express its length in millimeters, it would be appropriate to write 40350 millimeters, the dot over the 5 indicating that only the first four digits are certain, the final zero having been added to effect the change in unit. You do not guarantee that zero; this measurement is not correct to millimeters but only to ten millimeters. The real measurement in millimeters might be anywhere between 40345 and 40355. As before, you say the line contains 4035 units and each unit is ten millimeters.

To express the length of the line as 0.04035 kilometer would be to say that the unit is $\frac{1}{100,000}$ of a kilometer, and that the line contains 4035 such units. No matter in which way we express the length of this line, the measurement has four-digit accuracy, i.e., it contains four significant digits. These are the four digits in 4035, which tell *how many units*. Each of these digits may be called a counter. The position of the decimal point is quite unrelated to the number of significant digits with which a number is written, and therefore any zero used solely to fix the position of that decimal point is not considered a significant digit. It is not a counter but merely a place-holder.

In a number like 1.005, where zeros come between other digits, those zeros are significant. The number may be read as one thousand and five *thousandths*, where 1005 represents the number of thousandths. These zeros are counters, not place-holders.

Numbers like 1.20 and 0.040 require some special thought because most people have been incorrectly taught to believe that 1.2 and 1.20 have the same meaning. The number 1.20 may be read as one hundred and twenty *hundredths*, and has 3 significant digits because the number of units is 120, and the zero is a counter, not a place-holder. If the measurement has not really been taken to the nearest hundredth but only to the nearest tenth, then it should be written 1.2 because it is really twelve tenths and not one hundred and twenty hundredths. A zero added at the right of a decimal fraction is a pledge of the precision with which the measurement has been made, and should not be used unless the pledge is justified.

The number 4000 has an indeterminate number of significant digits. Inspection alone will not reveal how many of these zeros are counters and how many are place-holders. A dot or a bar * above the last significant digit would remove the ambiguity, thus:

$\bar{4}000$ means   4 thousands and has 1 significant digit
$4\bar{0}00$ means   40 hundreds and has 2 significant digits
$40\bar{0}0$ means 400 tens   and has 3 significant digits
$400\bar{0}$ means 4000 ones   and has 4 significant digits

Rounding a Number. "How many figures shall I retain in my answer?" is a question from which the statistical computer can never escape. When a computing machine is used, it is so easy to carry computations to a large number of places that there is a temptation to retain more digits in the final results than the accuracy of the original measurement justifies. If a computer discards too many places, he throws away valuable information and creates a false impression that his figures are less

---

* The dot and the bar are used interchangeably to indicate the last significant digit.

Exercise* 2

Study the examples below and supply the numbers to complete the table.

Number as Written	Size of Unit Indicated	Number of Units	Number of Significant Digits
71.3	0.1	713	3
$50\dot{2}00$	100	502	3
$5020\dot{0}$	1	50200	5
0.0600	0.0001	600	3
0.06	0.01	6	1
3600	?	?	?
9.01	—	—	—
10203	—	—	—
$102\overline{0}0$	—	—	—
7.20	—	—	—
0.0310	—	—	—
5.104	—	—	—
0.040	—	—	—
$461\overline{0}$	—	—	—
$3900\overline{0}$	—	—	—
390.00	—	—	—

reliable than they really are. If he retains too many places, he creates a show of false accuracy not justified by the precision of his original data.

The number of digits retained must be adjusted to the purpose the number is to serve. In an audit of the financial records of a company the last penny must be included, but in reporting the assets and liabilities and net earnings of that company to a group of laymen it is more useful to round off the pennies and perhaps the dollars. A layman will comprehend more quickly and remember longer a statement that there is a deficit of $35,000 than that there is a deficit of $34,618.21.

An amusing illustration of failure to sense this adjustment of precision to purpose is provided by a letter once written by the Victorian mathematician and philosopher, Charles Babbage, to Alfred Tennyson regarding the latter's lines,

> · Every moment dies a man
> Every moment one is born. ·

"I need hardly point out to you," wrote Mr. Babbage, "that this calculation would tend to keep the sum total of the world's population in a state of perpetual equipoise, whereas it is a well-known fact that the said sum is constantly on the increase. I would therefore take the liberty of suggesting that in the next edition of your excellent poem ('The Vision of Sin') the erroneous calculation to which I refer should be corrected as follows:

> Every moment dies a man
> And one and a sixteenth is born.

I may add that the exact figures are 1.067, but something must, of course be conceded to the laws of nature."

One of the Caspar Milquetoast cartoons provides another illustration of excessive and inappropriate meticulousness. Mr. Milquetoast has driven his new car exactly 499 miles and 1710 yards, and he says exultantly to his wife "Just 50 yards more and I can open her up to 31 miles an hour without risking an injury to the motor."

The number of digits retained in the result of a computation must be adjusted to the degree of precision present in the original data. To take rough measurements and to retain a great many digits in the outcome of the statistical treatment applied to them smacks of statistical incompetency, but so does throwing away too many digits in a study made with very accurate measurements.

The procedure of rounding off a number is simple. When the first (or left-hand) digit of those to be dropped is less than 5, no change is made in the last digit retained.

Thus   783,102 rounded to 2 significant digits becomes 780,000
            62,459 rounded to 2 significant digits becomes   62,000
        0.34349 rounded to 3 significant digits becomes   0.343

When the first (or left-hand) digit is more than 5, or is 5 followed by digits not all zero, the last digit retained is increased by 1.

Thus   944,521 rounded to 3 significant digits becomes 945,000
        0.0162 rounded to 1 significant digit becomes   0.02
        71.876 rounded to 3 significant digits becomes   71.9
        264,501 rounded to 3 significant digits becomes 265,000

When the digit to be dropped is a lone 5, or a 5 followed by zeros only, it is customary to make no change in the last digit retained if that digit is even, and to increase it by one if that digit is odd. Any other arbitrary rule which would increase the last digit in half the cases in which this situation occurs and would fail to increase it in half of them would serve just as well. Aside from the waste of time and energy involved, spinning a penny to decide the issue would produce satisfactory results.

Thus   74,350 rounded to 3 significant digits becomes   74,$\overline{4}$00
96.65 rounded to 3 significant digits becomes 96.6
249,500 rounded to 3 significant digits becomes 25$\overline{0}$,000
0.985 rounded to 2 significant digits becomes   0.98

The Number of Digits To Be Retained in the Results of Computation.
Computations based on exact numbers are valid for as many places as
the computer thinks it expedient to report them. Computations based on
approximate numbers are valid for a limited number of digits only and
must not be carried further.

Multiplication. When two or more approximate numbers are multiplied together, if the one with the fewer significant digits has n significant
digits, then the product cannot be relied upon for more than n digits.

This rule becomes clear upon considering the product of 754.32 and
6.4. If both are approximate, the lowest value this product could have
would be the product of 754.315 and 6.35, which is 4789.90025. The
highest value it could have would be the product of 754.325 and 6.45,
which is 4865.39625. These are not in agreement even in the second digit,
and certainly no subsequent digits are meaningful. If, therefore, we
multiply 754.32 by 6.4 and obtain 4827.648, the answer should be rounded
to 4$\overline{8}$00, and we should keep in mind that even the second digit, 8, is not
wholly dependable. Note that if the longer number had been rounded to
three digits before multiplying, and then the final product had been
rounded to two digits, we should have obtained 754 $\times$ 6.4 = 4825.6
$\doteq$ 4$\overline{8}$00, the symbol $\doteq$ being read "approximates" or "is approximately
equal to."

Illustrations:

16% of 24216 = 3874.56 if both numbers are exact
16% of 24216 = 3874.6 if 16 is exact and 24216 is approximate
16% of 24216 = 3$\overline{9}$00   if 16 is approximate and 24216 is exact
16% of 24216 = 3$\overline{9}$00   if both numbers are approximate

Division. When one approximate number is divided by another, **if**
the one with the fewer significant digits has n such digits, the quotient
should be written with n digits only. It is immaterial whether the number with the fewer digits is the dividend or divisor. The following examples will serve to make clear the meaning of this rule.

The quotient 83.642 $\div$ 72
cannot be less than 83.6415 $\div$ 72.5 = 1.15367586 $\cdot \cdot$
nor more than   83.6425 $\div$ 71.5 = 1.16982517 $\cdot \cdot$

and these results agree if rounded to two digits. Therefore if 83.642 is divided by 72, the result 1.1617 · · · should be rounded to 1.2 or to 1.16.

The quotient 72 ÷ 83.642
cannot be less than 71.5 ÷ 83.6425 = 0.8548 · · ·
nor more than   72.5 ÷ 83.6415 = 0.8668 · · ·

and these results agree only in the first digit. Therefore if 72 is divided by 83.642, the result, 0.8608, should be rounded to 0.86.

It should be noted that in either case a satisfactory result is obtained if the number with the greater number of significant digits is rounded before division to one more place than is to be retained in the final result. It should also be noted that the last place retained according to the rule may be in error.

Illustrations:

7683 ÷ 29 = 264.9 if 29 is exact and 7683 is approximate
7683 ÷ 29 = 2$\bar{6}$0   if 29 is approximate and 7683 is exact
7683 ÷ 29 = 2$\bar{6}$0 if both numbers are approximate

29 ÷ 7683 = 0.003775 if 29 is exact and 7683 is approximate
29 ÷ 7683 = 0.0038   if 29 is approximate and 7683 is exact
29 ÷ 7683 = 0.0038   if both numbers are approximate

Square Root. If a number contains n significant digits, its square root can in general be relied upon for n digits. There may be an error in the nth digit of the root. Consider the following illustrations.

$\sqrt{30.74}$ cannot be less   than $\sqrt{30.735} = 5.54392$ · · ·
$\sqrt{30.74}$ cannot be more than $\sqrt{30.745} = 5.54482$ · · ·

These are in agreement for 3 digits and differ only slightly in the fourth. $\sqrt{30.74} = 5.544$.

$\sqrt{3.07}$ cannot be less than $\sqrt{3.065} = 1.75071$ · · ·
$\sqrt{3.07}$ cannot be more than $\sqrt{3.075} = 1.75357$ · · ·

These are in agreement for 3 digits and confirm the rule that $\sqrt{3.07}$ should, if 3.07 is not an exact number, be written with 3 places as 1.75.

Addition and Subtraction. In addition and subtraction we are not concerned with which number has the fewest significant digits, but we wish to note in which number the non-significant digits occur farthest to the left. The digits of the sum or the difference are not significant to the right of that place in which the last significant digit occurs in any one of the numbers to be added or subtracted. Suppose, for example, that we wish to add

$$4\bar{8}00 + 13.4 + 7.065.$$

In the first number, the last significant digit is in hundreds place, in the next number in tenths place, in the third number in thousandths. Therefore, no digits in the sum are significant beyond hundreds place, and $4\overline{8}00 + 13.4 + 7.065 = 4\overline{8}00$, not 4820.465. It is clear that $4\overline{8}00$ may represent a number as small as 4750 or one as large as 4850, and therefore the third digit in the answer is completely untrustworthy.

Suppose for example, that 5 items of estimated expenditure are to be combined as follows:

$$\$4\overline{2}00 + \$10.25 + \$18 + \$364 + \$2.50$$

If these are added as they stand and the result reported as an estimated expenditure of \$4594.75, the result is grossly misleading, inasmuch as the first item alone may be in error by as much as \$50, and therefore no digits after the first two can be relied upon. The general procedure in such cases is to note which number has its last significant digit occurring farthest to the left. Then round all the numbers off one digit to the right of this position, add, and round off one more place.

Original Numbers	Rounded Numbers Ready to add
\$4$\overline{2}$00	\$4$\overline{2}$00
10.25	$\overline{1}$0
18	$\overline{2}$0
364	3$\overline{6}$0
2.50	0
\$4594.75	\$4590 rounded to \$4$\overline{6}$00

Exercise 3

1. How many significant digits has each of the following numbers?

(1) 0.047   (3) 0.010   (5) 750$\overline{0}$ (7) $\overline{5}$000   (9) 36.0   (11) 3.001

(2) 7.20   (4) 0.002   (6) 6001   (8) 4000   (10) 4.002   (12) 10$\overline{2}$00

2. Round each of the following numbers so that it contains three significant digits.

(1) 768501   (4) 271.6   (7) 3.6207

(2) 372486   (5) 89976   (8) 47639

(3) 42.9981   (6) 4.815   (9) 5635

3. Assume that all of the numbers involved in the following computations are approximations, and round the results to the number of digits which is appropriate.

(1) $(55.4)^2 = 3069.16$ (6) 390.625   (7) 14.37

(2) $\sqrt{951} = 30.8382879$ 3.11   5.2

(3) $\sqrt{3171} = 56.311633$ 23.4   431

(4) $(56.82)(1.7) = 96.594$ 17.3726   3.7245

(5) $(9863.2) \div 7.2 = 1369.89$ 434.5076

Rank, Score, Scale, Measure. If it is possible to arrange individuals in an ordered sequence with respect to some trait, the ordinal number corresponding to an individual's position in the series is his *rank* as to that trait in that particular group. Only relations of "less than" or "more than" need be established. Equality of units is not required. It is necessary only to know that A surpasses B, but not to know by what amount.

A *score* is a numerical tag attached to an individual in such a way that if *A* has more of a trait than *B*, *A*'s score on that trait will be larger than *B*'s. *A*'s score does not necessarily tell either the position *A* holds in his group, or the amount of the trait he possesses, but it does increase as amount of the trait increases, though not of necessity in proportion to that amount. Several individuals can have the same score.

If score units can be made equal, then these scores are said to be *scaled*, proceeding by equal steps. Unless scores are scaled, it is meaningless to add or subtract them, to try to say how much one individual exceeds another.

In order to know how much of a trait an individual has or to say that one thing is twice another, it is necessary not only to have equality of units but also to establish a zero point. Only when these two conditions are met can scores properly be spoken of as *measures*.

Unless equality of units can be established either by direct comparison or by some reasonable definition, measurement is impossible. Much that is called measurement in educational work is really not that at all. You cannot "measure" height with an elastic yardstick. Unless units are equal, it is useless to count them. Six books, 2 horses, 5 marbles and 1 hat may constitute 14 "possessions," but no sane man would assert that 14 of such "possessions" was more or less valuable than 10 "possessions."

Establishing the Equality of Units. *1. By Direct Comparison.* In the physical world, there are a few traits in which the equality of units can be established by comparing them directly. One unit of length can be superimposed on another unit of length, and it can be determined by direct observation that the first is, or is not, greater than the second. Two units of angular rotation can be similarly superimposed. Two units of weight can be placed on balance scales and compared with each other. Mass and volume also are of such a nature that the equality of units can be directly established. Most persons are amazed to discover that even in the physical world there are relatively few traits in which units can be directly compared.

2. By Definition. Consider time. Can an hour of yesterday be laid against an hour of today to determine which is longer? Is an hour at noonday really the same length as an hour near dawn? Since direct comparison is impossible, men have resorted to establishing a kind of equality by definition. Two periods of time may be defined to be equal if they correspond to equal volumes of sand passing through an hourglass, to equal angular rotation of the stars, or to equal decrease in the length of a burning candle, to equal angular rotation in the hands of a watch, to equal number of furrows plowed in a field, to equal increase in the length of shadow on a sundial, to equal number of swings of a pendulum of fixed length, to equal distances traversed by a horseback rider at full gallop. Some of these, the reader is saying, are very poor measures.

What is a "good" measure of time and what is a "poor" one? Suppose a primitive man undertakes to measure time simultaneously by the change in length of a burning candle and by the change in length of a shadow of a post. He will find that units which are defined as equal by one method cannot be defined as equal by the other, and he must conclude that at least one of the two devices is an indefensible one. If, later, he finds that there is fair agreement between the units of time as determined by equal angular change in the position of the stars, by equal volumes of sand passing through a small aperture, and by equal change in the length of a burning candle, whereas the units of time defined by equal change in the length of shadow of a post do not agree well with any of the others, he is likely to reject the definition by length of shadow in favor of one of the other three methods of definition.

Consider temperature. There is no direct way by which we can compare a rise in temperature from 10° to 12° with a rise from 70° to 72° and observe their equality. We may define them as equal because they correspond to equal changes in the height of a column of mercury, or to equal changes in the volume of a gas under constant pressure, and both definitions are considered successful because of the close correspondence between their results.

Consider intelligence. Can you lay the intelligence of one child beside that of another and say "These two are exactly equal"? Like temperature and time, intelligence units must be made equal by definition, if at all. The various testing instruments are attempts to do this, i.e., to say that two inaccessible units of intelligence will be considered to be equal if they correspond to equal units of score on the testing instrument.

Grouping Measures into Larger Intervals. Sometimes data gathered in small units are grouped into larger units before they are published. Imagine that after a group of children have been weighed to the nearest pound it seems best to arrange their weights in intervals of 3 pounds, placing children who weigh 41, 42, or 43 in one group, those who weigh 44, 45, or 46 in another, and so on. On the scale of weights, 41 covers the range indicated from the point 40½ to 41½, 42 covers the range 41½

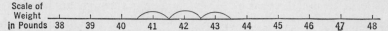

Scale of Weight in Pounds 38 39 40 41 42 43 44 45 46 47 48

to 42½, and 43 covers the range 42½ to 43½. These three scores together then cover the interval from 40½ to 43½. It must be understood that a point, such as 40½, is a mere mathematical abstraction, the division between two line segments, having position but no width.

Note the following and fix their meaning clearly in mind. The *width of interval* here is 3 (in this case 3 lbs.). The *real limits* of this interval are 40.5 and 43.5. The *score limits* of this interval are 41 and 43. The *class mark, class value,* or *class index* of the interval is the *midpoint*, which is 42. The interval is also called the *class sort,* or *step interval,* or *class interval.*

Exercise 4

1. Discuss each item in the following list in regard to these points:

a. Can the equality of units be established by direct comparison? If the answer is yes, disregard the other question.

b. If the answer to question (a) is no, can you find some other trait in which units can be directly compared, which is so related to this trait that it offers a reasonable method of making units equal by definition? Discuss the reasonableness of the definition.

(1) Chronological age
(2) Mental age
(3) Height
(4) Salary
(5) Pitch of voice
(6) Arithmetic comprehension
(7) Information about public affairs
(8) Socio-economic status
(9) Pain
(10) Happiness

2. In regard to each of the following traits, would you be justified in saying that (a) A's score is such and such a percent of B's, (b) A's score is so and so many units larger than B's, (c) A has a higher rank than B, or (d) there is no basis for comparing A with B? Note that (b) includes (c) while (a) includes both (b) and (c).

(1) Chronological age
(2) Score on a test of art appreciation
(3) Pitch of voice
(4) Mean annual temperature of various cities
(5) Socio-economic status of college students
(6) Salary
(7) Truancy
(8) I.Q.

3. a. On the scale of weight, above, draw a brace to indicate the interval which includes the next three scores above the interval we have been discussing, and state its real limits, score limits, class value, and width.

b. Do the same for an interval which would include the scores 40, 41, 42, 43, and 44.

c. Do the same for an interval to include all the scores from 40 to 49 inclusive.

d. Do the same for an interval to include scores 50 and 51.

4. Each row of the following table represents a separate set of data. Assume the original measurements were in units of the size indicated, and fill in the blanks in the table.

Problem	Size of Unit of Measure	Class Index	Consecutive Scores Included in Interval	Score Limits	Real Limits	Number of Units in Interval
A	0.5	39				3
B	1	55				5
C	1			26–29		
D					27.5–34.5	7
E			76, 76½, 77, 77½, 78			
F	0.25	19				3
G	0.2	8				5
H			48, 49, 50, 51			
I	1			30–39		

Method of Designating Class Interval. From the preceding exercise it is apparent that there are several ways in which it is possible to define an interval unambiguously. Any one of them may be used as a name for the interval. Compare the following designations to see which you think most practical as a description of class intervals:

(1)	(2)	(3)	(4)	(5)
75	73–77	72.5–77.5	73–	72.5–
70	68–72	67.5–72.5	68–	67.5–
65	63–67	62.5–67.5	63–	62.5–
60	58–62	57.5–62.5	58–	57.5–
55	53–57	52.5–57.5	53–	52.5–

Methods (1), (4), and (5) call for a good deal of concentration from the person tabulating in order to remember the limits of the interval. A good statistician arranges to have everything automatic which can be made automatic. Mental arithmetic and feats of memory are less praiseworthy in a statistician than careful organization of data to provide automatic checks. Method (3) actually invites the tabulator to err by placing 72 in the interval 72.5–77.5 instead of in the interval 67.5–72.5. Method (2), using score limits, takes up less space than (3) and probably facilitates accuracy of tabulation. (No figures are available to substantiate this point, but a test could readily be made.)

Choice of Class Interval. No hard and fast rule can be given for the selection of a class interval, but certain considerations should be kept in mind.

1. The number of intervals should seldom be less than 10 or more than 20, and 15 is a good number, in general. If the difference between the highest and the lowest score is divided by 15 and the quotient rounded off to the nearest integer, the result will provide a helpful suggestion as to width of interval.

Illustrations:

Highest Score	Lowest Score	Difference Divided by 15	Suggested Width of Interval	Number of Intervals †
79	36	$43 \div 15 = 2.9$	3	15
115	52	$63 \div 15 = 4.2$	5 *	13
184	98	$86 \div 15 = 5.7$	5 *	18
152	39	$113 \div 15 = 7.5$	7	17
264	101	$163 \div 15 = 10.9$	10 *	17
91	53	$38 \div 15 = 2.5$	3	13
61	37	$24 \div 15 = 1.6$	2	13

2. An interval of 10 units is generally preferred to one of 9 or 11, partly because human beings like to work with groups of 10, and partly because tabulation by tens is particularly easy. Therefore, in the fifth illustration above, the quotient 10.9 was considered to indicate an interval of 10 rather than 11. If the lowest integer in each interval can be a multiple of 10, then in tabulation no attention need be paid to the units digit. Note that in the interval whose score limits are 80–89, the real limits are $79\frac{1}{2}$–$89\frac{1}{2}$, and the midpoint is $84\frac{1}{2}$.

3. In general an interval with an odd number of units is easier to work with than one with an even number. Thus 4, 6, and 8 are not popular widths, and in the preceding illustrations 5 was suggested as the interval width even when 4 and 6 seemed indicated as nearer one-fifteenth of the range. It is often necessary to use an interval of width 2, however, as in the final illustration above, where a width of 1 unit would have given rise to 24 intervals and a width of 3 units to only 8.

When a score is considered to be located at the middle of a score inter-

---

* The numbers marked with an asterisk are discussed in sections 2 and 3, following.

† If lowest score is used as first integer in lowest interval.

val, the class interval with odd number of units has the advantage of having an integer as its midpoint, whereas the class interval with even number of units has a fraction as its midpoint. This is the chief reason for preferring the odd number.

Illustration:

Score Limits	Number of Units in Interval	Midpoint
40–41	2	40.5
40–42	3	41
40–43	4	41.5
40–44	5	42
40–45	6	42.5
40–46	7	43
40–49	10	44.5

4. After the width of interval has been determined, the beginning point should be adjusted with consideration of any natural groupings of the data, so as to avoid distortion. In subsequent computations, scores will be treated as if they were located at the middle of their class intervals. Therefore, an arrangement by which several high frequencies were placed at the very bottom of an interval with no compensating high frequencies at the top, or *vice versa*, would cause a slight error in the outcome of computations. Usually, however, this is an unimportant matter and may be disregarded unless the data are scanty or show an obvious rhythm.

5. When data are to be represented graphically, it is often advantageous to use a smaller number of broader intervals than would be recommended for computational purposes, especially if the number of cases in the distribution is small.

CHAPTER III

THE FREQUENCY DISTRIBUTION

Statistics are the only tools by which an opening can be cut through the formidable thicket of difficulties that bars the path of those who pursue the Science of Man.   Sir Francis Galton

Need for Organizing Mass Data. A mass of raw data is usually unwieldy and difficult to interpret or to comprehend if it is left in the form in which it has been collected. Consider the scores listed in Appendix A. Without reorganizing these data, what can you learn from them about the reading speed of pupils in this group? A cursory survey yields a general impression that most of the scores fall in the 20's and 30's. A more laborious examination shows the lowest score to be 7 and the highest 50, so that the range may be stated as 50 − 7 = 43. Beyond this it is hard to go with the data in their present form.

One thing which might be done is to rewrite these 109 scores in order from the highest to the lowest, as in Table I. An inspection of this table provides a much clearer impression of the distribution of scores than could be obtained from the unordered scores in the original compilation. The highest and lowest scores are immediately seen and the middle score, or midscore, can be readily obtained by counting from either end. It is the 55th score, and is the number 27 printed in italic type in the table on page 29.

The scores which occur most frequently are readily identified as 24, which occurs 10 times, and 30, which occurs 9 times. No other scores are as popular as these. Approximately one-half of the scores lie within the range from 23 to 34 inclusive, approximately one-fourth being smaller than 23 and one-fourth, larger than 34.

The tabulation presented in Table I, however, is rather tedious to prepare, cumbersome to print, and not particularly effective in its presentation. In order to present the data so that the eye can take them in easily, the mind comprehend them, and computational method deal with them efficiently, condensation is necessary. A first step in such a condensation would be achieved by representing the repetitions of a particular score by tallies rather than by rewriting the score itself, as in Table II. The number of tallies corresponding to any given score is the *frequency* of that score, commonly represented by the letter f. The

TABLE I

Data Arranged in Order of Size *

*Scores on Modern School Achievement Test of Reading Speed Made by
109 Fourth-Grade Children, City X, Dec. 2, 1940.*

(Data from column 6 of Table A, in Appendix)

50	44	40	33	30	28	26	24	23	17	13
50	43	40	33	30	28	26	24	22	17	12
49	43	39	32	30	28	26	24	22	17	11
48	42	39	31	30	27	26	24	21	16	10
46	42	36	31	29	27	26	24	21	16	10
45	41	35	30	29	27	25	24	21	16	10
45	41	35	30	29	27	25	24	20	16	8
45	41	35	30	28	26	25	24	20	15	8
44	40	34	30	28	26	25	24	18	14	7
44	40	34	30	28	26	24	23	18	14	

preparation of such a table is facilitated by having one person read the scores aloud from the original data sheet while another records tally marks opposite the corresponding values in a previously prepared list of scores. However, this is not twice as rapid as the work of one person alone, and therefore is not usually an economical procedure. Tabulation should always be checked by retabulating. Mistakes in tabulation are easy to make and cannot be discovered through computational checks unless an independent tabulation is available.

An arrangement of data showing the frequency with which a measure of a given size occurs is called a frequency distribution. This frequency distribution may be displayed in a frequency table, such as Tables II, III, IV, etc., or in a frequency chart, frequency curve, frequency polygon, or histogram, as discussed in later sections of this chapter.

Choice of Class Sort, or Class Interval, or Step Interval. The form of the distribution of scores is presented to the eye more vividly in Table II than in Table I, but it still appears diffuse and wasteful of space. Irregularities of distribution blur the pattern. Such irregularities would undoubtedly be somewhat reduced if the number of cases could be greatly increased. Even for a small group, however, some of these irregularities could be overcome by grouping together the frequencies corresponding

* The titles of tables and charts in this text are planned to emphasize form and pattern of treatment rather than content. This is exactly contrary to ordinary good usage in a treatise dealing with subject matter. See page 54 for a discussion of the standards for titles.

TABLE II

Frequency Distribution, Made in Intervals of One Unit

(*From Data of Table I*)

Score	Tallies	Frequency
50	/ /	2
49	/	1
48	/	1
47		
46	/	1
45	/ / /	3
44	/ / /	3
43	/ /	2
42	/ /	2
41	/ / /	3
40	/ / / /	4
39	/ /	2
38		
37		
36	/	1
35	/ / /	3
34	/ /	2
33	/ /	2
32	/	1
31	/ /	2
30	///// ////	9
29	/ / /	3
28	///// /	6
27	/ / / /	4
26	///// ///	8
25	/ / / /	4
24	///// /////	10
23	/ /	2
22	/ /	2
21	/ / /	3
20	/ /	2
19		
18	/ /	2
17	/ / /	3
16	/ / / /	4
15	/	1
14	/ /	2
13	/	1
12	/	1
11	/	1
10	/ / /	3
9		
8	/ /	2
7	/	1
Total		109

to a number of adjacent scores, thus forming step intervals, as discussed in the latter part of Chapter II.

A choice must be made as to the size or *width of the interval* and as to its beginning point. Both decisions are of necessity somewhat arbitrary. The relative advantages and disadvantages of having a coarser or a finer grouping may be seen by comparing Tables II to VI. The effect of choosing a different beginning point for the interval may be seen by comparing the different portions of Table IV, in which the width of interval is the same but the position of the interval on the scale is different. Of these three sections, it cannot be said that one is right and the others wrong, although the pictures they present are not identical. Section C has a certain advantage because the scores of 24 and 30, at which large frequencies occur in the original data, are placed at the middle of a step interval, while in sections A and B these large frequencies are not at the center of an interval.

Other tabulations of the same data, in which the interval is wider, are presented in Table V and Table VI. In Table VI the interval is so wide that the fundamental pattern of distribution is concealed.

TABLE III

Frequency Distribution Made in Intervals of Three Units

(From Data of Table I)

Score	Tallies	Frequency
49–51	/ / /	3
46–48	/ /	2
43–45	////·/·/ /	8
40–42	//// / / / /	9
37–39	/ /	2
34–36	//// /	6
31–33	////	5
28–30	//// //// //// / / /	18
25–27	//// //// //// /	16
22–24	//// //// / / / /	14
19–21	////	5
16–18	//// / / / /	9
13–15	/ / / /	4
10–12	////	5
7– 9	/ / /	3
Total		109

TABLE IV

Frequency Distribution, Data Grouped in Intervals of Three Units, Using Different Limits

(From Data of Table I)

A		B		C	
Score	f	Score	f	Score	f
49–51	3	48–50	4	50–52	2
46–48	2	45–47	4	47–49	2
43–45	8	42–44	7	44–46	7
40–42	9	39–41	9	41–43	7
37–39	2	36–38	1	38–40	6
34–36	6	33–35	7	35–37	4
31–33	5	30–32	12	32–34	5
28–30	18	27–29	13	29–31	14
25–27	16	24–26	22	26–28	18
22–24	14	21–23	7	23–25	16
19–21	5	18–20	4	20–22	7
16–18	9	15–17	8	17–19	5
13–15	4	12–14	4	14–16	7
10–12	5	9–11	4	11–13	3
7– 9	3	6– 8	3	8–10	5
				5– 7	1
Total	109	Total	109	Total	109

TABLE V

Frequency Distribution, Data Grouped in Intervals of Seven Units

(From Data of Table I)

Score	f
48–54	4
41–47	14
34–40	12
27–33	27
20–26	31
13–19	13
6–12	8
Total	109

TABLE VI

Frequency Distribution, Data Grouped in Intervals of Ten Units

(From Data of Table I)

Score	f
50–59	2
40–49	20
30–39	22
20–29	44
10–19	18
0– 9	3
Total	109

TABLE VII

Ungrouped Data

Number of Years of Previous Teaching in the Local School System for the 267 Teachers of City X

Number of Years	Number of Teachers	Number of Years	Number of Teachers	Number of Years	Number of Teachers
0	15	15	5	30	3
1	25	16	8	31	1
2	30	17	5	32	
3	26	18	4	33	
4	12	19	2	34	1
5	7	20	3	35	
6	11	21	2	36	2
7	15	22	1	37	
8	21	23	2	38	1
9	16	24	3	39	
10	9	25	1	40	
11	12	26		41	1
12	8	27	1	42	
13	4	28	2	43	
14	6	29	1	44	1

Use of Unequal Intervals. Suppose that a city school system is assembling information as to the training and experience of its teachers, and a table is to be made showing the number of years previous to the present each teacher has taught in the local system. Table VII shows the result of the first tabulation, year by year. To reduce this to a table with 15 intervals of 3 years each would be most unsatisfactory, because an increment of one year at the lower end of the scale is important, while an increment of one year at the upper end of the scale is negligible. Combining frequencies at the lower end of the scale would conceal valuable information. In such situations the width of interval is customarily adjusted to show fine gradations of scale where such detail is of importance and to employ coarser grouping where that is sufficient, as illustrated in Table VIII. Considerable care must be taken in reading such a table, and in presenting it graphically (see later section of this chapter) or in making computations based upon it (see Chapter VIII). In general, unequal intervals should be employed only when there is a very strong reason for doing so.

TABLE VIII

Data Grouped in Unequal Intervals:

Number of Years of Previous Teaching in the Local School System for the 267 Teachers of City X

Number of Years	Number of Teachers
0	15
1	25
2	30
3	26
4–6	30
7–9	52
10–14	39
15–19	24
20–24	11
25–34	10
35–44	5
Total	267

Errors Created by Grouping Scores in Intervals. In the ungrouped data of Table I and Table II, the range was seen to be from 7 to 50, the midscore to be 27, and the score with largest frequency, usually called the mode, to be 24. It will be interesting to see how the procedure of grouping scores into larger intervals affects these values.

The four largest scores in Table II are 50, 50, 49, and 48. After these have been grouped together into one interval in Table V, the only information available is that they fall somewhere between 47.5 and 54.5. Lacking more precise information, one might make various assumptions about them, such as that all four are concentrated at the midpoint of the interval (or 51) or that all four are distributed evenly throughout the interval, each occupying one-fourth of its width. The latter assumption is commonly made, and underlies the computations which are discussed in Chapter V. It is a fairly reasonable assumption when the class intervals are narrow, but appears less satisfactory when they are wide.

To estimate the range of scores from Table V, it is possible only to say that there may be one or more scores as small as 6 and one or more as large as 54. In this case, some statisticians would say that the range is from 6 to 54, defining it as extending from the smallest to the largest possible score; some would say from $5\frac{1}{2}$ to $54\frac{1}{2}$, defining it from the lower limit of the lowest interval to the upper limit of the highest interval; and some would say from 9 to 51, defining it as from the midpoint of the lowest to the midpoint of the highest interval. The choice of definition is not very important. In this text we have used the first, i.e., we have defined the range as extending from the smallest to the largest possible score. In discussing Table I, the term midscore was used to describe a score exactly at the middle of the ordered list of scores. For 109 scores, this would be the 55th from either end. In Table V, the 55th score is one of the group of 27 scores in the interval 27–33, presumably one of those near the lower limit, inasmuch as there are 52 scores below this interval, and so if the 27 scores in this interval could be arranged in order, the midscore, or the 55th score, would be the 3rd score counting up from the bottom of the interval. Often the original data are not accessible, and any estimate of the midscore must be obtained from the grouped distribution. Two expedients are commonly employed: (1) The midpoint of the interval in which the midscore falls is used as a rough approximation to the midscore. (2) An interpolated score is obtained on the assumption that all scores in the interval are evenly distributed throughout that interval. The value thus obtained is ordinarily called the median. It will be discussed more fully in Chapter V.

Examination of Tables II, IV (A), IV (B), IV (C), and VI will show that the midpoint of the interval with the largest frequency is considerably affected by the choice of interval, being for these five tables respectively 24, 29, 25, 27, and 24.5. The range of scores is also affected, being respectively 7 to 50, 7 to 51, 6 to 50, 5 to 52, and 0 to 59. When you have learned to compute the arithmetic mean and standard deviation, you will see that these measures are affected also by grouping errors, but not so greatly.

Gain and Loss of Information in Going from Original Data to a Frequency Distribution. In passing from the original data to any frequency distribution, all information about individuals is lost. This information about the individual case is deliberately relinquished in order that the group pattern may appear.

The use of a very small classification interval, as in Table II, presents the group data with precision, but may not throw the group pattern into high relief. As the width of the interval is increased, precision is sacrificed, but up to a certain point the group pattern emerges more and more vividly. When the width of interval is increased beyond this optimum point, the group pattern again becomes obscure. The optimum width of interval depends partly upon the number of cases in the tabulation, a larger number of narrower intervals being more appropriate to a large group, and a smaller number of broader intervals being more appropriate to a small group. In general, the form of distribution appears to greatest advantage when the number of intervals is not less than 10 nor more than 20.

Graphic Representation of Frequency. While there are many different ways of picturing a frequency distribution, certain devices contribute especially to the general understanding of the statistical measures which will be discussed in later chapters. Among such devices are the histogram, the frequency polygon, the smoothed frequency curve, and the cumulative frequency curve.

*1. The Histogram.** The rows of tallies in the frequency tables presented earlier in this chapter appeal to the eye and suggest the use of parallel bars or parallel columns as a graphic means of representing frequency.

To prepare a histogram from the data of Table IV (C), lay off the scale of scores on a horizontal axis, the scale increasing from left to right. This scale must be marked in such a way that the division points between

---

* The term "histogram" was first used by Karl Pearson in 1895 as a term for a common form of graphic representation, i.e., "by columns marking as areas the frequency corresponding to the range of their base." The term is not related in its origin to "history" as is sometimes erroneously stated.

intervals can be identified. With infinitely many points on the scale to select from, a few must be chosen to mark for identification. The sketches in Figure 1 show four possible, and equally correct, methods of marking the scale. In *a*, the numerical values of the division points only are shown; in *b*, the numerical values of the midpoints; in *c* and *d*, the numerical values of other selected scores which locate the scale. Try to imagine

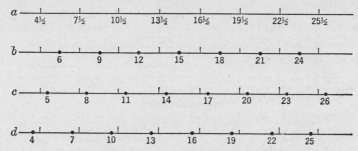

Fig. 1. Various methods of marking the same scale.
    a. Division points between intervals
    b. Midpoints of intervals
    c. First integer in each interval
    d. Last integer in each interval

these four superimposed, and you will see that each is imparting the same information, and that it is immaterial which method of marking is used. In any case the placing of the division points between intervals and the naming of score values on the scale must be consistent with the definitions of score and interval used in the original collection of data.

At right angles to the scale of scores, erect a scale of frequency. *The zero point must be shown on the frequency scale,* but not necessarily on the scale of scores.

We shall now represent each of the 109 individuals in Table IV (C) by a small rectangle whose horizontal distance is one interval on the scale of scores and whose vertical distance is one unit on the scale of frequency. This small rectangle is one area unit representing one frequency unit. There are 7 individuals with scores in the interval from $13\frac{1}{2}$ to $16\frac{1}{2}$, and the corresponding 7 area units form one column whose height is 7 units on the frequency scale and whose width is one interval on the scale of scores. In Figure 2 the 109 individual rectangles are shown, but ordinarily only the column outlines need be indicated. Sometimes even the vertical lines which separate columns are omitted. However, the beginner is likely to have a clearer understanding of what such a chart means if he sees these vertical lines.

In Figure 2 the frequency appears to be satisfactorily represented

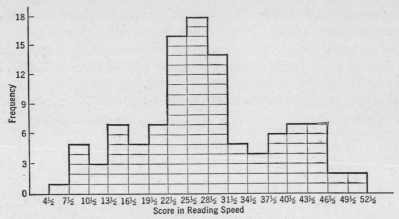

Fig. 2. Histogram: distribution of scores of 109 fourth-grade children of city X on Modern School Achievement Test of Reading Speed. (Based on frequency distribution of Table IV, C.)

either by the area of a bar or by its height. However, it is much better to think of the frequency as represented by the area. In a smoothed frequency curve (discussed subsequently) and in such theoretical curves as

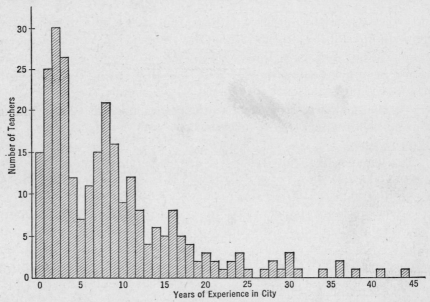

Fig. 3. Histogram: number of years of previous teaching in the local school system for the 267 teachers of city X. (From data of Table VII.)

the normal curve, frequency cannot be represented by the height of an ordinate but only by the area between two ordinates. The close parallelism between area and frequency is basic to an understanding of tables of probability needed for advanced work, and students who permit themselves to identify frequency with ordinate are seriously handicapped later.

If data are grouped in unequal intervals, such as those of Table VIII, the unwary are likely to commit a fallacy when trying to represent them graphically. Figure 3 shows a histogram based on Table VII and Figure 4 shows one based on Table VIII. Note that one frequency unit is

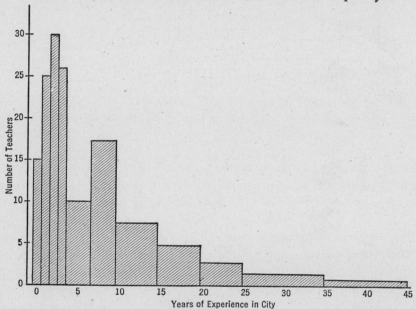

Fig. 4. Histogram illustrating treatment of unequal intervals. (From data of Table VIII.)

represented by a rectangle of length equal to one unit on the scale of scores and one unit on the scale of frequency. The 10 scores in the interval from $24\frac{1}{2}$ to $34\frac{1}{2}$ are represented by a rectangle equal in area to 10 such unit rectangles, and since this rectangle is 10 score units long, it can be only 1 unit high. Therefore, the frequency in the interval is represented not by the height but by the area of the rectangle. Similarly the 24 cases between $14\frac{1}{2}$ and $19\frac{1}{2}$ are represented by a rectangle 5 score units in length and $\frac{24}{5} = 4.8$ units in height.

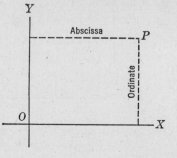

It will be convenient in discussing frequency graphs to use the conventional mathematical terms *ordinate* and *abscissa*. The vertical distance to a point from the horizontal axis is called the ordinate of that point. The horizontal distance to a point from the vertical axis is called the abscissa of that point.* Together, the ordinate and abscissa are called *coordinates* of the point.

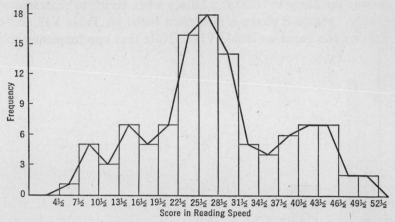

Fig. 5. Frequency polygon superimposed on histogram. (From data of Table IV, C. Compare with Fig. 2.)

2. The Frequency Polygon. The midpoints of the tops of the rectangles of the histogram have, in Figure 5, been connected by straight lines to form what is called a frequency polygon. Note that in Figure 6 the triangles 1, 2, · · · 7, are congruent respectively to triangles 1′, 2′, · · · 7′. (Vertical angles are equal; right angles are equal; sides which are halves of tops of bars are equal; by a well-known theorem of plane geometry this makes the triangles congruent.) Therefore, by drawing the frequency polygon through the midpoints of the rectangles, we make the area of the polygon equivalent to the area of the histogram. However, only one ordinate in each rectangle is preserved when we go from histogram to polygon. These are the ordinates at B, C, D, E, F, and G. All the other ordinates have been changed. It is desirable to use a representation of the frequency which will remain invariant (unchanged) when a frequency polygon is constructed and so area is used rather than ordinate.

When two or more frequency distributions are to be compared, the frequency polygon gives a clearer picture than the histogram. If two histograms are placed on the same pair of axes the lines of one are likely to be confused with the lines of the other. Two superimposed frequency

* The term originated in old surveying manuals written in Latin, in which that portion of a horizontal distance cut off by the shadow of a vertical staff was called the *pars abscissa*, or the "part cut off."

polygons, on the contrary, are usually quite distinct. The ogive curves described in Chapter V are still more effective in presenting overlapping distributions.

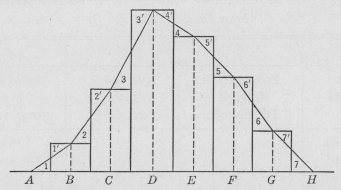

Fig. 6. Illustration of the relation of area and ordinates of frequency polygon to area and ordinates of histogram. Triangle 1 = triangle 1′, triangle 2 = triangle 2′, etc. The ordinates at B, C, D, E, F, and G are identical for the two figures. At no other points are ordinates identical for the two figures.

3. Smoothed Frequency Curve. As more and more cases are added to a distribution, there is a tendency for the frequency polygon to lose its jagged effect and to assume a more regular pattern. As the size of the class interval is made smaller and smaller, the frequency polygon takes on more and more the appearance of a smooth, flowing curve. When both changes take place simultaneously, the number of cases being made very large and the width of class interval very small, the frequency polygon takes on an appearance which often suggests the curve of a mathematical equation.

A simple device, called the moving average, is often used to smooth out what are thought to be chance irregularities in an observed frequency distribution or chance irregularities in a time series. There is usually no way of telling whether a particular hump or hollow in the curve is due to a chance error in the choice of cases or is an indication of some meaningful trend in the data. The moving average reduces one as well as the other.

The procedure is illustrated in Table IX and Figure 7. The original frequencies as given in Table IV (C) are reproduced in the second column of this table, and zero frequencies in cells immediately beyond the range of the original distribution are also shown. Any 3 adjacent frequencies are then added and their sum divided by 3 to produce the number in the third column which is written opposite the middle one of the three added frequencies. Thus $\dfrac{0 + 0 + 2}{3} = 0.7$ and $\dfrac{0 + 2 + 2}{3} = 1.3$ are the first two

TABLE IX

Frequency Distribution Smoothed by Moving Average

(From Data of Table IV, C)

1	2	3	4
Score	Frequency in Original Distribution	Average of Three Frequencies	Average of Five Frequencies
62–64	0	0	0
59–61	0	0	0
56–58	0	0	0.4
53–55	0	0.7	0.8
50–52	2	1.3	2.2
47–49	2	3.7	3.6
44–46	7	5.3	4.8
41–43	7	6.7	5.2
38–40	6	5.7	5.8
35–37	4	5.0	7.2
32–34	5	7.7	9.4
29–31	14	12.3	11.4
26–28	18	16.0	12.0
23–25	16	13.7	12.0
20–22	7	9.3	10.6
17–19	5	6.3	7.6
14–16	7	5.0	5.4
11–13	3	5.0	4.2
8–10	5	3.0	3.2
5– 7	1	2.0	1.8
2– 4	0	0.3	1.2
−1– 1	0	0	0.2
−4– −2	0	0	0
Total	109	109	109

entries in this column. The last column is obtained in similar fashion, the sum of 5 adjacent frequencies being divided by 5. Note that the first frequency in column 4 is $\dfrac{0 + 0 + 0 + 0 + 2}{5} = 0.4$. The smoothed distribution has frequencies beyond the range of the original distribution, and these must not be overlooked, else the total number of cases in the

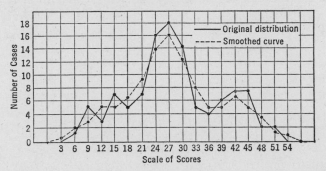

Fig. 7. Frequency polygon smoothed by moving average. (From distribution in column 3 of Table IX.)

smoothed distribution will be incorrect. Figure 7 shows frequency polygons based on the original distribution and on the distribution smoothed by a moving average of 3 frequencies.

In general, the use of a moving average has these effects which, in a particular problem, may or may not be desirable:

1. It makes the distribution more regular.
2. It makes the distribution flatter, less peaked.
3. It increases the spread of the distribution.

4. *Cumulative Frequency Polygon and Cumulative Percentage Polygon.* An extremely useful type of frequency distribution is one in which the ordinate erected at any given point on the scale of scores represents the number of cases with score less than the given score, as in Figure 8.

In Table X, the frequencies in the column headed f are the same as those of Table IV (C). In the next column these frequencies have been cumulated from the bottom of the table. Cumulation is merely a process of addition in which, as each new number is added, the resulting sum is recorded. These cumulative frequencies have been changed to cumulative percentages by dividing each by 109, and the results recorded in the last column.* To be sure you understand this table, find in it the entries

* If a computing machine is available, the reciprocal of 109, that is, $1 \div 109 = 0.009174\cdots$, can be put into the machine and multiplied in turn by each of the cumulative frequencies. If a copy of Crelle's *Computing Tables* is available, all the quotients can be read from a single page.

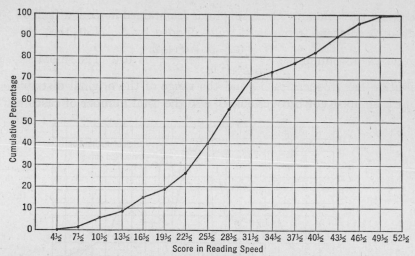

Fig. 8. Cumulative percentage polygon: percentage of children with reading speed score less than a given score. (From data of Table X.)

which justify the following statements, and complete those statements in which there are omissions:

44 cases have scores below 25.5.
___96___ % of the cases have scores below 46.5.
85 cases have scores below _37.5_.
The percentage of cases with scores below 31.5 is ___70___.
Below 52.5 or below any point on the scale above 52.5, there are _100_ % of cases.

There are no cases below 4.5 or any lower point on the scale. If the scale of scores is laid off on the horizontal axis and the scale of frequency on the vertical, a cumulative frequency curve may be drawn. Note that the cumulative frequency is plotted opposite the *upper limit* of the corresponding interval; that is, a cumulative frequency of 62 is plotted against a score value of 28.5.

If cumulative percentage instead of frequency is on the vertical scale, as in Figure 8, a cumulative percentage curve results. The cumulative percentage curve has great advantage over the cumulative frequency curve whenever two or more distributions are to be compared by plotting them on the same pair of axes. This topic will be treated in Chapter V, after a discussion of the meaning of medians and percentiles.

The fundamental relationship between an ordinary frequency distribution and its cumulative frequency distribution is illustrated * in Figure 9.

* This arrangement was probably first used by Robert E. Chaddock. Readers who have studied the calculus will recognize that the cumulative frequency curve bears the same rela-

TABLE X

Cumulative Frequency and Percentage Distributions

(From Data of Table IV, C)

Score	f	Number of Cases with Score Less than Upper Limit of Interval	Percentage of Cases with Score Less than Upper Limit of Interval
50–52	2	109	100%
47–49	2	107	98
44–46	7	105	96
41–43	7	98	90
38–40	6	91	83
35–37	4	85	78
32–34	5	81	74
29–31	14	76	70
26–28	18	62	57
23–25	16	44	40
20–22	7	28	26
17–19	5	21	19
14–16	7	16	15
11–13	3	9	8
8–10	5	6	6
5– 7	1	1	1
Total	109		

Note that the single shaded strip under the cumulative curve is equal in area to the sum of the shaded rectangles under the frequency curve.

The graphs of these cumulative frequency curves are reflex curves, the center of curvature lying to the right in one portion of the curve and to

tion to an ordinary frequency curve that the integral of a function bears to the function. The highest point on the frequency curve determines the point of inflection on the cumulative curve.

the left in another portion. In architecture, an ogive arch (also called ogee) is one which has. a reflex curve. Because cumulative frequency graphs and percentile graphs (which will be discussed in Chapter V) are usually reflex, Francis Galton termed them *ogives*. The name is now used for this type of presentation even if the curve of the graph is not reflex.

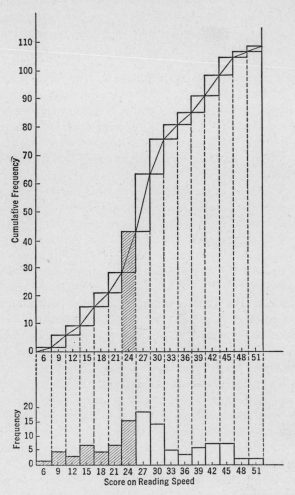

Fig. 9. Frequency and cumulative frequency charts: scores of 109 fourth-grade children on test of reading speed.

If frequencies were cumulated down from the top instead of up from the bottom, the resulting curve would show the number of children having a reading score greater than a given score. Its shape would be the same as that of the curve in Figure 8, but upside down.

The Bivariate Frequency Distribution.* The simultaneous distribution of frequency in two variables can be prepared from the data in Appendix A, and such a table will be suggestive of the general relationship between the traits. In fact, such a table will later be used in the computation of a coefficient of correlation between two traits. Such simultaneous, or joint, distributions of two variables are often called *bivariate* distributions. To illustrate this type of tabulation, the records of 109 children as to chronological age and reading speed will be used. The steps to be followed in setting up such tables are as follows:

1. Decide upon an appropriate step interval for each of the traits.
2. Lay off two axes at right angles to each other. On one axis lay off the step intervals for one variable and on the other axis the step intervals for the second variable. In Table XI the age scale has been placed on the horizontal axis and the scale of reading speed on the vertical. In the present instance it is relatively unimportant which variable is placed on the horizontal axis.
3. Draw horizontal and vertical lines across the page through the division points of the scale to form a grid or use paper already ruled.
4. Let one person read the pair of scores aloud from Appendix A while a second records on the prepared grid one tally for each pair of scores. Here the first pair of scores on the list is "Age, 121; reading speed, 27." Just as soon as he hears "121," the recorder should locate the vertical column in which an age score of 121 months belongs. This is the column with the heading 119–123. The recorder will next locate the horizontal row in which a reading score of 27 falls. This is the row with heading 25–27. He will then place *one tally* in the cell belonging to this column and this row. Cardboard guides can be used by both the reader and the recorder to reduce errors. The reader needs some device to keep his eye from jumping to the wrong row or wrong column on the data sheet. The recorder will find it advantageous to prepare a strip of cardboard with an exact duplicate of the reading-speed scale, which he can slide across the page. As the age score is read, he moves this strip so that the scale appears directly at the left of the appropriate age column, with zero point properly aligned. It is a simple matter then to place the tally in the proper cell.
5. When a tally has been recorded for every score, the marginal frequencies are obtained by adding along each row and by adding along each column.

Examination of Table XI shows that the set of marginal frequencies at the right of the table is the distribution of reading speed, as given in Table III. The set of marginal frequencies across the bottom of the table

---

* This section may be deferred until the chapter on correlation is studied. There are, however, some advantages in considering this material at the present stage.

TABLE XI

Bivariate Frequency Distribution: Scores of 109 Fourth-Grade Children on Test of Reading Speed Distributed by Age Groups

Score in Reading Speed	Number of Children at Given Age with Given Score													Total Number of Children with Given Score
	94–98*	99–103	104–108	109–113	114–118	119–123	124–128	129–133	134–138	139–143	144–148	149–153	154–158	
49–51			1	1	1									3
46–48			2											2
43–45		1	4	5	2									8
40–42		1		1	3									9
37–39			2											2
34–36		1		3	1	1								6
31–33	1		5	2	2	1								5
28–30		1	2	3	3		3	1		1			1	18
25–27			2	4	7	2								16
22–24			1	6	3	1		2						14
19–21	1			2				1						5
16–18			1	1	4	2	1		1		1			9
13–15				2			2					1		4
10–12			1	1		1								5
7–9						1		1		1				3
Total Number of Children at Given Age	2	4	21	31	26	8	6	5	1	2	1	1	1	109

* Age to nearest month.

is the frequency distribution of age. Apparently there is a slight, though not very pronounced tendency for the younger children to read more rapidly. This observation should be made tentatively, in due recognition of the fact that we do not yet know how either to establish or to disprove it. No such generalization should be announced by a novice. Yet even the novice may note the absence of very rapid readers among the older children and the numerous cases of older children who are slow readers and of younger children who are rapid readers.

To represent this joint frequency distribution graphically, a column perpendicular to the plane of the distribution might be erected on each cell of the table, the height of the column being proportional to the frequency in the cell. This would produce a figure in three dimensions which is a natural extension of the histogram used to display the distribution of frequency in a single trait. In the accompanying sketch, the vertical column has 7 volume units to represent the 7 children whose reading-speed score falls in the interval 25–27 and whose chronological age falls in the interval 114–118.

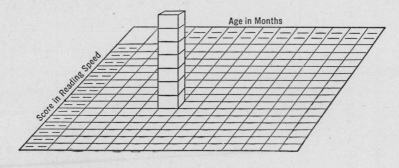

Exercise 5

1. For the data in Appendix A, what would be an appropriate class interval for use in tabulating the scores for each variable?

2. Using a class interval of 5, with 60–64 as score limits of the lowest class, make a frequency distribution of the intelligence quotients, tabulating boys' scores and girls' scores separately and then combining them. Set up a table with proper title and column headings to display these data. (See Chapter IV for suggestions about title and headings.)

3. a. Make a histogram to show the distribution of intelligence quotients for all 109 pupils, boys and girls together. Mark clearly the division points on each scale, and give it an appropriate label. Give the histogram an appropriate title.

   b. Superimpose a frequency polygon on this histogram. Pay particular attention to the ends of the distribution. The polygon should meet the horizontal axis at the midpoint of the class interval lying next beyond the last interval in which frequency occurs.

4. Smooth the distribution of intelligence quotients with a moving average of 3 frequencies and plot the result.

5. a. From the distribution of intelligence quotients of boys, construct the cumulative *percentage* distribution and plot it.

b. Construct the cumulative percentage distribution for intelligence quotients of girls and plot on the same pair of axes used for the boys.

c. Because the number of girls is not the same as the number of boys, the *cumulative frequency* distributions would not be directly comparable, but the *cumulative percentage* distributions are comparable. This method will be more fully developed in Chapter V.

6. Plot the simultaneous frequency distribution of age and intelligence quotient. Save the result for later use in connection with the study of correlation.

CHAPTER IV

THE PRESENTATION OF DATA IN TABLES *

The Function To Be Served by a Table. A necessary initial step in any statistical study is the orderly arrangement of data. To plan a satisfactory logical arrangement of data in classes and subclasses, and to present it clearly for the benefit of the reader, may be a difficult task when data are complex, but the difficulties are chiefly difficulties of logic, not of technique.

There are two main types of table. A *general purpose* table or reference table is used to present a comprehensive set of data in such an arrangement that any particular item can be easily located. As illustrations one may note the extensive summaries in many census reports, or the tabulation of the original, unanalyzed raw data which is often published for reference in the appendix of a research study. In such tables great accuracy is usually desired, hence numbers are carried out to a good many places; ease of reference is important, hence the arrangement of items is often alphabetical. It is primarily a repository of information, and the information should be easy to locate. A *special purpose* table has as its goal clear analysis, and therefore the arrangement of rows and columns is planned to facilitate making important comparisons and showing important trends or relationships.

Tabular or Textual Presentation. Often the author of a monograph has a choice as to whether he will present a given set of data in a formal table with number and title, or verbally in a running paragraph, or in an informal tabulation which is actually part of a sentence. Examples of the latter method can be found in this book on pages 64, 82, and 174.

Several points should be considered in deciding which form to use. (1) Because the use of tabular form gives great emphasis to the facts presented, unimportant data should not be set in a table. Even very simple data which can be stated clearly in sentences may be placed in a table if it is desired to call special attention to them and to refer to them

---

* This chapter can be omitted without affecting the clarity of any subsequent material. If time is limited, it should be omitted or deferred to the end of the course. If time is not limited, the chapter may be expanded to include the criticism and reorganization of tables and charts taken from current sources. If a lantern is available, it can be used effectively for presenting material for this purpose. The discussion of tables presented here is largely abstracted from *Statistical Tables, Their Structure and Use*, by Walker and Durost (Teachers College Bureau of Publications, 1936) where the subject is treated more fully.

51

more than once. (2) A table is clear whether read in connection with one part of the material or another. Therefore, figures to which repeated reference is to be made should be placed in a table rather than a paragraph, whereas figures which must be read in a particular context to be understood, and to which no further reference is to be made, may appropriately be expressed verbally in the text. (3) If a list is long, most people find that its presentation in sentence form is hard to comprehend. If a list is long, presenting it in informal tabulation entails the risk of having it appear partly on one page and partly on another, which is not good typography. A formal table has the advantage that the printer can adjust its position to produce attractive paging. (4) Tabular material, whether arranged formally or informally, increases the cost of printing. (Once in reading a student's manuscript, the author noted that its extensive tabulations were without benefit of title or number and had no clear structural relationship to the context. The student explained that he had removed the titles because he had been told that the presence of tables would increase the cost of printing his material!) (5) Informal tabulation is appropriate only when it can properly be considered as part of a sentence, when the grammatical structure is straightforward and logical.

Table Format. The horizontal arrays of a table are called *lines* or *rows;* the vertical arrays are called *columns*. The space common to a particular row and column is called a *cell*.

Every column should have a heading referring to the subheadings or the tabular entries directly below it. A heading which extends over two or more columns is called a *box head*, or *box heading*, or *brace heading*. Each column under the box head has its own *subhead*. The box head and the subhead taken together usually name the entries in the column below.

All the subheads under one box head should be similar in phrasing. Every subhead must be logically derived from the box head under which it stands. Increasing the number of box heads and subheads increases the cost of printing and makes the table seem more complex, hence unnecessary subheads should be avoided.

Every line should have a heading which identifies the row and indicates how the entries in that row differ from the entries in other rows of the table. All the line headings together form what is called the *stub*. The stub presents one basis for classification of the data; the column headings—when there are more than one—present another. The stub itself should have a heading.

The general principle that the column headings should name that which is tabulated in the columns can be wisely disregarded in a few situations such as the following: (1) In a bivariate frequency distribution, such as that of Table XI, the emphasis is on mutuality of relationship, and there is no essential difference between rows and columns. It is so well understood that all entries are frequencies, that the words "frequency" or "number of cases" are seldom used in the headings. (2) Sometimes in an ordinary frequency distribution it is so obvious that the entries are frequencies, that even a careful author feels justified in omitting that information from the column headings. (3) Occasionally interchanging rows and columns makes it easier to adjust a table to the page as in Table XXXI of this text. In this case the row heading names the tabular entry and the column heading specifies the class to which it is referred. (4) When no possible ambiguity results because the name of the entry is clearly stated in the table title, it may seem satisfactory to omit the name from the column heading, though such omission is, by and large, not a very wise practice.

Table Title. The title of a table has two distinct purposes: it names what is listed in the table, and it serves as a display device to focus the attention of the reader. The first purpose makes clarity and completeness essential; the second makes brevity highly desirable. Unfortunately, brevity and clarity sometimes seem incompatible.

Whatever information is needed for understanding a table must appear with the table. A table fails of its purpose if the reader must hunt through adjacent pages to uncover its meaning. The title is the principal device for conveying such requisite information, although footnotes may also be employed. In general, the title (with the help of a subtitle or footnote) should tell what is listed in the table, where the data were obtained and when, for how many subjects, for what kind of subjects. If the data were gathered by someone other than the writer, proper credit must be given. If the data are measurements, the unit should be stated either in title, row, column heading, or footnote—wherever it seems most appropriate. If percentages are quoted, the base should be clearly indicated.

In formulating a title, it should be remembered that the initial word or words hold the position of greatest emphasis. That position should be used for the thing which it is most important to bring to the reader's attention. Usually this is the name of whatever is listed in the table. It is wasteful and inefficient to begin a title with such unimportant words as "Table showing the distribution of. . . ."

When several closely related tables are presented, it is well to use parallel phrasing for their titles, as well as similar format and similar arrangement of line and column headings. Some device must be found to draw attention to the essential differences between the related tables.*

The Titles of Tables in This Text. If the titles appended to the charts and tables in this text should appear in an ordinary book or article, they could quite properly be denounced as excessively bad titles. On the other hand, titles for these tables and charts constructed in accordance with the principles in the preceding section would be ineffectual for two reasons: (1) The same title would have to be used over and over again because the same data are presented in various patterns; and (2) these tables and charts are primarily designed to illustrate form and not content, and therefore it is appropriate that the title name the form to which attention is directed rather than the content, which is here relatively unimportant. This is exactly the reverse of the purpose usually served by tables and charts. Usually an author wants his reader to think about what is in a table or chart rather than about the manner in which he has chosen to arrange it. Such phrases as "Cumulative frequency distribution of . . ." or "Data grouped in intervals of . . ." or "Histogram illustrating . . ." or "Distributions illustrating . . ." would, in a content study, serve to draw the reader's attention from the essential aspects of content to the superficial aspects of form; here they are used to draw his attention from the superficial aspects of content to the essential aspects of form. *The titles used in this text cannot be taken as models for titles in another kind of treatise.*

Ruling. The logical structure of a table must be clear, else the table is useless. When the page is not crowded, white space between columns or between rows can often serve the same purpose as rules, but when the table is complex or when it crowds the page, it is not always possible to provide enough white space between the lines to help the reader's eye to locate any particular cell.

A table should stand out from the rest of the text, should be separated from the text either by horizontal rules or by a rather wide border of white space. Horizontal rules above and below a table, which are not intersected by vertical rules, do not add appreciably to its cost.

Boxing in a table by vertical rules at the side appears to serve no logical purpose and adds to the printing cost. The only reason for using such rules would seem to be that the author or publisher considers that they make a page attractive.

Intersecting vertical and horizontal rules call for expensive hand work where the two cross. Horizontal rules alone or vertical rules alone do not greatly increase printing costs.

* Several methods of doing this are illustrated in *Statistical Tables, Their Structure and Use*

When a box heading is used, a rule under it is almost necessary to show how many columns the box heading covers.

The plan of ruling adopted should be such as to facilitate whatever kind of reading is most appropriate for the data. One reads a table selectively, not line by line. The format should be such as to encourage making the important comparisons, and to keep the eye from straying to the wrong row or wrong column.

Totals. A row or column can properly be called a total only when its entries are obtained by adding the entries in other rows or other columns. For example, suppose a table presents data on illiteracy for each of the states and for the United States as a whole. If number of illiterates is recorded, the summary figure for the United States is a total, but if percentage is recorded, the summary is not a total, but is the percentage *for all the states*, and should be so labeled.

The totals for the columns should be separated from the rest of the table either by space or by a horizontal line extending only to the stub. This serves to draw attention to the total and also to prevent the reader's misreading it as another tabulated item.

Preparation of Dummy Format. One simple precaution against the dangers of failing to secure needed data, of securing data that are not in usable form, and of wasting effort on the collection of irrelevant data, is to draw up a dummy format of each table that is likely to appear in the study, and to do this before sending out any instrument for gathering data. This step will, of course, delay the initial stages of a study. It has, however, saved many persons from grief in later stages of their studies by revealing flaws in their instruments while such flaws could still be corrected. For example, it may seem very satisfactory to the maker of a questionnaire to use some such irregular classification for age as "Under 20, 20–29, 30–44, 45–65, over 65"; but when he comes to analyze his data he may decide that he wants a mean age, or the correlation of age with some other trait, and may find himself in difficulties which could readily have been avoided. Had he foreseen the form his tables were to take, he would have recognized the inadequacy of this classification. The experienced research worker may or may not need to commit such table formats to paper in advance. These may be so clearly in the background of his thinking as unconsciously to dominate the structure of his instruments. Similarly, an experienced writer who never prepares a written outline may adhere to sharply logical structure, but the writing of most novices would be vastly improved by the use of outlines.

Usually there is more than one way in which a table might be set up, one plan being more effective for one purpose and one for another. Until an author has secured a good deal of experience in planning tables, he should try out various arrangements of his data, drawing up different dummy formats. It is usually not necessary to enter any figures in these to see their strong and weak points.

Exercise 6

1. Below are short descriptions of a number of studies, the outcome of each of which is to be displayed in a table or series of tables. For each one draw up a dummy format, with stub, column headings, heading over the stub, and title.

a. For a particular state, the reported automobile accidents are classified as to type of accident, sex of driver, and ten-year period in which accident occurred.

b. For a particular state, the number of births, deaths, stillbirths, maternal deaths, and infant deaths, and the rate for each are classified by race as white, Negro, and other, and are classified by ten-year period.

c. Children referred to a particular clinic are classified as to sex and as to type of behavior problem they exhibit, a child being counted more than once if he exhibits more than one problem. Both number and percentage of children exhibiting a given problem are to be shown in the table.

d. For a large city system, the average daily register, the average daily attendance, and the percentage of attendance is to be shown for boys, girls, and both, for each of 25 elementary schools.

e. The number of children registered, the number promoted, and the percentage promoted at the end of the fall term and at the end of the spring term is to be shown for various types of handicapped children (blind, cardiopathic, crippled, etc.) in a city school system.

f. In a study of retardation in the junior high schools of a city school system, pupils are classified according to grade in which they are enrolled (7A, 7B, 8A, 8B, 9A and 9B) and according to whether they are underage, at normal age, or overage. Those who are underage are classified as to the extent of their underageness; $\frac{1}{2}$ year or less, $\frac{1}{2}$ to 1 year, 1 to $1\frac{1}{2}$ years, $1\frac{1}{2}$ to 2 years. Those overage are similarly classified. Summaries are shown for all grades, for all underage, for all overage.

2. Select several tables from current publications. Check on each to see that it meets these criteria: (a) Is it logically a unit, all the data closely related, with no extraneous facts included? (b) Is it autonomous, self-explanatory, self-sufficing? Can it stand alone if removed from the context? (c) Is the title unambiguous, concise, complete, clear, and logically accurate? (d) Are sources and units specified? (e) Does every column and every row have a heading? Are these well chosen? Does the column heading, taken with any box headings to which it is subordinate, name that which stands in the column? (f) Are all subclassifications logically subordinate to the main classification? (g) Does the arrangement facilitate logical analysis?

If the table is unsatisfactory in any way, see if you can rearrange it effectively.

Graphic Methods. A very considerable literature has in recent years grown up on the subject of graphic methods. With this literature, no person who plans to carry out statistical studies and to present the results of such studies to the public, can afford to remain unacquainted. Graphic devices for presenting statistical data of all kinds and standards of graphic presentation are discussed in the references at the end of this chapter. Because these references are readily accessible in most college libraries, it seems undesirable to treat here the general problems of graphic representation. At this point, the student is urged to examine one or more of these references. The histogram, frequency polygon, and frequency curve are treated here in some detail because of their contribution to an understanding of certain fundamental statistical concepts.*

BIBLIOGRAPHY

Graphic Methods
American Society of Mechanical Engineers, *Time-Series Charts: A Manual of Design and Construction*. New York, the Society, 1938.
Arkin, H. and Colton, R. R., *Graphs: How to Make and Use Them*. New York, Harper and Brothers, 1936.
Brinton, W. C., *Graphic Presentation*. New York, Brinton Associates, 1939.
Brown, T. H., Bingham, R. F., and Temnomeroff, V. A., *Laboratory Handbook of Statistical Methods*. Book 1, "Graphic Methods." New York, McGraw-Hill Book Co., 1931.
Chaddock, R. E., *Principles and Methods of Statistics*. Chapter XVI, "Graphic Representation." Boston, Houghton Mifflin Co., 1925.
Croxton, F. E., and Cowden, D. J., *Applied General Statistics*. New York, Prentice Hall, Inc., 1940. Chapters IV, V, and VI.
Funkhouser, H. G., "Historical development of the graphical representation of statistical data," *Osiris*, 3 (1937), 269–404. This contains an annotated bibliography of nearly 300 titles on graphic method.
Haskell, A. C., *Graphic Charts in Business*. New York, Codex Book Co., 1928.
Karsten, K. G., *Charts and Graphs*. New York, Prentice Hall, Inc., 1925.
Mills, F. C., *Statistical Methods Applied to Economics and Business*, revised edition, Chapter II, "Graphic Presentation." New York, Henry Holt and Co., 1938.
Paterson, D. D., *Statistical Technique in Agricultural Research*. Chapter IV, "Diagrams." New York, McGraw-Hill Book Co., 1939.

* The inventor of the graphic method of presenting statistical data was William Playfair (1759–1823). The first known bar graph occurs in his *Commercial and Political Atlas*, London, 1786, 1787, 1801, where it was used to compare the imports and exports of Scotland for a given year. See Funkhouser, H. Gray, "Historical development of the graphical representation of statistical data," *Osiris*, 3 (1937), 269–404, and Funkhouser, H. Gray, and Walker, Helen M., "Playfair and his charts," *Economic History*, 3 (February, 1935) 103–109.

Riggleman, J. R., *Graphic Methods for Presenting Business Statistics*. New York, McGraw-Hill Book Co., 1926.

Rugg, H. O., *Primer of Graphics and Statistics for Teachers*. Boston, Houghton Mifflin Co., 1925.

Williams, J. H., *Graphic Method in Education*. Boston, Houghton Mifflin Co., 1924.

Tabular Work

Croxton, F. E., and Cowden, D. J., *Applied General Statistics*. New York, Prentice Hall, Inc., 1940. Chapter III.

Mudgett, B. D., *Statistical Tables and Graphs*. Boston, Houghton Mifflin Co., 1930.

United States Government Printing Office., *Style Manual*, pp. 111–119. Washington, D. C., 1939.

Walker, H. M., and Durost, W. N., *Statistical Tables; Their Structure and Use*. New York, Bureau of Publications, Teachers College, Columbia University, 1936.

CHAPTER V

MEASURES OF RELATIVE POSITION

A measure of the absolute amount of any quantity usually has limited meaning until or unless it can be interpreted as a relative amount. Is an error of two inches in measuring height large or small? That depends on whether one is measuring the height of a child, of a building, of a cloud. The price of an article becomes meaningful only in relation to some standard such as the usual price of similar articles, the amount of cash available for its purchase, the hours of labor required to produce and market it, and the like. As a surveyor indicates location with reference to some bench mark, so do we seek for reference points, standards, bench marks, in all our experiences.

In measuring traits of human beings, a standard is naturally furnished by the group to which an individual belongs. It is difficult to think of any human trait in which amounts are interpreted without reference to what is usual of individuals of a given type. To say that a man's voice has a range of three octaves excites no surprise unless we know how rare are individuals with so great a range.

A child of 10 may feel very tall and very mature in a group of younger children, but if transferred to another group in which he is the youngest he may feel very small and inexperienced. The standard of comparison has changed and absolute measures of age, height, information, and the like do not reflect the change. A measure of the individual's relative position with respect to his group has obvious meaning for understanding persons and group behavior.

Galton put the matter very clearly when he wrote,*

A knowledge of the distribution of any quality enables us to ascertain the Rank that each man holds among his fellows, in respect to that quality. This is a valuable piece of knowledge in this struggling and competitive world, where success is to the foremost, and failure to the hindmost, irrespective of absolute efficiency. A blurred vision would be above all price to an individual man in a nation of blind men, though it would hardly enable him to earn his bread elsewhere. When the distribution of any faculty has been ascertained, we can tell from the measurement, say of our child, how he ranks among other children in respect to that faculty, whether it be a physical gift, or one of health, or of intellect, or of morals.

* *Natural Inheritance*, London, 1889, pp. 36–37.

59

Especially in the field of educational and psychological testing are scores completely without meaning unless they can be referred to some standard, some bench mark. What does it mean to say that a student scored 29 on a test? Nothing at all. This may have been a phenomenally high score or a phenomenally low one, or may be about the average of students with comparable training and age. The score itself provides no basis for interpretation.

Percentage, Percentile, Percentile Rank. An individual's position in his group with respect to any given trait can be described by a statement of the percentage of the group he exceeds in that trait. To say that John is older than 90% of his class at school, can run faster than 75% of them, is taller than 80%, has a higher intelligence quotient than 30%, exceeds 25% in score on an arithmetic test and 40% in score on an English test, and exceeds 95% in the number of absences he has had during the term, gives a certain description of John to one who knows the class and a certain description of the class to one who knows John. John's age would be called the *90th percentile (or centile)* of the age distribution of the class, and John is said to stand *at the 90th percentile* of the class in respect to age, or to *have a percentile rank of 90* in age.

One of the earliest suggestions for the use of such measures to describe a group was published in 1874 in a place where few persons would think of looking for statistical help, a handbook called *Notes and Queries on Anthropology for the Use of Travellers and Residents in Uncivilized Lands*. Galton contributed to this handbook a section on *Statistics* in which he urged travelers in little frequented regions to bring back as much anthropometric information as possible. A chieftain, Galton thought, would probably refuse to have all his men measured, but might be persuaded to have them drawn up in a line in order of height, and to allow the visitor to measure the heights of the men at the middle and quarter points. A report on these selected individuals could furnish a partial description of the entire group. A very amicable chieftain might even be persuaded to allow the 20th, 90th, 910th, and 980th man out of 1000 to be measured, thus providing rough values of what Galton later called the 20th, 90th, 910th, and 980th permilles, or what are now more commonly called the 2nd, 9th, 91st, and 98th percentile values.

If exactly $n\%$ of the cases in a distribution have scores less than a given value, that value is called the *nth percentile*. The *nth percentile* may also be defined as the score corresponding to a point on the scale of scores of a grouped frequency distribution such that $n\%$ of the area under the frequency curve lies below (i.e., to the left of) the ordinate drawn at that point. It may also be defined as the abscissa of that point.

We shall designate it as P_n. The term *centile* is sometimes advocated as a substitute for the term percentile on the ground that it is consistent in form with quartile and decile. The term centile seems to be a very satisfactory term, if one were creating statistical language *de novo*, but it has never come into general use.

Certain percentiles are so important that they have received special names. The 10th, 20th, 30th, etc., percentiles are called the 1st, 2nd, 3rd, etc., *deciles*. The 25th percentile is called the *lower quartile* or *first quartile*, designated as Q_L or Q_1. The 75th percentile is called the *upper quartile* or *third quartile*, designated as Q_U or Q_3. The 50th percentile is called the *median*, and is usually designated as Md. Obviously the median is also the 5th decile or the 2nd quartile. The 15th percentile is sometimes called the 150th *permille*, the 73rd percentile, the 730th permille. The *n*th permille would thus be the abscissa of a point on the scale of scores of a grouped frequency distribution such that *n* one-thousandths of the area under the curve lies below the point. Galton introduced this term, like all the preceding, but today it is seldom used. Galton also used the terms *octile* and *dodecile*, now practically obsolete.

A certain contrast in the use of the terms "rank" and "percentile rank" must be understood. The case which ranks first is the case at the top of the distribution. The case with percentile rank of 1 is at or near the bottom. The case with percentile rank of 50 is known to be at the middle of the distribution, with just as many cases above as below it. The case with rank 50 may be anywhere along the scale, depending upon the number of cases. If there are 10,000 people in the group, the case with rank 50 would be above the 99th percentile. If there are only 50 cases, it would be at the 1st percentile. The import of standing 50th from the top of a group depends upon the size and quality of the group. The import of exceeding 50% of a group depends upon the quality of the group but has little to do with its size.

Note that a percentile, a median, a decile, or quartile is a score represented by a point on the scale of scores, and not a range. No one who has clearly understood this graphic representation would say "in the upper decile" or "in the lower quartile" as though a decile or a quartile represented a range. The word quarter still keeps its normal meaning. The lower fourth of the scores is not the lower quartile but the lower quarter, and the lower quartile is the score below which the scores of the lower quarter of the group fall. "Percentile" is not, as a student once remarked "the new term they are using instead of percentage this year."

Obtaining a Percentile from a Histogram. The method of computation about to be presented is not the most expeditious one but is presented here in order to develop a basic understanding of what the process means. The writer believes that what are efficient methods to the experienced computer are often a source of confusion to the novice and that short cuts should usually not be studied until the underlying concepts are clear. Often this text will employ a somewhat cumbersome computational pattern when a topic is first introduced in order to bring out more vividly the basic ideas, and in a later section will present a more efficient computational pattern streamlined for quicker action. In obtaining percentiles or percentile ranks, the routine is self-explanatory when its graphic basis is understood.

The age distribution of the 109 cases in Appendix A is shown in Table XII and the corresponding histogram in Figure 10. Suppose the median is to be found for these data.

By definition, the median is located at a point on the base line of this histogram such that exactly 50% of the area lies to the left of an ordinate at that point, and 50% to the right. Now imagine you have been given a pair of scissors and you are asked to cut this histogram into two portions of equal area, cutting along a line perpendicular to the base. Where would you cut? Locate the point precisely.

TABLE XII

Cumulative Frequency Distribution: Chronological Age of 109 Children in Fourth Grade

Age to Nearest Month	f	Cumulative Frequency	
		Upward	Downward
155–159	1	109	1
150–154	1	108	2
145–149	1	107	3
140–144	2	106	5
135–139		104	5
130–134	3	104	8
125–129	6	101	14
120–124	8	95	22
115–119	22	87	44
110–114	25	65	69
105–109	31	40	100
100–104	7	9	107
95– 99	2	2	109

There should be $\frac{1}{2}(109) = 54.5$ units to the left of this ordinate and the same area to the right. Counting up from the lower end of the distribution, as in Table XII, we see that the ordinate must be located between the points 109.5 and 114.5 because $2 + 7 + 31 = 40$ units lie to the left of the ordinate at 109.5 while $2 + 7 + 31 + 25 = 65$ units

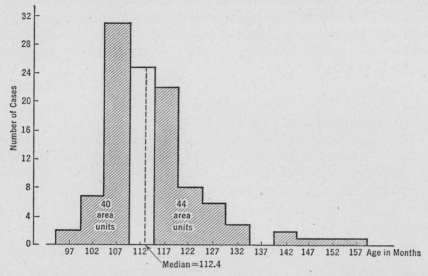

Fig. 10. Histogram divided in two portions of equal area by ordinate at median. (From data of Table XII.)

lie to the left of the ordinate at 114.5. We must cut through the unshaded portion in Figure 10 on a vertical line so placed that, out of 25 units in that interval, $54.5 - 40 = 14.5$ units are to the left of the line and $65 - 54.5 = 10.5$ are to the right. The point of division must therefore lie $\frac{14.5}{25}$ of an interval to the right of 109.5 or $\frac{10.5}{25}$ of an interval to the left of 114.5. As an interval contains 5 score units the point sought is either

$$109.5 + \frac{14.5}{25} \times 5 = 112.4$$

or

$$114.5 - \frac{10.5}{25} \times 5 = 112.4$$

This value is the median.

Any other percentile is obtained in similar fashion, using the appropriate percentage where, in this computation, 50% was used. Illustrations of the procedure for other percentiles will, however, be delayed until a shorter routine is described in the next section.

Obtaining a Percentile from a Cumulative Frequency Distribution.
It is not necessary or even expedient to draw a histogram once the process
is understood. Cumulating the frequency either from the bottom or
from the top of the distribution is an aid to quick computation if several
different percentiles are to be found for the same distribution.

The steps in the computation of any given percentile from a cumulative frequency distribution may be illustrated by the following example:

From the distribution given in Table XII compute the 82nd percentile.

A. Working from the low score
   of the distribution:

B. Working from the high score
   of the distribution:

82% of 109 = 89.38 cases

$100\% - 82\% = 18\%$
18% of 109 = 19.62 cases

Cumulative frequency less
than 119.5 = 87
Additional cases required to
locate percentile:
89.38 − 87 = 2.38
Frequency in the next higher
interval = 8
Width of interval = 5

$$P_{82} = 119.5 + \frac{2.38}{8}(5) = 121.0$$

Cumulative frequency greater
than 124.5 = 14
Additional cases required to
locate percentile:
19.62 − 14 = 5.62
Frequency in the next lower
interval = 8
Width of interval = 5

$$P_{82} = 124.5 - \frac{5.62}{8}(5) = 121.0$$

Exercise 7

1. Verify the following percentiles computed from the distribution of
chronological age in Table XII:

Percentage of Cases Exceeded	Percentile = Age in Months below Which the Given % of Cases Falls
05	102.0
10	104.8
15	105.7
20	106.6
25	107.4
30	108.3
35	109.2
40	110.2
45	111.3
50	112.4

Percentage of Cases Exceeded	Percentile = Age in Months below Which the Given % of Cases Falls
55	113.5
60	114.6
65	115.8
70	117.1
75	118.3
80	119.6
85	123.0
90	127.1
95	133.8

*2. In question 1, the percentages are listed with equal increments. Note that the corresponding percentiles do not have equal increments. Table XII indicates that the original scores cluster thickly in the lower part of the distribution and spread out more sparsely in the upper intervals. Where are the percentile values most widely spaced? Where do they occur most closely together?

3. Using the data of Table IV(A), compute the following percentiles: P_{13}, P_{27}, P_{41}, P_{50}, P_{62}, P_{97}. Compute the same percentiles from the arrangement of data in Table IV(B), Table IV(C), Table V, and Table VI. Set up a table, with proper headings and title, showing these six percentile values for each of the 5 tables, illustrating the effect upon these selected percentiles produced by grouping the same data in different class intervals.

4. No two students require the same amount of drill. Give yourself as much drill as you seem to need to achieve mastery of the computation of percentiles. Any of the following procedures would be useful:

a. Set down a purely arbitrary frequency distribution. Compute several percentiles working up from the low score as in illustration A above. Check by working down from the high score as in B. It is highly unlikely that your results will check unless they are correct.

b. Any two members of the class may set down an arbitrary frequency distribution, agree upon certain percentiles to be computed, compute them independently, and compare results. This does not provide a perfect check inasmuch as both persons could commit the same error, but it is helpful. If errors are made, this method is more likely to reveal their nature than is a.

c. In almost any published text of elementary statistics you are likely to find some problems with answers.

Percentile Rank of a Score. In the illustration of the routine for computing a percentile, it was found that for Table XII the 82nd percentile was 121.0 The same relationship might be stated inversely by saying that "the percentile rank of 121.0 is 82." The procedure for finding the percentile rank of a given score is exactly the reverse of that for finding a percentile value. To find the percentile rank of 121.0 we should first ask how many scores lie below 121.0 in the distribution, and then ask what percentage these scores are of all 109 scores.

The score 121.0 lies in the interval marked 120–124 in Table XII. Below this interval there are $2 + 7 + 31 + 25 + 22 = 87$ scores. What proportion of the 8 scores in the interval 120–124 must also be considered as below 121.0?

In the histogram which might be drawn to represent this distribution, the point 121.0 would lie 0.3 of a step interval above the point 119.5, because the width of the interval is $124.5 - 119.5 = 5$, and the point lies $121.0 - 119.5 = 1.5$ *score units* above the beginning of the interval, and $\frac{1.5}{5} = 0.3$. Therefore, of the 8 *area units* in the interval, $0.3 \times 8 = 2.4$ area units would lie to the left of an ordinate at 121.0 These 2.4 area units represent 2.4 scores to be added to the 87 scores in the intervals below the interval 120–124. The percentage of scores below 121.0 is therefore $\frac{87 + 2.4}{109} = 82.0\%$, and the score is said to have a percentile rank of 82.

Note that it is only *obtained scores* for which a percentile rank is likely to be sought and these are usually discrete integers. Therefore an obtained score of, say 114, will be treated here as a score of exactly 114.0, not 114.5 or any other fractional value.

Note also that in naming the percentile rank of a score, decimal places in the percentage are usually dropped. Thus if 76.3% of the area of a histogram lies below a given score, one would usually say that score has a percentile rank of 76, not of 76.3.

Exercise 8

*1. Give two translations of each of these statements, by filling blanks in the two sentences which follow the statement.

a. Exactly 57% of the teachers in a given school system receive salaries less than $1385.

_____ is the _____ percentile of the distribution of salaries. _____ is the percentile rank of _____.

b. Of the deaths recorded from a given disease for a given year in a given community, 87% were of persons under 12 years old.

_____ is the _____ percentile of the age of persons dying from this disease. _____ is the percentile rank of age _____.

c. The median of a given distribution is 72.0.

The _____ percentile is _____.

The percentile rank of _____ is _____.

d. Exactly 5% of all persons consulted had annual incomes larger than $2150.

The _____ percentile is _____.

The percentile rank of _____ is _____.

2. For the data of Table XII, verify the following percentile ranks:

Score	Percentile Rank
108	28
122	83
125	88
143	97
151	98

3. For the data of Table XII, compute the percentile ranks of the following scores:

Score	Percentile Rank
101	—
111	—
118	—
120	—
123	—
140	—
147	—
152	—

Distributions with Zero Frequencies. Because of the gap in Table XII, all scores from 134.5 to 139.5 have the same percentile rank. When a distribution is irregular, some intervals having no frequencies, a given percentile may appear indeterminate. For example, suppose P_{80} is to be found for Table XIII. What is the score below which 80% of the 30 cases, or 24 cases, lie? Clearly any score in the range from 30.5 to 33.5 provides a correct answer to this question. In such cases it has become customary to define the midpoint of the interval as the percentile in question. This is an arbitrary procedure, but reasonable because you obtain the same answer whether you cumulate from the top down or from the bottom up. Such cases are unimportant because a percentile has little meaning for so small and irregular a group. The addition of a few more cases would be likely to affect all percentile values considerably.

TABLE XIII

*Irregular Frequency Distribution
with Gaps: Fictitious Data*

Class Sort	f	Cum. f
40–42	1	30
37–39	3	29
34–36	2	26
31–33		24
28–30	4	24
25–27	5	20
22–24	6	15
19–21		9
16–18	4	9
13–15	3	5
10–12	2	2

Measures of Spread of Distribution. The *range* between the highest and lowest scores has already been mentioned as an interesting character of a distribution. Range, however, is a very unstable measure of spread, being greatly dependent upon the presence or absence of one or two extreme individuals. A widely used measure of spread is the range from the first to the third quartiles, called the *interquartile range*. Geometrically this is a distance along the scale of scores from Q_L to Q_U, and is indicated in Figure 11 by a brace. The *semi-interquartile range* is often used as a measure of spread or dispersion. In a perfectly symmetrical distribution, such as A and D in Figure 11, this would be the absolute value (i.e., the value taken without regard to sign) of the distance from the median to either quartile. It is commonly called by the misleading name of "quartile deviation." When Galton invented this term, he was thinking of distributions shaped like A, in which the semi-interquartile range is really the deviation of the quartile points from the median. In an asymmetrical distribution such as B or C, the semi-interquartile range has no obvious meaning and is certainly not the deviation of either quartile from the median.

The difference between any pair of symmetrically placed percentiles could be used as a measure of variability and the range $P_{90} - P_{10}$ is one that is often so used.

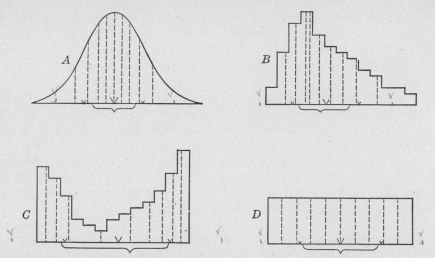

Fig. 11. Position of decile points in frequency distributions of different forms.

Dotted lines are erected at the decile points.

Brace extends from Q_L to Q_U with center at median.

Large arrow indicates mean.

Small arrows indicate points at distance of one standard deviation on either side of mean. (Standard deviation is treated in Chapter VIII.)

Spacing of Percentile Points. Figure 11 shows the position of the decile points for four different shapes of distribution. Study the spacing of these points on the base line. Only in rectangular distribution D is each pair of consecutive deciles separated by the same number of score units, and rectangular distributions are very rarely encountered.

Exercise 9

*1. Examine Figure 11 and make a statement as to why the percentile points are spaced evenly along the scale of scores in D and are not spaced evenly in A, B, or C. In what part of the distribution do they crowd most closely together? In what part are they more widely separated?

*2. Which of the following statements are true no matter what the shape of the distribution? Which are true for a symmetrical distribution but not necessarily for distribution of other shapes? (A symmetrical distribution is of such a form that if you folded the histogram on the ordinate at the median, the two halves would exactly coincide. See Figure 23 on page 161.)

a. The two quartiles are equally distant from the median.

b. Exactly 30% of the area lies to the left of an ordinate erected at P_{30}.

c. The difference between P_{20} and P_{10} is the same as the difference between P_{90} and P_{80}.

d. An ordinate at the median bisects the area of the histogram.

e. The percentiles are represented by points along the scale of scores.

f. The median is exactly halfway between P_{30} and P_{70}.

g. If an ordinate is erected at the median and at each of the quartile points, these ordinates will divide the area of the histogram into four equal parts.

h. The proportion of area lying between the ordinates at P_{10} and P_{20} is the same as the proportion lying between the ordinates at P_{20} and P_{30}.

i. The distance on the scale of scores between P_{10} and P_{20} is the same as between P_{20} and P_{30}.

3. In Table XXXVI on page 160 are six symmetrical distributions. Verify the values of the interquartile range, $Q_U - Q_L$, shown below the table, paying no attention for the present to the other measures listed there. Do the same for the five distributions in Table XXXVII on page 162.

Reading Percentile Values from a Cumulative Percentage Curve. Figure 12 is a cumulative percentage graph constructed from the data of Table XII. Age in months has been laid off on the horizontal axis, the scale being marked to show the division points between intervals. The cumulative frequencies of Table XII have been reduced to cumulative percentages and each such percentage is plotted against the upper limit of its interval.*

For example, Table XII shows that 65 cases, which is 60% of all the cases, lie below the score 114.5. Therefore a point is plotted where the vertical line through 114.5 crosses the horizontal line through 60. Similarly a point has been plotted opposite the upper limit of each interval, and a curve drawn through these points. This curve is brought to the base line at the lower limit of the lowest interval in which frequency occurs and is brought to the 100% line at the upper limit of the highest interval in which frequency occurs.

Percentile values can easily be read from this chart. For example, to find P_{25}, find the point on the vertical, or percentage scale, which represents 25%. Draw a horizontal line from this point to the ogive, and at the point of contact with the ogive drop a perpendicular to the base line. It meets the base line at A, and A is the lower quartile.

Exercise 10

1. From Figure 12, read off the values of P_{20}, P_{70}, and P_{35}, and compare your results with the figures listed in Question 1 of Exercise 7.

2. Make a large-scale copy of Figure 12 on finely ruled paper from which scale values can be read with fair precision. From this graph, estimate the

---

* The student who is not familiar with plotting should look up the subject of graphs in an elementary algebra or read Chapter XI in *Mathematics Essential for Elementary Statistics*.

approximate value of the twenty-third percentile and check by direct computation of that percentile from the original data.

3. On your graph, plot each of the percentile values stated in Problem 1 of
Exercise 7 and verify that each point so plotted falls exactly on the ogive.
For example, to show that the 20th percentile is 106.6, locate the point whose

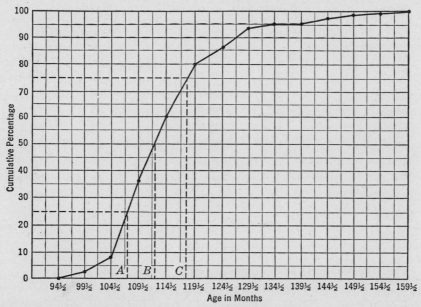

Fig. 12. Cumulative percentage curve showing positions of median and
quartile points. (From data of Table XII.)

$$A = \text{lower quartile}$$
$$B = \text{median}$$
$$C = \text{upper quartile}$$

ordinate on the percentage scale is 20 and whose abscissa on the age scale is
106.6.

4. Note that a percentile score is found on the horizontal axis, while the
corresponding percentage of cases with score less than the given score is on
the vertical axis. Where are the quartile points? Indicate by a brace the distance between the upper and lower quartiles. This is the interquartile range.

5. Indicate the range from P_{10} to P_{90}.

6. Compute the percentile rank of each of the following ages: 97, 102, 107,
132. Plot the computed values on your copy of Figure 12. They should lie on
the ogive already obtained. For example, the percentile rank of 112 is 48.
Below 112 there lie $2 + 7 + 31 + \frac{25}{2} = 52.5$ cases, and 52.5 cases is 48% of
109 cases. Find the point whose abscissa is 112 and whose ordinate on the
percentage scale is 48. This point also lies on the ogive.

TABLE XIV

Overlapping Frequency Distributions: Scores in Word Meaning
for Two Grade Groups from Different Schools *

Score	Group M (Grade 6B)			Group R (Grade 5A)		
	f	Cum. f	Cum. %	f	Cum. f	Cum. %
66–69	1	25	100.0	1	39	100.0
62–65		24	96.0		38	97.4
58–61	2	24	96.0	1	38	97.4
54–57	5	22	88.0	5	37	94.9
50–53	4	17	68.0	4	32	82.1
46–49	1	13	52.0	5	28	71.8
42–45	3	12	48.0	5	23	59.0
38–41	7	9	36.0	8	18	46.2
34–37	1	2	8.0	5	10	25.6
30–33	1	1	4.0	5	5	12.8
Total	25			39		

The Use of Ogives to Compare Groups. In his *Study of Ability Grouping in the Elementary School*,† Parl West makes an analysis of the overlapping of groups. Table XIV, adapted from his study, shows the distribution of scores on a test of word meaning made by two groups of pupils from two different grades in two different schools in the same city. He called these two groups "M" and "R." It is not necessary to go into the purpose of his study here, as that would take our attention away from the graphic device used. The median score of group M is 47.5, and of group R is 42.7, so that on the median the groups differ by 4.8 score points. In terms of range, however, the overlapping appears to be complete.

In Figure 13, where the two frequency distributions are shown on the same pair of axes, the extent of overlapping is difficult to interpret. In Figure 14, where the two ogives are shown, interpretation is much easier. Points A and B represent the 10-percentile points of the two curves, points C and D the 90-percentile points. Thus for group M, the range $P_{90}-P_{10}$ is represented by the line segment BD, and for group R by the line segment AC. Although the two groups happen to coincide as to

* From West, Parl, *A Study of Ability Grouping in the Elementary School*, Bureau of Publications of Teachers College, Columbia University, 1933, page 10.
 † *Ibid.*

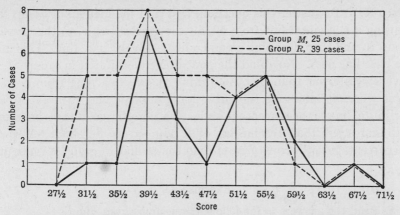

Fig. 13. Overlapping frequency polygons: scores in word meaning for two grade groups from different schools. (From data of Table XIV.)

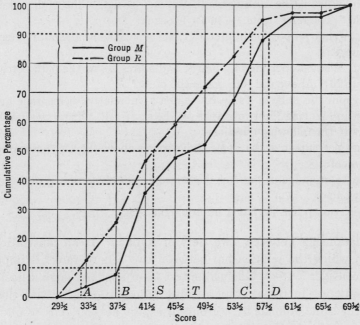

Fig. 14. Comparison of two groups by ogive curves. (From data of Table XIV.)

total range, it is clear that the middle 80% of group M are placed higher on the scale than the middle 80% of group R. The points S and T represent the two medians, and the median of group M is seen to be higher on the scale of scores than the median of group R.

The chart can also provide an answer to such questions as "What percentage of children in group M have scores that exceed the median of group R?" To answer this question, first find the median of group R by drawing a horizontal line from 50, on the vertical scale, to the curve for group R, and then dropping a perpendicular to the base line. This meets the base line at S. Now find the percentage of children in group M who have scores lower than S, by following the vertical line from S to the point where it intersects the curve for group M, and then extending a horizontal line to the percentage scale. The percentage of cases in group M with scores less than the median of R appears to be about 39, so that the percentage with scores greater than the median of group R is about 61.

Exercise 11

1. Read the answers to the following questions from Figure 14.

a. What proportion of group M had scores less than 50? Greater than 50? What proportion of group R had scores less than 50? Greater than 50?

b. What is the 10th percentile of each group? The 90th percentile of each? The range from P_{10} to P_{90} for each?

c. What proportion of group M had scores below the 40th percentile of group R?

d. What proportion of group R had scores below the 60th percentile of group M? Above the 70th percentile of M?

2. From the data in Table XV make a cumulative percentage graph for each group, placing the two graphs on the same grid. From the graphs, read answers to the following questions:

What percentage of the women have scores above the 80th percentile of the men?

What percentage of the men have scores below the lower quartile of the women?

Which group has the larger interquartile range?

Relationship between Two Sets of Ranks.* As an illustration of a case in which the relationship between two sets of ranks is important, let us consider a stock judging contest in which three high school teams are competing in the attempt to rank 10 cows to agree with the ranks given the same animals by a group of expert judges. The results are as shown in Table XVI.

The prize goes to the team able to place the cows in a rank order most nearly similar to that of the judges. How is that team to be selected? A natural first suggestion is that the teams be scored in terms of number of agreements. Team I has agreed with the judges on the placement of 5 cows, A, C, E, H, and J; Team II, on the placement of two cows, C

---

* As no subsequent material depends on this section, it may be omitted now and taken up when the chapter on correlation is studied, or omitted altogether in a minimum course.

TABLE XV

*Overlapping Distributions: Scores on the Science Section of the Cooperative
Contemporary Affairs Test Made by 120 Men and 130 Women
in the Sophomore Class of a Liberal Arts College*

Score	Number of	
	Men	Women
22	1	1
21		
20	1	
19		1
18	2	1
17	2	
16	1	2
15	3	3
14	5	5
13	5	3
12	7	4
11	4	5
10	6	7
9	10	6
8	8	7
7	13	9
6	7	10
5	9	11
4	8	12
3	9	15
2	6	12
1	9	9
0	4	7
Total	120	130

TABLE XVI

Rank Given to Each of Ten Cows by the Official Judges and by Three High School Teams

Cow	Rank Given by			
	Judges	Team I	Team II	Team III
A	1	1	2	1
B	2	6	1	2
C	3	3	3	5
D	4	9	5	6
E	5	5	4	8
F	6	7	8	7
G	7	2	7	10
H	8	8	6	4
I	9	4	10	3
J	10	10	9	9

and G; Team III, on the placement of two cows, A and B. A glance at Figure 15 where these rank relationships are shown graphically, suggests, however, that the errors made by Team II, while more numerous than those of Team I, are much smaller.

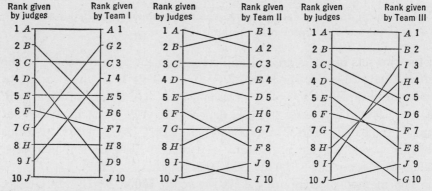

Fig. 15. Agreement by three high school teams with the official judges on rank given to each of ten cows. (From data of Table XVI.)

The charts in Figure 16 illustrate various degrees of agreement or disagreement between sets of ranks, ranging from the chart on the left, in which each of 10 individuals holds exactly the same position in the two sets of ranks, to the chart on the right in which the order of the ranks is exactly reversed.

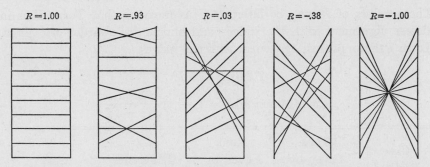

Fig. 16. Charts showing various degrees of relationship between two sets of ranks.

The formula commonly used to measure the closeness of relationship between two sets of ranks is

$$R = 1 - \frac{6\Sigma d^2}{N(N^2 - 1)}$$

In this formula,

R is the measure of relationship sought.

N is the number of individuals ranked, which in this particular case is 10.

6 is a number which comes out of the mathematical derivation of the formula and is always the same for all problems.

d is the difference between the two ranks given to the same individual. (The sum of all the values of d is always zero.)

Σ is the capital Greek letter *Sigma*, which corresponds to S in our alphabet, and is to be interpreted as meaning "the sum of."

If the two sets of ranks are in complete agreement as in the chart at the left of Figure 16, every d is zero, $\Sigma d^2 = 0$, and $R = 1$. If the two sets of ranks are completely reversed, as in the chart at the right of Figure 16, $R = -1.00$. The reason for this depends upon a mathematical proof outside the scope of this introductory treatment.* Degrees of relationship between perfect agreement in rank and perfect disagreement will have values of R between +1.00 and −1.00.

The method of computing R is shown in Table XVII. In similar fashion compute the value of R for each team and verify the following:

---

* The mathematically trained student may wish to consult the following: Jackson, Dunham, "The algebra of correlation," *American Mathematical Monthly*, 31 (March, 1924), 110–121.

For Team I and the judges, $R = .44$
For Team II and the judges, $R = .92$
For Team III and the judges, $R = .52$

These values of R may be interpreted as meaning that Team II is in closest agreement with the judges and should be awarded the prize. Team I shows poorest agreement with the judges.

TABLE XVII

Computation of $R = 1 - \dfrac{6\Sigma d^2}{N(N^2 - 1)}$

Case Ranked	Rank Given by Judges	Rank Given by Team I	$d =$ Difference in Ranks	d^2
A	1	1	0	0
B	2	6	4	16
C	3	3	0	0
D	4	9	5	25
E	5	5	0	0
F	6	7	1	1
G	7	2	-5	25
H	8	8	0	0
I	9	4	-5	25
J	10	10	0	0
			$0 = \Sigma d$	$92 = \Sigma d^2$

$$R = 1 - \frac{6(92)}{10(99)} = .44$$

It may also be of some interest to see how closely the three teams agree with each other. In the same manner we obtain values of R for each pair of teams as follows:

For Team I and Team II, $R = .33$
For Team I and Team III, $R = .27$
For Team II and Team III, $R = .48$

This topic will be developed further in Chapter XIII.

BIBLIOGRAPHY

Elderton, W. P. and E. M., *Primer of Statistics*, Adam and Charles Black, London, 1909. This thoroughly delightful little book, written with great simplicity by two scholars, presents the concepts of median and cumulative frequency in their most elementary manner.

Galton, Francis, "Statistics by intercomparison, with remarks on the law of frequency of error," *Philosophical Magazine*, 4th Series, 49 (1875), 33–46.

Otis, Arthur, *Statistical Method in Educational Measurement*. World Book Co., Yonkers-on-Hudson, New York, 1926. Chapter V, "The Percentile Graph," Chapter VII, "Percentile Curves," Chapter IX, "Percentile Rank in a Normal Distribution."

Thurstone, L. L., "Note on the calculation of percentile ranks," *Journal of Educational Psychology*, 18 (1927), 617–620. This paper describes a very quick method for obtaining percentile ranks with the help of a computing machine.

Walker, H. M., *Studies in the History of Statistical Method*. The Williams & Wilkins Co., Baltimore, Maryland, 1929. Chapter IV, "Percentiles."

West, Parl, *A Study of Ability Grouping in the Elementary School*, Teachers College, Columbia University Bureau of Publications, New York City, 1933. This study makes consistent use of overlapping ogives.

CHAPTER VI

SYMBOLISM IN STATISTICS

The human mind has never invented a labor-saving machine equal to algebra.   Editorial in *The Nation*

It is characteristic of all symbolism that there is a constant tendency for the symbol to replace the thing symbolized; and it is very easy to allow mathematical symbols to obscure mathematical ideas. If one should memorize and reproduce correctly the sounds which constitute a sentence in the Russian language without knowing anything of their significance, he would not be speaking Russian—he would merely be making Russian noises. And if a student in the classroom goes through a correct manipulation of mathematical forms without understanding the meaning and significance of the processes, his work is not mathematics at all—he is merely making mathematical marks. The vast short-hand symbolism we have invented to record and communicate ideas is only the language of mathematics, and language is a very doubtful asset to anyone who has no ideas to communicate.   W. B. Carver

On this Occasion, I must take notice to such of my Readers as are well vers'd in Vulgar Arithmetick, that it would not be difficult for them to make themselves Masters, not only of all the Practical Rules in this Book, but also of more useful Discoveries, if they would take the small Pains of being acquainted with the bare Notation of Algebra, which might be done in the hundredth part of the Time that is spent in learning to read Short-hand.   Abraham De Moivre

The scientist resorts to symbolism because words often fail to meet his needs for clear, precise, and unambiguous statements. A single formula can often tell more than a page of verbal material, and tell it in such a way that it means the same thing to all competent readers. To Voltaire's aphorism that "One merit of poetry few will deny, it says more, and in fewer words, than prose," David Eugene Smith aptly adds, "One merit of mathematics few will deny; it says more, and in fewer words, than any other science. The world knows no such brevity outside this particular field. Poetry and mathematics, therefore, have this in common—that they say more and in fewer words than any other written form."

Use of Symbolism in Statistics.* Valuable as is the brevity of mathematical language, its clarity is even more important to the statistician. A vague idea of the purposes and procedures of statistical method can be conveyed by words, but precise ideas are excessively difficult to achieve without the use of symbolism. The difficulty which many students have with elementary statistical method is due in large part to their habit of looking at a formula as though it were an Egyptian hieroglyph, never having learned to read a formula as a sentence. A conversation between two college boys overheard on the top of a Fifth Avenue bus expresses a state of mind inimical to an understanding of statistical method. Said the first boy, "But I don't understand it." Replied his companion, "Understand it! Heavens, man, why do you try to? It's a formula!"

The language of statistical method is highly symbolic, but many persons studying an elementary course have had insufficient mathematical training and are unaccustomed to thinking in symbolic language. It is the writer's experience that time spent by such students in an effort to understand the symbolic language of statistical method will result in time saved through greater ease and confidence in reading and utilizing the material presented in this and other textbooks on the subject.

Unfortunately for the beginning student, the language and symbolism of statistics have not as yet been standardized, so that as he goes from one book to another he must learn, if not a new language, at least a new dialect. Annoying as this may be to the student, it has probably been fortunate for the field of statistics itself. The methods of statistical inquiry are expanding with enormous rapidity. Had a committee attempted a decade ago to standardize the symbolism, it is almost certain that the best selection they could have made then would fit like a straight-jacket today.

A list of the symbols employed in this text, as well as many of those employed by other writers, has been placed in Appendix E. The student will find this list a useful study aid.

General Principles of Symbolic Representation. Certain general principles are so commonly observed in mathematical work that they form a sort of grammar. Knowing the rules of this grammar facilitates using the language.

1. Individual letters of the alphabet are generally used to represent numbers or quantities. For instance, the letter h might be used to represent the number of inches in the height of a child. It should be borne in mind that the letter thus used represents a number and not an abstract

---

* This section and the one immediately following may be omitted by the mathematically trained reader, who can go on at once to the section on *multiple subscripts.*

quality or trait. It is not correct to say that h represents height, unless "height" is understood as an abbreviation for "number of inches in height," or "number of centimeters in height," or "number of feet in height," as the case may be. In the long run, the use of initial letters of words may become impractical, because too many words begin with the same letter. Therefore it is customary to make extensive use of letters x, y, and z to represent variables in general.

2. The letters of the alphabet soon prove inadequate in representing all the variables which need to be discussed. One way of extending the alphabet is to use *capital* letters, *small* letters, and *Greek* letters. Thus the scores of a child on three successive tests might be designated as A, a, α; those of a second child as B, b, and β; etc.

3. A second way of extending the alphabet is by the use of *super-scripts*. The number of cases in several different groups might be indicated as N, N', N'', N''', etc. This superscript is not to be confused with an exponent, the superscript having a descriptive meaning only, whereas an exponent indicates that a certain operation is to be performed.

4. A third way, more convenient than either of the preceding, is to use *subscripts*. A subscript, like a superscript, has the force of an adjective, and has no numerical significance. Thus the number of boys and the number of girls in a class might be designated as N_b and N_g, or as N_B and N_G and the scores of different children in a class as X_1, X_2, X_3, etc.

5. The use of groups of letters to represent a single number is bad form, and most confusing in a formula. The modal salary paid to men and the modal salary paid to women in city A and in city B might be represented as: S_{MA}, S_{WA}, S_{MB}, S_{WB}: or as $_AS_M$, $_AS_W$, $_BS_M$, $_BS_W$: or as S_M, S_W, S'_M, S'_W: but not as SMA, SWA, SMB, SWB, and not as $MSMA$, $MSWA$, $MSMB$, $MSWB$.*

6. Relationships between numbers are expressed by certain conventional signs. They are to an algebraic formula what a verb is to a sentence. The following are commonly employed in statistical formulas:

Sign	Verbal equivalent
$=$	is equal to
$<$	is less than
$>$	is greater than
$\leqq$ or $\leqslant$	is equal to or less than (is not greater than)
$\geqq$ or $\geqslant$	is equal to or greater than (is not less than)
$\doteqdot$	is approximately equal to
$\neq$	is not equal to

* A number of abbreviations, such as IQ, MA, CA, and Md for intelligence quotient, mental age, chronological age, and median, respectively, are so firmly established that attempts

7. The use of such signs of operation as $+$, $-$, $\times$, $\div$ and $\sqrt{\ }$ is very familiar. Because of possible confusion with the letter x, the sign $\times$ is seldom used in a formula but the product of two numbers may be indicated by writing the symbols together without a sign or with only a raised dot between them, as pq or $\left(\dfrac{a-2}{3}\right)\left(\dfrac{a+2}{7}\right)$ or $\frac{3}{4} \cdot \frac{2}{7}$. (It should be noted that in England and Canada the raised dot is a decimal point, whereas the dot on the line indicates multiplication.) The division sign is almost never used except when it facilitates typesetting. The quotient of $a + b$ divided by $c + d$ might be written $\dfrac{a+b}{c+d}$ or $(a + b)/(c + d)$. The chief reason for writing $(a + b) \div (c + d)$ is that it takes up only one line of print; the same result, however, is achieved by using the slanting bar instead of the symbol $\div$ to indicate division.

8. Signs of *grouping*, or aggregation, are used to indicate that an expression of more than one term is to be treated like a single number. Such signs are parentheses ( ), square brackets [ ], brace { }, and a horizontal bar placed above the expression. Sometimes parentheses are placed around numbers merely to avoid confusion, as $(\frac{3}{4})$ $(1\frac{1}{2})$ or $y = \left(r\dfrac{s_y}{s_x}\right) x$.

9. An *exponent* which is a positive integer indicates how many times a number is to be used as a factor, as $x^4 = xxxx$. A negative integer used as an exponent indicates a reciprocal of the number with the positive exponent, as $x^{-4} = \dfrac{1}{x^4}$. A fraction used as an exponent indicates that the number is to be raised to a power corresponding to the numerator of the fraction, and then a root of this is to be taken, the order of the root corresponding to the denominator of the fraction. For example: $x^{\frac{1}{2}} = \sqrt{x}$ and $x^{\frac{2}{3}} = \sqrt[3]{x^2}$. In statistical formulas, the exponent $\frac{1}{2}$ will often be used instead of the square root sign, for convenience, when a square root is to be extracted from a complicated expression. *An exponent indicates that a certain operation is to be performed, and is therefore different in meaning from a subscript or a superscript.*

10. Another sign of operation, used continually by statisticians, is the sign of *summation*, usually written as Σ, which is the large Greek letter *sigma*. The sum of X_1, X_2, X_3, and X_4 could be written as $\displaystyle\sum_{i=1}^{4} X_i$

to supplant them have met with little success. Nevertheless, they are poor symbols, very awkward to combine with other symbols.

and could be read "the sum of all the X's, from X_1 to X_4." The subscript of the first term to be added is written below the summation sign; the subscript of the last term is written above it. These are called the limits of summation. The subscript attached to the letter X indicates that this subscript varies from term to term.

The sum of $ax_{10} + ax_{11} + ax_{12} + \cdots + ax_{40}$ could be written as $\sum_{i=10}^{40} ax_i$ and the subscript i would show that x is a variable and a is not. In more advanced work, it is quite essential to indicate the limits of summation carefully. In a first course, summations are almost always taken from 1 to N, and the short form ΣX is used instead of $\sum_{i=1}^{N} X_i$. A mathematician might read ΣX as "sigma X," but a statistician would be more likely to say "the sum of the X's," or "summation X," because the statistician also makes a great deal of use of the small Greek sigma, σ, in another connection to be described later.

Multiple Subscripts. When data have to be classified on more than one basis, the use of double or even triple subscripts is very helpful. Confronted for the first time with such symbols, a student not trained in mathematics is sometimes needlessly alarmed. A small amount of practice on symbolism at this stage will greatly increase the ease with which later portions of this text, or any other text, can be studied.

As a simple illustration of multiple classification, suppose that each of 50 pupils has been given 4 different reading tests, making 200 measures in all. Let X_{12} (read "X sub one two" or "X one two") represent the score of pupil 1 on test 2; X_{54} the score of pupil 5 on test 4; and, in general, X_{ij}, the score of pupil i on test j. The 200 scores can be arranged in a *matrix* (or rectangular formation) as follows:

$$
\begin{array}{cccc}
X_{11} & X_{12} & X_{13} & X_{14} \\
X_{21} & X_{22} & X_{23} & X_{24} \\
X_{31} & X_{32} & X_{33} & X_{34} \\
\cdot & \cdot & \cdot & \cdot \\
\cdot & \cdot & \cdot & \cdot \\
\cdot & \cdot & \cdot & \cdot \\
X_{i1} & X_{i2} & X_{i3} & X_{i4} \\
\cdot & \cdot & \cdot & \cdot \\
\cdot & \cdot & \cdot & \cdot \\
\cdot & \cdot & \cdot & \cdot \\
X_{50,1} & X_{50,2} & X_{50,3} & X_{50,4}
\end{array}
$$

In this matrix, each row represents the four scores belonging to a single pupil. The row of scores X_{i1}, X_{i2}, X_{i3}, X_{i4} represents the scores of some unspecified pupil. Each column represents the 50 scores of all the pupils on one particular test. To avoid the tedium of writing out 50 scores, dots have been inserted, indicating omission. X_{3j} would indicate the score of pupil 3 on some test, X_{i3} would indicate the score of some pupil on test 3, X_{ij} would indicate the score of some pupil on some test, any pupil on any test.

We might wish to know the sum of the four scores for one particular pupil, or the sum of the scores of the 50 pupils on one particular test, or the sum of all 200 scores.

To write each of these sums, for example, as ΣX, would be most confusing. It is necessary to make clear whether the summation extends over all the test scores for one individual or over all the individual scores on one test. When the pupil is the variable, the first subscript is replaced by some convenient letter, as for example, i. When the test is the variable, the second subscript is replaced by some convenient letter, as j, different from the first. The limits of summation for this variable will be written above and below the summation sign.

Study carefully the following identities, putting each into words as you read it.

For the scores of individual 2,

$$X_{21} + X_{22} + X_{23} + X_{24} = \sum_{j=1}^{4} X_{2j} \qquad (\text{``The sum of } X_{2j}, \text{ where } j \text{ runs from 1 to 4''})$$

For the scores on test 2,

$$X_{12} + X_{22} + \cdots + X_{49,2} + X_{50,2} = \sum_{i=1}^{50} X_{i2} \qquad (\text{``The sum of } X_{i2}, \text{ where } i \text{ runs from 1 to 50''})$$

For the scores of individual i,

$$X_{i1} + X_{i2} + X_{i3} + X_{i4} = \sum_{j=1}^{4} X_{ij}$$

For the scores on test j,

$$X_{1j} + X_{2j} + \cdots + X_{49j} + X_{50j} = \sum_{i=1}^{50} X_{ij}$$

For all 200 scores, adding first by columns and then by rows,

$$(X_{11} + \cdots + X_{50,1}) + (X_{12} + \cdots + X_{50,2}) + (X_{13} + \cdots + X_{50,3})$$
$$+ (X_{14} + \cdots + X_{50,4}) = \sum_{j=1}^{4} \sum_{i=1}^{50} X_{ij}$$

Also for all 200 scores, adding first by rows and then by columns,

$$(X_{11} + \cdots + X_{14}) + (X_{21} + \cdots + X_{24}) + \cdots + (X_{50,1} + \cdots$$
$$+ X_{50,4}) = \sum_{i=1}^{50} \sum_{j=1}^{4} X_{ij}$$

Obviously the sum of the 200 scores is independent of the order in which the addition is performed, and therefore

$$\sum_{j=1}^{4} \sum_{i=1}^{50} X_{ij} = \sum_{i=1}^{50} \sum_{j=1}^{4} X_{ij}$$

In elementary work, no confusion arises from omitting the limits of summation, and assuming that $\sum X$ always means $\sum_{i=1}^{N} X_i$. In more advanced work, the limits of summation may be omitted whenever the meaning is unambiguous.

Exercise 12

(Practice material will be found in *Mathematics Essential for Elementary Statistics*, Chapters VII and XIII.)

1. Write out in full the summation represented by each of the following:

$$\sum_{i=1}^{6} X_i \qquad \sum_{i=1}^{3} (X_i - a) \qquad \sum_{i=12}^{15} ax_i^2$$

$$\sum_{i=1}^{4} f_i X_i \qquad \sum_{i=6}^{9} x_i y_i \qquad \sum_{i=1}^{3} \tfrac{1}{2} x_i^2$$

$$\sum_{i=10}^{12} dX_i \qquad \sum_{i=2}^{5} ab_i c$$

2. Referring to the matrix of scores on page 84, state in words the meaning of each of the following:

a. X_{34} e. $\displaystyle\sum_{j=1}^{4} X_{3j}$

b. X_{71} f. $\displaystyle\sum_{i=1}^{50} X_{i2}$

c. $X_{\cdot 2}$ g. $\displaystyle\sum_{i=1}^{50} \sum_{j=1}^{4} X_{ij}$

d. X_{3j}

3. Referring to the matrix of scores on page 84, write the symbol for each of the following:

    a. The score of the 7th pupil on the 3rd test

    b. The score of any pupil on the 2nd test

    c. The score of the 5th pupil on some test

    d. The sum of the scores of the 8th pupil on all four tests

    e. The sum of the scores of all 50 pupils on the 4th test

    f. The sum of all 200 scores.

4. Suppose a study has been carried out with 150 pairs of children equated as to age, intelligence quotient, and sex, one member of each pair being assigned to a group that is taught by one method, the other member being assigned to a group taught by a second method. Let us suppose further that at the end of the experiment, each child is measured with respect to gain on three different measuring instruments. Altogether there will be $150 \times 2 \times 3 = 900$ scores available for study.

Let X_{ijk} represent the gain made by a child of pair i taught by method j and measured on test k, where i runs from 1 to 150, j runs from 1 to 2, and k runs from 1 to 3.

Translate the following symbols into words:

a. X_{213}	d. X_{i23}	g. X_{ij2}
b. X_{223}	e. X_{8j2}	h. X_{i2k}
c. X_{712}	f. X_{81k}	i. X_{7jk}

    j. $X_{213} - X_{223}$ ("The difference in the scores on test 3 made by the two children of the second pair," or better "the amount by which the child in pair 2 who was taught by the first method exceeds his mate taught by the second method, measurements being made with test 3." Note how much clearer and briefer is the symbolic language.)

    k. $\displaystyle\sum_{i=1}^{150}(X_{i13} - X_{i23})$

    l. $X_{211} + X_{212} + X_{213}$

    m. $X_{123} + X_{223} + X_{323} + \cdots + X_{i23} + \cdots + X_{150,23}$

    n. $\displaystyle\sum_{k=1}^{3}X_{21k}$

    o. $\displaystyle\sum_{i=1}^{150}X_{i23}$

    p. $\displaystyle\sum_{i=1}^{150}\sum_{k=1}^{3}X_{i2k}$

5. For the data described in Problem 4, express each of the following in symbols:

    a. The score on test 1 of the child in pair 6 who was taught by the second method.

    b. The score on test 2 of one of the children in pair 4, the method not being specified.

c. The amount by which the score of the child in pair 5 taught by method 2 exceeds the score of his mate, both being measured on the second test.

d. The sum of all the scores made by the child in pair 9 taught by the first method.

e. The sum for all 3 tests and for all 150 children of the amount by which the score of the child taught by method 1 exceeds the score of his mate.

f. The sum of all 900 scores.

Statistical Symbols. The reader is advised to familiarize himself as soon as possible with the symbols commonly employed in statistical formulas, and to learn to translate each symbol and each formula into appropriate words and sentences. Many of the concepts for which symbols are employed in statistics will be understood only as they are introduced and discussed in later chapters, but a few illustrations will be given here of the use of symbols to represent certain concepts with which the reader is already acquainted, or which he can understand without much difficulty at this stage.

Frequencies in a Frequency Distribution. The letter f is used to indicate the frequency of a score or value, or the frequency of scores falling within a class sort or interval. The frequencies of successive class sorts might be indicated as f_1, f_2, f_3, etc. The sum of all class frequencies in a frequency table is equal to the total number of scores or cases, which is represented by the letter N. Therefore, in symbolic language, $\Sigma f = N$.

Arithmetic Mean. The sum of a set of scores divided by the number of the scores is the arithmetic mean. The letter M is often used to represent the arithmetic mean. Because of certain advantages which will be apparent in later stages of the study, this measure will be represented in this text by a horizontal bar placed over the letter which denotes the variable in question. Thus the arithmetic mean of a set of X's will be represented by $\overline{X}$, which may be read either "the mean of X," or "X bar," or "bar X." Since the arithmetic mean is obtained by adding all the scores and dividing by the number of the scores, this relationship is adequately expressed by the formula $\overline{X} = \dfrac{\Sigma X}{N}$.

Score Measured from Different Origins. The number attached to a point on a scale indicates the distance to that point from some origin. If the origin is moved, the numerical designation of the point changes. In the sketch at top of page 89, the same point P changes its scale value from 6 to 8 to 1 as the origin shifts from A to B to C, yet in each system its position is definitely described. Suppose that X represents the value of

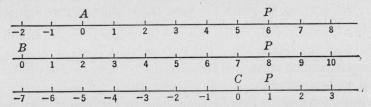

the point on the first scale, then X' and X'' might be used to designate the same point on the other scales.

In statistics the deviation of a score from the mean is of great importance, and therefore calls for a special symbol. When a capital letter, such as X, is used to represent the value of the score from zero origin, the corresponding small letter, as x, is generally used to designate its deviation from the mean.

Thus

$$x = X - \overline{X} \tag{1}$$

both defines the value x and indicates the relationship existing between X and x. Sometimes the origin is arbitrarily chosen at some point on the scale which may be neither zero nor the mean, and deviations are reckoned from this arbitrary origin rather than from the mean. In such case, denoting the arbitrary origin by A, the deviation of a score X from this arbitrary origin may be expressed by

$$x' = X - A \tag{2}$$

The deviation of the mean from the arbitrary origin may be expressed as

$$a = \overline{X} - A \tag{3}$$

The different relationships between $X, \overline{X}, x, x'$, and a may be seen from the accompanying sketch.

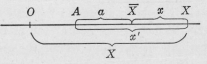

Scores Expressed in Different Units. For convenience in computation, a score may be designated in terms of interval units from the origin, rather than in terms of the original score units. A glance at the following diagram will show that there is no

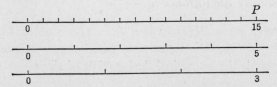

change of position on the scale involved, and that the numerical values of the point merely differ because of difference in width of interval used.

If two scales have the same origin, all that is necessary for the conversion of a score from one scale to the other is to multiply by the appropriate ratio between the two scales. Thus to translate a score in interval units to a score in original units, it is necessary to multiply by the width of the interval, and conversely.

A classic and familiar example is provided by the hero of *The Pirates of Penzance*, who, because he was born on February 29, had a birthday only once in four years and so measured his age in four-year units.

> Though counting in the usual way
>   Years twenty-one I've been alive
> Yet reckoning by my natal day
>   I am a little boy of five.

CHAPTER VII

AVERAGES

So careful of the type she seems,
So careless of the single life.
Tennyson

The great body of physical science, a great deal of the essential facts of financial science, and endless social and political problems are only accessible and only thinkable to those who have had a sound training in mathematical analysis, and the time may not be far remote when it will be understood that for complete initiation as an efficient citizen of one of the great new complex worldwide states that are now developing it is as necessary to be able to compute, to think in averages and maxima and minima as it is now to be able to read and to write.   H. G. Wells

One of the important tasks of descriptive statistics is to render mass data comprehensible by providing certain single values which can serve as a family type to represent the entire group. There are many group characteristics which one might wish to describe and which will be discussed in later sections. In this chapter we shall consider measures which may be used to represent the central position of the group. All such measures of central position are called *averages*.

Various Measures of Central Position. A reasonably resourceful person could invent a large variety of measures each of which would be called a measure of central position, or an average, because it is found near the middle of the distribution and in some way typifies the group. Measures which have been invented and used for this purpose include the following:

1. The score which occurs most frequently. This is the *mode*, to be discussed in a later section of this chapter.

2. The abscissa of a point on the scale of scores such that an ordinate erected at that point cuts off half of the area of the histogram. This is the *median*, with which the reader is already familiar.

3. The sum of all the scores divided by the number of scores. This is the *arithmetic mean*, popularly called "the average."

4. One-half the sum of the highest score and the lowest score. This would be so unstable that an experienced person would not be likely to use it. It has no name.

5. One-half the sum of the upper and lower quartiles. This also has no name. It is a poor measure of central position, though not so poor as the one last named.

6. The Nth root of the product of N scores, as $\sqrt[5]{X_1 \cdot X_2 \cdot X_3 \cdot X_4 \cdot X_5}$ or $\sqrt[8]{Y_1 \cdot Y_2 \cdot Y_3 \cdot Y_4 \cdot Y_5 \cdot Y_6 \cdot Y_7 \cdot Y_8}$. This measure is known as the *geometric mean* and has great usefulness in problems of one particular type, described on page 110 and in Appendix C.

7. The reciprocal of the mean of the reciprocals of the scores, as $\dfrac{3}{\dfrac{1}{x_1} + \dfrac{1}{x_2} + \dfrac{1}{x_3}}$. This is known as the *harmonic mean*. Though not often encountered, it is needed in problems of one particular type, described on page 109 and in Appendix C.

8. The square root of the mean of the squares of the scores, as $\sqrt{\dfrac{X_1{}^2 + X_2{}^2 + X_3{}^2 + \cdots + X_N{}^2}{N}}$. This is called the *root mean square*.

There is no limit to the number of measures of central position which could be devised. The early period of statistical development was characterized by the rapid invention of new devices and new formulas, and the man who could devise a new statistic was acclaimed as having done something valuable and clever. Today, the invention of plausible devices is recognized as not very difficult and not necessarily very valuable, and the ardent search for new tools has given place to a critical examination of tools, with a view to substituting efficient for inefficient methods.

Qualities Desirable in an Average. It is not always possible to secure at one time all the qualities which one might wish an average to possess, but the following are advantageous properties:

1. It should be located near the center of the distribution. Each of the eight averages listed in the preceding paragraph meets this criterion.

2. It should give to extreme scores such an influence as best represents the data in a particular problem. When the median is chosen over the mean, it is usually because, in that particular situation, the mean gives too great weight to extreme cases. This occurs chiefly when a distribution is very asymmetrical.

3. It should be easy to comprehend. Mean, median, and mode satisfy this criterion.

4. It should be easy to compute. Mean, median, and mode satisfy this criterion.

5. It should be an algebraic function of all the scores in the distribution. This means that the measure can be obtained from the scores by

addition, subtraction, multiplication, division, taking a root, or by a combination of these. Finding either the median or the mode involves an element of inspection which is not included among these operations. This property makes possible many time-saving computational devices, such as the method of obtaining statistics for a combined group from the statistics of its component groups. This property facilitates theoretical work, so that we know a great deal more about those averages which possess it than about those which do not. Inability to satisfy this criterion is one of the chief weaknesses of the mode and the median. Each of the three means (arithmetic, geometric, harmonic) satisfies it.

6. It should be relatively stable with respect to grouping errors (see page 35). The mode is particularly weak in respect to this criterion, a change in the step interval sometimes causing a very large change in the position of the mode.

7. It should be relatively stable from sample to sample. This concept of the variation of a statistic from sample to sample is developed more fully in Chapter XV. The second book of this series, intended for a more advanced course, will be devoted almost entirely to matters related to sampling variability. As a general introduction to the idea, however, let us suppose that a research worker wants to know the average height of all 8-year-old boys in the United States. Instead of measuring them all, he takes a sample of 2000 scattered throughout the states and selected according to a careful plan. Later he takes a second sample of 2000 selected by the same general plan. No matter which form of average is used, the two samples cannot be expected to yield exactly the same average. If, in the long run, it can be shown that one of the averages tends to fluctuate less from sample to sample than the other averages, that average is better in this respect. The arithmetic mean is more stable than any of the others in this regard, and is technically called an *efficient statistic* to indicate that it has a smaller variation from sample to sample than other averages. (This statement is true for the common types of distribution likely to be encountered in practical work. It is not true for certain rather rare types of theoretical curves which the student of mathematical statistics may encounter in more advanced studies.)

The Mode. The measure which occurs most frequently in a distribution is the mode, just as the style of dress or hat or coat which occurs most frequently in a given season is called the mode. In a grouped frequency distribution, the mode is considered to be at the midpoint of the interval in which the largest frequency occurs. If two or more adjacent intervals have the same frequency, and it is larger than the frequency in other intervals, the mode is considered to be at the midpoint of the entire range covered by such intervals. In a smooth frequency curve, the mode is the abscissa corresponding to the highest point on the curve. Two kinds of mode should be distinguished. The *mathematical mode* is a concept of considerable interest in theoretical work and is far more useful than the *crude mode.* However, the mathematical mode is difficult to obtain; can, in fact, be obtained only if the equation of a theoretical frequency curve is known, so that its maximum point can be found. This is almost always a task calling for some mathematical erudition. Therefore the mathematical mode is not discussed in elementary treatises, and the term mode

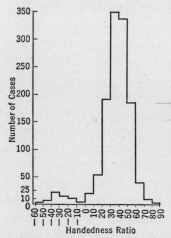

Fig. 17. Bimodal frequency distribution: handedness ratios. (From Durost, p. 302.)

is ordinarily applied to what is more properly called the crude mode.

The crude mode is the measure described in the first three sentences of the preceding paragraph. It is extremely easy to obtain, requiring no computation but merely inspection of the distribution. It is not an algebraic measure of the scores, and it is highly undependable, being subject to large variations from sample to sample, and subject to large changes produced by a change in choice of step interval. It is, indeed, so unstable that when it is published one of the other averages is almost always published with it.

Sometimes in a distribution there are two different intervals each of which has a frequency conspicuously larger than the frequencies in adjacent intervals, as is illustrated in Figure 17. The midpoint of each of these intervals is then called a mode, and the distribution is referred to as *bimodal*.

Sometimes two groups which ought to be treated separately are thrown together so that an artificially bimodal distribution is formed. As a rather extreme example, if a group of 10-year-olds and a group of 16-year-olds were to be combined, the distribution of their height, their weight, their mental age, their scores on almost any educational test, would be likely to be bimodal. The only thing to say about bimodal distributions of this sort is that the procedure of combining widely disparate groups is wrong and should be avoided. However, some truly bimodal distributions arise in homogeneous groups. Durost found that handedness has a continuous distribution with two humps, as represented in Figure 17. If the origin is taken at the point which represents complete ambidexterity, one hump is about as far to the left of this point as the other is to the right, but the one to the right is much higher.*

The cloudiness at the Greenwich Observatory during July is a classic example of a bimodal distribution. A glance at Table XVIII reveals that there were relatively few days of moderate cloudiness but many very clear days and many very cloudy days. This is an extreme instance of bimodality, producing the type of frequency distribution appropriately termed a *U-shaped distribution*. To state any average of these measures of cloudiness would tell very little about Greenwich weather. To give either the mean or the median of Durost's handedness ratios would provide less information than it would conceal.

TABLE XVIII

Bimodal Frequency Distribution: Frequencies of Different Degrees of Cloudiness as Observed at Greenwich During the Years 1890–1904 (Excluding 1901) for the Month of July †

Degree of Cloudiness	Frequency
10	676
9	148
8	90
7	65
6	55
5	45
4	45
3	68
2	74
1	129
0	320
Total	1715

† From Gertrude E. Pearse, "On corrections for the moment-coefficients of frequency distributions when there are infinite ordinates at one or both of the terminals of the range." *Biometrika*, 20A (1928), 336.

No standard symbol has been adopted for the mode. Some authors use *Mo*, but for several reasons this is not very satisfactory. Some authors

* Durost, W. N., "The development of a battery of objective group tests of manual laterality, with the results of their application to 1,300 children," *Genetic Psychology Monographs*, 16 (October. 1934), 225–335.

designate the mode by placing the symbol ⌣ above whatever letter is used to represent the variable in question. Thus if H represents height, $\breve{H}$ could be used to represent the mode of height. In general $\breve{X}$ (read "X arc" or "arc X" or "mode of X") could be used to indicate the mode of variable X.

The Median. It has been made clear in Chapter V that the median is easy to comprehend and to compute. Its chief weaknesses are that it fluctuates from sample to sample more than the mean and that it is not an algebraic function of all the scores, and therefore when several groups are to be combined there is no way of obtaining the median of the combined group from the medians of the component groups. Relatively little use can be made of the median in the mathematical theory of statistics, because of its non-algebraic nature, and consequently less is known about its properties than about the properties of the mean. When a correlation coefficient or a standard deviation (which will be treated later) is to be computed, the median is not appropriate as a measure of central position, for it cannot enter into algebraic relationship with them as the mean does.

TABLE XIX

Different Distributions with Same Median: Fictitious Data

Class Sort	Number of Cases			
	A	B	C	D
77–79		2		5
74–76		2		1
71–73		2		3
68–70	6	7		9
65–67	7	9	13	8
62–64	20	15	20	11
59–61	24	18	24	18
56–58	18	16	18	15
53–55	11	9	17	12
50–52	6	5	6	9
47–49	2	3		7
44–46		7		
41–43	3	1		
38–40	1	2		
Total	98	98	98	98
Median	59.5	59.5	59.5	59.5
Mean	58.8	59.0	59.3	60.2

The principal reason for the popularity of the median is that *extreme cases have no effect on it*. This is illustrated in Table XIX, in which four distributions have been constructed to have the same median, although they differ greatly as to extremes of the distribution. If each of the four extremely low cases in *A* were increased by 15 points the median would not be changed at all. Only if some score, or scores, were moved from one side of the median to the other would the value of the median be affected. This insensitivity of the median to extreme values may be either a strength or a weakness, depending on the circumstances of a particular problem.

For a distribution like that of Table XX, in which the end intervals have an unspecified range, a median can be computed, but not a mean.

TABLE XX

Frequency Distribution with Open Ends: Non-Farm Homes Classified by Monthly Rental, 1930 *

Monthly Rental	Number of Homes
$200 and over	45,750
150–199	46,297
100–149	163,292
75– 99	343,071
50– 74	1,503,401
30– 49	3,191,435
20– 29	2,545,208
15– 19	1,302,387
10– 14	1,330,927
Under $10	1,563,952
Not reported	315,829
Total	12,351,549

* *Statistical Abstract of the United States*, 1939.

The Mean. The sum of all the scores in a distribution divided by the number of the scores, popularly spoken of as "the average," is technically called the *arithmetic mean*. The geometric and the harmonic mean are encountered so rarely that the arithmetic mean is usually referred to as "*the* mean." Symbolically, its definition is:

$$\overline{X} = \frac{\Sigma X}{N} \quad \text{or} \quad \overline{X} = \frac{\sum_{i=1}^{N} X_i}{N} \tag{4}$$

From the discussion of qualities desirable in an average, it is clear why the mean is more widely used than any other measure of central tendency. There are other advantages enjoyed by the mean which can be discussed only in more advanced work, such as its very important relation to the theory of probability and to the normal curve. In certain circumstances, however, some other average is preferable.

Many methods of computing a mean are available, the choice between them being a matter of convenience and related to the form of the data. Several of the more common methods will now be described in connection with the same set of data.

The amount of practice needed by the members of any class varies widely and this text makes no pretence of providing enough exercises for all students to acquire computational skill. Anyone can provide practice for himself merely by writing down a series of numbers, computing the mean by several different methods, and comparing results. Throughout this text are numerous distributions for which the mean value is given. These may be used as practice material.

Computation of the Mean from Ungrouped Gross Scores. The scores in Appendix A have not been systematized in any way. The sum of the scores in any column of the table might be obtained by adding all the scores together. In thus adding the 109 scores of reading speed, which make up ΣX, the number 24 would have to be added ten separate times, for ten different children have that score. When the scores are arranged in order as in Table I on page 29 or in Table II on page 30, it would obviously be more efficient to add $10 \times 24 = 240$ once than to add 24 ten separate times. This suggests that the mean can be found by multiplying each score value by the corresponding frequency, adding the products, and dividing by N. The formula is now written

$$\overline{X} = \frac{\Sigma fX}{N} \tag{5}$$

in which f tells the novice not to overlook the frequency in his computations. Later, when the student thoroughly understands that ΣX means the sum of *all* the scores in the distribution, including every repetition, the omission of f from the formula will do no particular harm.

Table XXI suggests the method of computing the mean of Table II. The reader should complete the work, verifying the value $\overline{X} = 28.14$ as computed from the raw data.

Computation of the Mean from a Grouped Frequency Distribution. If raw data are not available and we compute the mean reading speed from the grouped distribution of Table III, a small grouping error is to

TABLE XXI

*Illustration of the Method of Computing the Mean from the Ungrouped Distribution of Table II ***

Score	f	fX	
50	2	100	
49	1	49	
48	1	48	
47			$N = \Sigma f = 109$
46	1	46	$\Sigma fX = 3067$
45	3	135	$\overline{X} = \dfrac{3067}{109} = 28.14$
.	.	.	
.	.	.	
.	.	.	
8	2	16	
7	1	7	
Total	109	3067	

*Note the omission of scores in the middle of the distribution. The student should supply these and complete the computation.

be expected in the mean. Such a grouping error is usually negligible. The reason for it can be seen by comparing Table II with Table III. The 9 scores in the interval 16 to 18 of Table III will now be treated as though each score was 17, so that their total contribution to the mean will be $9 \times 17 = 153$. Actually, however, the contribution of these scores is $4 \times 16 + 3 \times 17 + 2 \times 18 = 151$. An excess in one interval is likely to be balanced by a deficiency in another, so that the total sum is not likely to be much affected by errors of grouping.

Table XXII illustrates three computations of the mean from the grouped data of Table III.

Use of Gross Scores. The entry in the column headed X is the gross score value of the midpoint of the interval. In the column headed fX, each value of X has been multiplied by the corresponding frequency. The sum of this column should be a close approximation to ΣfX obtained in Table XXI. The computation is completed by dividing by N.

Use of a Code. The entries in the column headed x' are deviations in interval units from an arbitrary origin so placed that all deviations are positive but as small as possible. This origin is taken at the midpoint of

TABLE XXII

Three Computations of the Mean of a Grouped Frequency Distribution Using Different Origins

(Data from Table III)

Class Sort	f	A Use of Gross Scores		B Use of Step-Interval Units with Origin at Midpoint of Lowest Interval		C Use of Step-Interval Units with Origin in Middle of Distribution	
		X	fX	x'	fx'	x''	fx''
49–51	3	50	150	14	42	7	21
46–48	2	47	94	13	26	6	12
43–45	8	44	352	12	96	5	40
40–42	9	41	369	11	99	4	36
37–39	2	38	76	10	20	3	6
34–36	6	35	210	9	54	2	12
31–33	5	32	160	8	40	1	5
28–30	18	29	522	7	126	0	0
25–27	16	26	416	6	96	−1	−16
22–24	14	23	322	5	70	−2	−28
19–21	5	20	100	4	20	−3	−15
16–18	9	17	153	3	27	−4	−36
13–15	4	14	56	2	8	−5	−20
10–12	5	11	55	1	5	−6	−30
7– 9	3	8	24	0	0	−7	−21
Total	109		3059		729		−34

Method A: $\Sigma fX = 3059$ $\overline{X} = \dfrac{3059}{109} = 28.06$

Method B: $\Sigma fx' = 729$
$\qquad\qquad\quad A = 8$ $\overline{X} = 8 + \dfrac{3(729)}{109} = 28.06$
$\qquad\qquad\quad i = 3$

Method C: $\Sigma fx'' = -34$
$\qquad\qquad\quad A = 29$ $\overline{X} = 29 - \dfrac{3(34)}{109} = 28.06$
$\qquad\qquad\quad i = 3$

the lowest interval in which frequency occurs, so that for these data $A = 8$. The scores in the X column have been reduced in two ways to produce the scores in the x' column, first by subtracting the value of the midpoint of the lowest interval, $A = 8$, and then by dividing the remainder by the width of the step interval, which for these data is $i = 3$. The resulting set of cardinal numbers, beginning with zero and proceeding by unity, may be called *coded scores*.

Think now of the frequency distribution of these coded scores. When the coded scores are multiplied by their corresponding frequencies the entries in Column fx' are obtained, and the mean coded score is seen to be $729/109 = 6.688$. But the goal of the computation was not to find the mean coded score but the mean gross score. The mean coded score is 6.688 *interval units* above its origin, which would be $6.688 \times 3 = 20.06$ *score units* above $A = 8$, which would be 28.06 score units above zero. The formula for this computation is

$$\overline{X} = A + i\left(\frac{\Sigma fx'}{N}\right) \tag{6}$$

where i is the width of the step interval. When score units are employed, $i = 1$.

This method is particularly convenient for machine computation.

Use of an Arbitrary Origin Near the Center of the Distribution. When computations are to be made with pencil and paper, it is desirable to keep the numbers as small as possible, and so it is convenient to place the arbitrary origin near the middle of the distribution. This has caused some writers to call the reference point a "guessed average" or an "assumed mean." In reality it is neither, and the terms are unfortunate and misleading. Note that *the reference point is always placed at the midpoint of an interval.* The midpoint of the next higher interval is then $+1$ interval unit from the origin, the midpoint of the next lower interval -1 interval unit, and so on. When the reduced scores of Column x'' are multiplied by their corresponding frequencies, the entries in Column fx'' are obtained. The mean of the reduced scores is $-34/109 = -0.312$ interval units from its origin, which would be $0.312 \times 3 = 0.94$ score units below that origin. But the origin is 29. Hence the location of the mean of the reduced scores is -0.312 on its own scale, and this corresponds to $29 - \frac{(34)(3)}{109} = 28.06$ on the scale of raw scores.

Check for Computation of the Arithmetic Mean. A convenient check can be obtained by moving the origin up or down by one interval. When the origin is moved up one interval, $\Sigma fx'$ is decreased by N, when it is moved down one interval, $\Sigma fx'$ is increased by N. Thus if the origin is taken at the midpoint of the interval 31–33, $\Sigma fx''$ will be $-34 - 109 = -143$; if at the midpoint of the interval 25–27, $\Sigma fx''$ will be $-34 + 109 = 75$. No matter what origin is chosen, the value of $\overline{X}$ is invariant, that is, unchanging. Trying to find an error by looking over the figures of a completed computation is usually fruitless. The good computer employs checks which are something other than sheer repetition.

The student should verify these values by computing the mean from different reference points.

Computation of the Mean of a Small Number of Scattered Scores. When N is small, grouping scores into larger intervals is likely to produce a large error, and should therefore be avoided. If a computing machine is available, or if the scores are not too large, they may be added as they stand. However, it is often economical to reduce them first by subtracting from each score some convenient constant, then to find the mean of the reduced scores and add it to the constant.

Illustration:

Original Scores	Scores Reduced by Subtracting 150
159	9
162	12
171	21
143	−7
158	8
165	15
174	24
161	11
	93

$$\overline{X} = \tfrac{93}{8} + 150 = 161.625 \text{ or } 161.6$$

If A is the value subtracted, the procedure may be expressed by the formula

$$\overline{X} = \frac{\Sigma X}{N} = \frac{\Sigma(X - A)}{N} + A \tag{7}$$

Computation of the Mean by Cumulation or Successive Addition. This method has been placed in Appendix C. It does not belong in a minimum course, but is a very useful procedure, leading to valuable short cuts in connection with the computation of standard deviation and correlation coefficient. A procedure of computing the mean by "folding" the distribution will also be found in Appendix C.

The Mean as a Member of the Moment System. The mean and certain other measures used to describe the characteristics of a distribution are sometimes called the *moments* of the distribution through an analogy with certain concepts and terms in physics.

Consider a rigid rod or lever AB free to turn about some fixed point F called the fulcrum. The tendency of AB to turn depends upon the amount of the force brought to bear on it, and the place where the force is applied. The larger the force applied at some given point, the more easily the bar will turn. If the force were moved farther out from the fulcrum F, it would have a

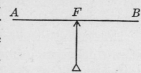

greater tendency to produce rotation of AB around F. This tendency to produce rotation is called the *moment of the force.*

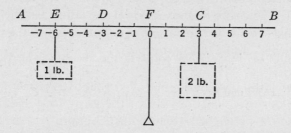

Suppose now that we had a rod marked off in inches, and we placed a weight of 2 lb. at C, 3 inches to the right of F. Obviously, we could keep the rod from rotating if we took another 2-lb. weight and placed it at D, 3 inches to the left of F. However, *we could also keep AB from rotating if we placed a 1-lb. weight at E, 6 inches to the left of F.* In the language of physics, this illustrates the fact that the magnitude of the force tending to produce the rotation is measured by the product of the number of units in the force (1 lb.) times the number of units in the force arm (6 inches), where the force arm is the perpendicular distance from the fulcrum to the line of direction of the force.

No matter where the 2-lb. weight is placed on FB, or where the 1-lb. weight is placed on FA, if the lever is balanced, or is in equilibrium, the product of the 2-lb. weight and its distance from the fulcrum must be equal to the product of the 1-lb. weight and its distance from the fulcrum, or $2 \times CF = 1 \times EF$. This statement may be generalized to include any number of weights of any size. Imagine that for the small frequency distribution on page 104 a histogram has been drawn, that it has been cut out of material having weight, and that it rests upon a lever arm with fulcrum at zero, as in Figure 18a.

Score	f
43–47	2
38–42	10
33–37	18
28–32	8
23–27	6
18–22	5
13–17	1
	$N = 50$

How much force does the entire histogram exert upon the lever? The weight of each column is proportional to its frequency. Each column exerts a force equal to the weight of the column multiplied by its distance from the fulcrum, which is the product of f for that column by the corresponding X. The entire force is ΣfX. If the entire frequency, concentrated at a single point, were to exert the same force, the score value of that point would be $\dfrac{\Sigma fX}{N}$. This point is the mean. The turning force exerted by the entire distribution is called the first *moment* around zero. This illustration corresponds exactly to the gross score method of computing the mean of a grouped frequency distribution.

Suppose now that the fulcrum is moved to the point corresponding to the mean. The lever will be in equilibrium, the positive and negative forces being perfectly balanced, as in Figure 18b. Therefore the mean may be defined as that point on the scale which is the center of equilibrium for the distribution.

Suppose now that the fulcrum had been placed at some point other than the mean. For convenience let it be the midpoint of an interval, as it usually is in computation. The lever, as in Figure 18c, is not in equilibrium but tips downward on the right. How far must the fulcrum be moved to bring the lever into equilibrium? We must see what is the moment of force exerted around the fulcrum. The two columns to the left of the fulcrum exert a counterclockwise force of $1 \times 2 + 5 \times 1 = 7$ units, the step interval being used as the unit of distance. The column directly over the fulcrum is balanced, exerting no force in either direction. The four columns to the right of the fulcrum exert a clockwise force of $8 \times 1 + 18 \times 2 + 10 \times 3 + 2 \times 4 = 82$ units. The total turning force therefore is $82 - 7 = 75$ units in a clockwise direction. If the fulcrum were moved one scale unit to the right, the turning force would be reduced by one unit for every individual in the distribution, that is, by N units of force. In this case, $N = 50$. Therefore, to eliminate 75 units of turning power, the fulcrum must be shifted $\frac{75}{50} \times 5$ score units or 7.5 score units. Thus the lever will be in equilibrium if the fulcrum is placed at $25 + 7.5 = 32.5$. This point is the mean. The illustration parallels the computation of a mean from an arbitrary origin.

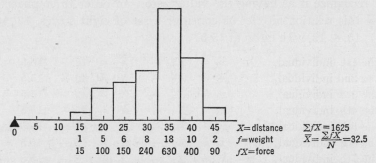

0	5	10	15	20	25	30	35	40	45
			1	5	6	8	18	10	2
			15	100	150	240	630	400	90

X=distance $\Sigma fX = 1625$
f=weight $\overline{X} = \frac{\Sigma fX}{N} = 32.5$
fX=force

Fig. 18a. Graphic representation of gross score method of computing the mean.

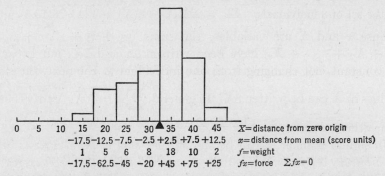

0	5	10	15	20	25	30	35	40	45
			−17.5	−12.5	−7.5	−2.5	+2.5	+7.5	+12.5
			1	5	6	8	18	10	2
			−17.5	−62.5	−45	−20	+45	+75	+25

X=distance from zero origin
x=distance from mean (score units)
f=weight
fx=force $\Sigma fx = 0$

Fig. 18b. Graphic representation of the mean as the center of equilibrium.

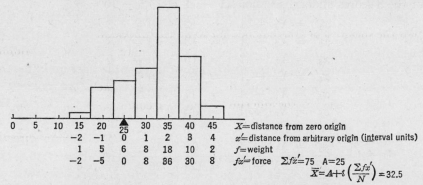

0	5	10	15	20	25	30	35	40	45
			−2	−1	0	1	2	3	4
			1	5	6	8	18	10	2
			−2	−5	0	8	36	30	8

X=distance from zero origin
x'=distance from arbitrary origin (interval units)
f=weight
fx'=force $\Sigma fx' = 75$ $A = 25$
$\overline{X} = A + i \left(\frac{\Sigma fx'}{N} \right) = 32.5$

Fig. 18c. Graphic representation of computing the mean from an arbitrary origin.

The fact that *the sum of the deviations from the mean is zero*, as shown in Figure 18b, is a very important property of the mean to which reference will be made again and again in succeeding pages. The student will find that his understanding of many other relationships is facilitated if, whenever he meets the symbol Σfx, where x represents the deviation of a score from the mean, or the equivalent expression, $\Sigma f(X - \overline{X})$, he can immediately recognize it as having the value zero. In order to emphasize and clarify this relationship, let us consider a set of eight scores, 12, 18, 10, 25, 17, 15, 8, 19, with mean at 15.5.

For the 1st individual, $x_1 = X_1 - \overline{X} = 12 - 15.5 = -3.5$
For the 2nd individual, $x_2 = X_2 - \overline{X} = 18 - 15.5 = +2.5$
For the 3rd individual, $x_3 = X_3 - \overline{X} = 10 - 15.5 = -5.5$
For the 4th individual, $x_4 = X_4 - \overline{X} = 25 - 15.5 = +9.5$
For the 5th individual, $x_5 = X_5 - \overline{X} = 17 - 15.5 = +1.5$
For the 6th individual, $x_6 = X_6 - \overline{X} = 15 - 15.5 = -\ .5$
For the 7th individual, $x_7 = X_7 - \overline{X} = 8 - 15.5 = -7.5$
For the 8th individual, $x_8 = X_8 - \overline{X} = 19 - 15.5 = +3.5$

For the set of 8 individuals, $\Sigma x = \Sigma X\ (-)\ 8(\overline{X}) = 124 - 8(15.5) = 0$

Because x and X are variables, the sums $(x_1 + x_2 + \cdots + x_8)$ and $(X_1 + X_2 + \cdots + X_8)$ have been written Σx and ΣX, but because $\overline{X}$ is a constant, not changing from one individual to the next, the sum of 8 values of $\overline{X}$ can be written $8\overline{X}$. In general, $\displaystyle\sum_1^N \overline{X} = N\overline{X}$. Verify the sums of the other columns.

In similar manner, it can be shown that *sum of the deviations around any arbitrary origin is N times the amount by which the mean exceeds that origin*, or $\Sigma fx' = N(\overline{X} - A)$. Suppose, for example, that $A = 10$. Then for the 8 scores under discussion, $\overline{X} - A = 15.5 - 10 = 5.5$.

$$x_1' = X_1 - A = 12 - 10 = 2$$
$$x_2' = X_2 - A = 18 - 10 = 8$$
$$x_3' = X_3 - A = 10 - 10 = 0$$
$$x_4' = X_4 - A = 25 - 10 = 15$$
$$x_5' = X_5 - A = 17 - 10 = 7$$
$$x_6' = X_6 - A = 15 - 10 = 5$$
$$x_7' = X_7 - A = 8 - 10 = -2$$
$$x_8' = X_8 - A = 19 - 10 = 9$$

$$\Sigma x' = \Sigma X - NA = 124 - 80 = 44$$
$$\Sigma x' = N\overline{X} - NA = 8(5.5)$$

or

$$\frac{\Sigma x'}{N} = \overline{X} - A = 5.5$$

When scores are grouped, this becomes $\dfrac{\Sigma fx'}{N} = \overline{X} - A$.

Exercise 13*

1. The set of numbers 27, 22, 30, 20, 41, 28 has mean at 28. Write down the value of x for each score as it was done in the preceding paragraph, and verify $\Sigma x = 0$.

2. For the same set of numbers write down the deviation of each number from 30. Complete the set, and verify that $\Sigma x' = 6(28-30) = -12$.

3. Write down the deviations of these numbers from any arbitrary value you may select. If this value is called A, verify that $\Sigma x' = 6(28 - A)$.

Geometric Representation of Mode, Median, Mean. To illustrate the relative positions of these three measures of central position, draw a smooth curve, such as Figure 19. From the highest point on this curve, drop a perpendicular to the base line. The foot of this perpendicular is the

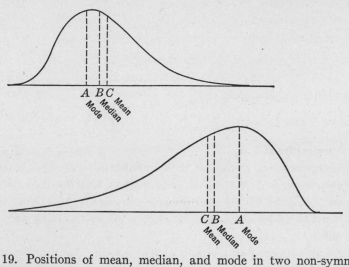

Fig. 19. Positions of mean, median, and mode in two non-symmetrical distributions.

A = mode = foot of perpendicular dropped from highest point on curve.
B = median = foot of perpendicular which bisects area under curve.
C = mean = center of equilibrium.

mode, indicated by A in the sketch shown here. To locate the median geometrically, it is necessary to draw an ordinate which will bisect the area under the curve. In Figure 19 this is done by the ordinate at B, and so B is the median. Now imagine that the figure is resting on a fulcrum at B. Half of the area is on each side of B, but that area is stretched out farther to one side than to the other. Therefore the situation is like that of a teeter-totter with two children of the same weight, sitting at unequal distances from the fulcrum. The lever will not balance until the fulcrum is moved to the center of equilibrium, which is the mean. *Note that the mean, median, and mode are represented by points in the scale of scores.* In a smooth non-symmetrical frequency distribution, the median is usually found between the mean and mode and nearer to the mean.

Misleading Use of Mean, Median, or Mode. Any statistical measure can be misleading if used or interpreted by someone who does not understand it, or whose thinking is illogical. Several typical abuses of averages should be noted.

Use of Wrong Average. 1. Suppose that a school board wishes to prove to the community that the teachers in the system are well paid. The salary distribution is as follows:

Salary	Number of Teachers		
$5,000	1		
2,600	1		
2,400	2	Mean	= $1,730
2,100	1		
1,800	2	Median	= $1,550
1,600	8		
1,500	10	Mode	= $1,500
1,200	5		

For these data, the median is really indeterminate; 50% of the cases receive salaries of $1,600 or more, 50% receive salaries of $1,500 or less. Any value between $1,500 and $1,600 will satisfy the definition of a median, and the point half-way between them is the most satisfactory, though arbitrary, choice.

Should the Board publish only the mean, the community would be misled into thinking that the typical teacher receives $1,730 a year, whereas only 7 out of 30 receive so large a salary. In such a case, it is better to use the median if only one average is quoted, still better to use all three, or to show the entire distribution.

2. Much has been written of the recent increase in mean age at death, and this is often understood to imply that the number of old people is increasing rapidly. A large part of the change, however, is due to a reduction in infant mortality; such reduction would have little effect on the median age at death, while increasing the mean in striking fashion.

Use of an Average When Some Other Measure is Called For. 1. Sometimes variability is more important than central position. Two cities may have the same mean annual temperature without being much alike as to climate, because in one the temperature is equable, never going to extremes, while in the other the temperature passes from extreme heat to extreme cold. Today's cold is not mitigated by last summer's heat, and an average temperature has little meaning unless the range is also given.

2. Sometimes a maximum value, or a minimum, is all that matters. An engineer designing a bridge or an elevator is not concerned so much with the average load it will carry as with the maximum load.

3. The data on handedness and on cloudiness, quoted on page 94, illustrate situations in which a mean would have little meaning. It would be more valuable, in such bimodal distributions, to state both modes than any single mean or median, and still better to show the entire distribution.

Use of an Average to Describe Data That Do Not Properly Belong in the Same Group. Age-weight or age-height tables based upon the average weight or the average height of persons of a given age would obviously be of little value if the two sexes were combined, because so far as weight and height go, the sexes belong to clearly differentiated groups In regard to many other traits there is no known difference between them, and sex groups can properly be combined. Suppose that in a residential section on the outskirts of a small city, a number of very wealthy men have built homes, and that in another section of the same city several hundred unemployed live on relief. The average annual income of all families in the city would be deceptive. *An average is intended to describe a group*. It has no value and no meaning when applied to two discrete groups artificially thrown together.

The Harmonic and Geometric Means. Each of these averages is applicable to one particular type of problem in which no other average is equally meaningful. Because their use is not often required, it seems inadvisable to include them in the text proper. Because their use is sometimes essential they are presented in Appendix C, together with a selected bibliography. At this point, we shall describe very briefly the types of problem in which these measures are used, in order that the reader who has such a problem may be warned that he should study the appropriate mean before proceeding further.

The harmonic mean is typically called for in problems about work, time, and rate, where the amount of work is held constant and an average rate is required; or in problems about total cost, number of persons and per capita cost, when the total cost is held constant and an average per capita cost is called for; or in problems of similar nature involving rates.

The geometric mean is typically used in obtaining the average rate of change of a variable which may be assumed to be changing at a relatively constant rate. Finding the average growth of the population of a community over a period of time, or the average rate of change in the enrollment of an institution, or the average percentage rate of learning or forgetting of an individual in successive periods, demands the use of the geometric mean.

The geometric mean of two numbers is the mean proportional between them, which is the square root of their product. It will be seen later that the correlation coefficient is the geometric mean of the two regression coefficients.

CHAPTER VIII

MEASURES OF VARIABILITY

It is difficult to understand why statisticians commonly limit their inquiries to averages, and do not revel in more comprehensive views. Their souls seem as dull to the charm of variety as that of the native of one of our flat English counties, whose retrospect of Switzerland was that, if its mountains could be thrown into its lakes, two nuisances would be got rid of at once. An average is but a solitary fact, whereas if a single other fact be added to it, an entire normal scheme, which nearly corresponds to the observed one, starts potentially into existence.

Francis Galton

In almost every situation in which an average is needed, there is also needed a measure of the *scattering, dispersion, fluctuation, spread, or variability* of the individuals within the group.

Total Range. The method of describing the variability of a group which is likely to come first to mind is a statement of the range from lowest to highest score. In some cases this is more meaningful than any other measure. Particularly in situations where the extremes involve some hazard for which preparation should be made, it may be more important to know the most extreme case to be encountered than to know anything else about a distribution. An explorer would want to know the lowest and the highest temperatures on record in the region he was about to enter. In general, however, the range is a somewhat unsatisfactory measure of spread because it is so dependent upon the performance of the extreme individuals. If either the oldest or the youngest child in a group happens to drop out, the age range may be considerably changed, whereas the removal of any number of other individuals would not affect it at all. Usually the number of individuals near the ends of the distribution is small so that the total range is a function of the scores of a few extreme individuals only.

Table XXIII has been constructed to illustrate three groups with the same mean which are very unlike in their total distribution. The removal of two extreme individuals from group A would reduce its range below that of B. The greater range of A is not a description of the entire group of 124 individuals but of the two most extreme individuals only.

While groups B and C have the same range, the members of B cluster more closely around the middle of the group. The range, as a measure of

111

scatter, fails to reveal the greater homogeneity of B, the greater dispersion of C.

TABLE XXIII

Distributions Having the Same Mean
but Different Variability

Class Sort	Frequency		
	A	B	C
77–79	1		
74–76	6	7	28
71–73	11	12	20
68–70	16	14	11
65–67	20	16	7
62–64	18	17	5
59–61	14	20	3
56–58	12	14	3
53–55	11	13	7
50–52	7	7	12
47–49	7	3	17
44–46		1	11
41–43			
38–40	1		
Total	124	124	124
Mean	62.3	62.3	62.3
Range	41	32	32
$P_{90} - P_{10}$	20.6	19.3	28.4
$P_{93} - P_{07}$	23.3	21.6	29.6

Interpercentile Range. When central position is measured by the median, the range between any two symmetrically placed percentiles may be used to indicate the spread of scores. The interquartile range, or the range within which the middle half of the cases fall, is very frequently used as a measure of scatter.*

* When Galton invented the "quartile deviation" or $\frac{1}{2}(Q_U - Q_L)$, he had been reading Quetelet's *Letters on the Theory of Probability*, addressed to Prince Albert, Queen Victoria's consort, in which he had encountered the concept of "probable error." The German astron-

The range from the 10th to the 90th percentile, or still better, the range from the 7th to the 93rd percentile,* includes most of the cases yet excludes the erratic few at the ends of the range which make the total range unreliable.

Measures Based on Deviations. To find the amount by which each score deviates from some measure of central position and to average all such deviations seems a natural way of estimating the total amount of dispersion. It has already been noted, however, that the algebraic sum of the deviations from the mean is always zero, no matter whether the scores cluster closely around the mean or depart widely from it. Since the algebraic sum of the deviations from the mean is zero, the mean of those deviations is also zero. Being invariant, it does not differentiate one distribution from another and so is useless as a measure.

Some method must be found to prevent the positive and negative deviations from cancelling each other, that is, some method which will take account of size of deviation only, and will disregard direction. Two methods suggest themselves at once: (1) to ignore signs or, (2) to square the deviations. The first method produces what is called *the mean deviation*, the second, what is called *the standard deviation*.

When the sign of a number is disregarded, only its *numerical* or *arithmetic* or *absolute* value is considered. Thus a debt of $50 has the same absolute value as a credit of $50, but not the same signed value. The signed value is also called the *directed* or *algebraic* value. The absolute values of -3 and of $+3$ are the same. If n represents a given number, which may be either positive or negative, $|n|$ represents the absolute value of n. Suppose that $n_1 = 10$, $n_2 = -4$, $n_3 = -9$, $n_4 = 6$, $n_5 = -7$. The *algebraic sum* of these numbers is $\Sigma n = 10 - 4 - 9 + 6 - 7 = -4$. The sum of their *arithmetic values*, or their *absolute values* is $\Sigma |n|$ which is read "The sum of the absolute values of n" or "The sum of all the n's taken without regard to sign," and is equal to $|10| + |-4| + |-9| + |6| + |-7| = |36|$.

omers of the first half of the nineteenth century were familiar with the probability curve— now often called the "normal" curve—as describing the errors made in repeated observations of the same astronomical object. This is a symmetrical curve, with mean at zero. The half of the errors which are nearest zero lie between two points which are equally distant from the mean. The distance from one of these points to the mean the German astronomers called "der wahrscheinliche Fehler," or "the probable error." Galton called half the interquartile range the "quartile deviation" or Q and used it as a short cut for obtaining the probable error. However, in an asymmetrical distribution the quartile points are not equally distant from the median, and Q is not a deviation at all. Furthermore, the probable error is a term used today only in connection with the reliability of sampling, never to describe the variability of a set of observed data.

* This range $P_{93} - P_{07}$ has been shown to vary less from sample to sample than any other range. See Kelley, Truman L., "A new measure of dispersion," *Quarterly Publications of the American Statistical Association*, 17 (1920–21), 743–749.

The Mean Deviation. *The mean deviation* of a frequency distribution is the mean of the absolute values of the deviations from some measure of central position. It is an unsatisfactory measure of scatter. Once the signs of the deviations have been thrown away, the algebraic nature of any measure based upon them is lost. Therefore the mean deviation lacks those algebraic properties which would facilitate its computation and establish its relation to other measures. It is not particularly easy to compute. It does not enter into algebraic combinations with other measures. It has no advantages whatever over the standard deviation, and its computation will not even be illustrated here.* At one time a median deviation, or the median of the absolute values of the deviations, was proposed as a measure of scatter, but it is now completely obsolete.

The Variance and the Standard Deviation. To get rid of negative signs without committing algebraic violence, all the deviations may be squared, and the mean of these squares taken. The result is called the *mean square deviation* or *variance*. The variance is a measure of variation, but it is a square rather than a linear measure. The square root of the variance is called the *root mean square deviation* or the *standard deviation*. We shall designate it as *s*. The standard deviation is in reality a standard with which deviations of individual scores may be compared. Again and again, for other statistics to be used later, we shall resort to this device of squaring to get rid of negative signs, averaging, and then taking the square root to change the mean square back to a linear measure.

When Karl Pearson first used the term *standard deviation* in 1893, he employed the small Greek sigma, σ, to designate it, and since then that symbol has been almost universally used. Recently there has developed a tendency to distinguish between the statistics observed in particular samples and the corresponding unknown value in the universe from which those samples are drawn, by using a Latin letter for the sample statistic, and the corresponding Greek letter for the value in the universe. In conformity with this practice, we shall use *s* for the standard deviation of a particular sample and reserve σ to refer to the standard deviation of a universe. Usually the standard deviation of the universe from which the sample is drawn is an unknown value, and so an observed value of *s* is used to obtain an estimate of the unknown σ. Such problems belong to the field of statistical inference rather than descriptive statistics, and are mentioned here only to explain why *s* rather than σ has been adopted as the symbol for the standard deviation. This subject is discussed further in Chapter XV.

* The reader who may wish to study the mean deviation and its computation will find a number of references given at the end of this chapter.

So common is the use of σ as a symbol for the standard deviation that some persons speak of "the sigma of the distribution" when they mean its standard deviation, and some speak of "sigmatized scores" meaning scores expressed as multiples of the standard deviation.

Symbolic Definition and Computational Formulas for the Variance. Verbally, the variance may be defined as the sum of the squares of the deviations from the mean divided by their number.* Translated into symbolism, this becomes:

Definition:
$$s^2 = \frac{\Sigma f(X - \overline{X})^2}{N} = \frac{\Sigma fx^2}{N} \tag{8}$$

This definition does not offer an efficient routine for computation. The mean is seldom an integer, and to take deviations from the mean usually requires an unnecessary amount of labor. It is better to use an arbitrary reference point, and to make computations by one of the following formulas:

For any position of the origin and any width of interval
$$s^2 = i^2\left[\frac{\Sigma f(x')^2}{N} - \left(\frac{\Sigma fx'}{N}\right)^2\right] \tag{9}$$

For origin at zero and measures in score units
$$s^2 = \frac{\Sigma fX^2}{N} - \left(\frac{\Sigma fX}{N}\right)^2 \tag{10}$$

or
$$s^2 = \frac{\Sigma fX^2}{N} - (\overline{X})^2 \tag{11}$$

The width of interval i need not be written into formula (10) because when score units are employed $i = 1$. Formulas (10) and (11) are merely a special case of (9), but are shown separately because of the great economy in computation which they afford.

If formulas (8) to (10) are each multiplied by N, we have relationships (12) to (14), which will be useful to remember. Formula (15) states that the right hand members of formulas (12), (13) and (14) are equal.

$$Ns^2 = \Sigma fx^2 \tag{12}$$

$$Ns^2 = i^2\left[\Sigma f(x')^2 - \frac{(\Sigma fx')^2}{N}\right] \tag{13}$$

$$Ns^2 = \Sigma fX^2 - \frac{(\Sigma fX)^2}{N} \tag{14}$$

$$\Sigma fx^2 = i^2\left[\Sigma f(x')^2 - \frac{(\Sigma fx')^2}{N}\right] = \Sigma fX^2 - \frac{(\Sigma fX)^2}{N} \tag{15}$$

* For discussion of an alternative definition preferred by some statisticians, see Chapter XV.

Symbolic Definition and Computational Formulas for the Standard Deviation. From the corresponding formulas for the variance we have:

Definition:
$$s = \sqrt{\frac{\Sigma f(X - \overline{X})^2}{N}} = \sqrt{\frac{\Sigma fx^2}{N}} \quad (8a)$$

For any position of the origin and any width of interval
$$s = i\sqrt{\frac{\Sigma f(x')^2}{N} - \left(\frac{\Sigma fx'}{N}\right)^2} \quad (9a)$$

For origin at zero and measures in score units
$$s = \sqrt{\frac{\Sigma fX^2}{N} - \left(\frac{\Sigma fX}{N}\right)^2} \quad (10a)$$

or
$$s = \sqrt{\frac{\Sigma fX^2}{N} - (\overline{X})^2} \quad (11a)$$

A proof that formulas (9), (10), and (11) follow from the definition in (8) will be found in Appendix B.

TABLE XXIV

Computation of the Standard Deviation from a Grouped Frequency Distribution, Using an Arbitrary Origin and Showing Checks

(Data from Table III)

Class Sort	f	A			B		
		x'	fx'	$f(x')^2$	$x' + 1$	$f(x' + 1)$	$f(x' + 1)^2$
49–51	3	7	21	147	8	24	192
46–48	2	6	12	72	7	14	98
43–45	8	5	40	200	6	48	288
40–42	9	4	36	144	5	45	225
37–39	2	3	6	18	4	8	32
34–36	6	2	12	24	3	18	54
31–33	5	1	5	5	2	10	20
28–30	18	0	0	0	1	18	18
25–27	16	−1	−16	16	0	0	0
22–24	14	−2	−28	56	−1	−14	14
19–21	5	−3	−15	45	−2	−10	20
16–18	9	−4	−36	144	−3	−27	81
13–15	4	−5	−20	100	−4	−16	64
10–12	5	−6	−30	180	−5	−25	125
7– 9	3	−7	−21	147	−6	−18	108
Total	109		−34	1298		+75	1339

Check: $\Sigma f(x' + 1)^2 = \Sigma f(x')^2 + 2\Sigma fx' + N$

$1339 = 1298 \quad - 68 \quad + 109$

$$s^2 = 3^2 \left[\frac{1298}{109} - \left(\frac{-34}{109} \right)^2 \right] = 9(11.81) = 106.3$$

or $\quad s^2 = 3^2 \left[\frac{1339}{109} - \left(\frac{75}{109} \right)^2 \right] = 9(11.81) = 106.3$

$\quad s = 3\sqrt{11.81} = 10.3$

Computation of the Standard Deviation from a Grouped Frequency Distribution Using an Arbitrary Origin. When no machine is available, the computer naturally wishes to keep all figures as small as possible, and so he reduces the scores by taking an arbitrary origin near the center of the distribution and using the class interval as unit. Compare the method of computing a mean in section C of Table XXII in the preceding chapter. Table XXIV shows two computations of the standard deviation either of which may be considered a check on the other. The origin used in section B of this table is taken one interval lower than the origin used in section A.

Steps in the Computation of a Variance or Standard Deviation, with Origin in Middle of Distribution

1. Prepare a grouped frequency distribution of the measures.
2. Choose an arbitrary origin. Code the intervals using zero for the interval in which the origin is placed, and coding the intervals above that origin successively 1, 2, 3, · · · and below it -1, -2, -3, · · ·. Call these coded scores x'.
3. Multiply each x' by the corresponding f and enter the product in the fx' column.
4. Multiply each fx' by the corresponding x' and enter the product in the $f(x')^2$ column.
5. Find the algebraic sum of the entries in the fx' column and divide by N obtaining $\frac{\Sigma fx'}{N}$. From section A of Table XXIV this is $\frac{-34}{109} = -0.312$.

6. Square this result, obtaining $\left(\frac{\Sigma fx'}{N} \right)^2$. From section A of Table XXIV this is $\left(\frac{-34}{109} \right)^2 = 0.097$.

7. Find the sum of the entries in the $f(x')^2$ column and divide by N, obtaining $\frac{\Sigma f(x')^2}{N}$. From section A this is $\frac{1298}{109} = 11.908$.

8. Subtract the result of step 6 from that of step 7, obtaining $\dfrac{\Sigma f(x')^2}{N}$ $- \left(\dfrac{\Sigma fx'}{N}\right)^2$, which is here equal to $\dfrac{1298}{109} - \left(\dfrac{-34}{109}\right)^2 = 11.81$. This is the variance expressed in step interval units.

9. If the variance is wanted in score units, multiply the result of step 8 by the square of the width of the interval. Here this is $3^2(11.81) = 106.3$.

10. To obtain the standard deviation in score units, either take the square root of the result of step 9 or multiply the square root of the result of step 8 by the width of the interval.

$$\sqrt{106.3} = 10.3 \qquad \text{or} \qquad 3\sqrt{11.81} = 3(3.44) = 10.3$$

Check Steps

Take an origin one interval lower or one interval higher than that used in step 2. Repeat steps 2, 3, 4, 5, 6, 7, working with the new origin. If the new origin is lower, deviations from it may be labeled $x' + 1$ as in section B, and the check formulas are

$$\Sigma(x' + 1) = \Sigma x' + N$$
or
$$75 = -34 + 109$$
and
$$\Sigma(x' + 1)^2 = \Sigma(x')^2 + 2\Sigma x' + N$$
or
$$1339 = 1298 + 2(-34) + 109$$

If the new origin is taken one interval higher than the first, deviations from it may be labeled $x' - 1$ and the check formulas are

$$\Sigma(x' - 1) = \Sigma x' - N$$
and
$$\Sigma(x' - 1)^2 = \Sigma(x')^2 - 2\Sigma x' + N$$

If Table **XXIV** contained a third section with origin at **32**, computation would yield

$$\Sigma(x' - 1) = -143 \qquad \text{and} \qquad \Sigma(x' - 1)^2 = 1475$$

and the checks would be

$$-143 = -34 - 109$$
and
$$1475 = 1298 - 2(-34) + 109$$
$$= 1298 + 68 + 109$$

Caution. The inexperienced computer makes certain typical errors. Some have been known to try to obtain the $f(x')^2$ values by squaring the fx' values. This would produce $f^2(x')^2$ and not $f(x')^2$.

A fairly common error relates to the width of interval. In obtaining the mean by the formula $\overline{X} = A + i\dfrac{\Sigma fx'}{N}$, if x' is in interval units, $\dfrac{\Sigma fx'}{N}$ will be in interval units. A is in score units. Therefore $\dfrac{\Sigma fx'}{N}$ must be changed to score units by multiplying it by i before it can be added to A. The matter is exactly like adding feet to inches—they must first be reduced to the same denomination. In computing the variance one does *not* multiply $\left(\dfrac{\Sigma fx'}{N}\right)$ by i^2 before combining it with $\dfrac{\Sigma f(x')^2}{N}$, because the two expressions are already in the same denomination.

When the variance is translated from interval to score units, the multiplier to be used is i^2, the square of the width of interval, since variance is given in square units, and not linear units.

Computation of the Standard Deviation When a Machine Is Available. In this case, large numbers are less inconvenient than negative signs. Hence the origin is usually placed at the midpoint of the lowest step interval or at the zero point in the scale of scores. Detailed instruction for machine computation of a standard deviation may be found in Dunlap's *Computation of Descriptive Statistics*, New York, Ralph C. Coxhead Corporation, 1937.

TABLE XXV

Computation of Mean and Standard Deviation of a Small Number of Unclassified Scores Without Arranging Them in a Frequency Distribution

Individual	X	X^2	x'	$(x')^2$
A	31	961	6	36
B	25	625	0	0
C	37	1369	12	144
D	41	1681	16	256
E	29	841	4	16
F	36	1296	11	121
G	25	625	0	0
H	35	1225	10	100
I	32	1024	7	49
J	41	1681	16	256
Total	332	11328	82	978

$$\overline{X} = \frac{332}{10} = 33.2 \qquad \overline{X} = 25 + \frac{82}{10} = 33.2$$

$$s^2 = \frac{11328}{10} - (33.2)^2 \qquad s^2 = \frac{978}{10} - (8.2)^2$$

$$= 1132.8 - 1102.24 \qquad = 97.8 - 67.24$$

$$= 30.56 \qquad\qquad = 30.56$$

$$s = 5.53 \qquad\qquad s = 5.53$$

Computation of the Standard Deviation of a Small Number of Un-classified Scores. When N is small, grouping the scores into intervals may cause a large error. It is better to square each score separately, if they are not too large and use the gross score formula (10a); or to reduce each score by a convenient constant, square the remainder and use formula (9a), taking each score as it comes without setting up a frequency distribution, as illustrated in Table XXV.

Computation of Mean and Standard Deviation from Data Classified in Unequal Intervals. When the frequency piles up at one end of a distribution, use of a unit which is fine enough to bring out the form of the

TABLE XXVI

Computation of Mean and Standard Deviation from Data
Grouped in Unequal Step Intervals

(Data from Table VIII)

Class Sort	f	A			B		
		X	fX	fX^2	x'	fx'	$f(x')^2$
35–44	5	39.5	197.5	7801.25	31.5	157.5	4961.25
25–34	10	29.5	295	8702.5	21.5	215	4622.5
20–24	11	22	242	5324	14	154	2156
15–19	24	17	408	6936	9	216	1944
10–14	39	12	468	5616	4	156	624
7– 9	52	8	416	3328	0	0	0
4– 6	30	5	150	750	−3	−90	270
3	26	3	78	234	−5	−130	650
2	30	2	60	120	−6	−180	1080
1	25	1	25	25	−7	−175	1225
0	15	0	0	0	−8	−120	960
Total	267		2339.5	38836.75		+203.5	18492.75

$$\overline{X} = \frac{2339.5}{267} = 8.76 \qquad \overline{X} = 8 + \frac{203.5}{267} = 8.76$$

$$s^2 = \frac{38837}{267} - (8.76)^2 = 68.7 \qquad s^2 = \frac{18493}{267} - \left(\frac{204}{267}\right)^2 = 68.7$$

$$s = 8.29 \qquad s = 8.29$$

distribution in that part of the range where the number of cases is large may produce a very long table if the same interval is used throughout. In such cases, the width of interval is sometimes changed from one part of the range to another. While this is not a good practice, the student of statistics should know what to do with such data when he wishes to use figures gathered by another person. Deviations obviously cannot be taken in interval form. Computations may be carried out with the gross scores which correspond to the midpoints of the various intervals, as in method A of Table XXVI, or they may be carried out with the deviations of these midpoints from some arbitrary origin as in method B. Check the computations in Table XXVI by using method B but taking a different origin.

Graphic Representation of Standard Deviation. Attempts to visualize the standard deviation and the variance are not very rewarding, and it is wiser to accept these as abstract concepts whose meaning will develop through use. Only two pictorial explanations are known to the writer. One of these is an analogy to *torque*, but so few students have been found who did not consider the explanation more difficult than the concept to be explained that it will not be given here. The other applies to a very special kind of frequency curve only, the "normal" curve, shown in Figure 20. In this curve, the standard deviation is the abscissa of the point of

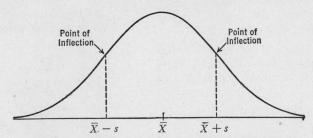

Fig. 20. Standard deviation in a normal curve.

inflection. If you will lay the edge of a card in a position tangent to this curve at the mean, the tangent line will lie altogether above the curve. Slide the card along the curve, keeping it tangent, until you reach a point where the tangent line cuts the curve. The abscissa of that point is the standard deviation. In this particular form of distribution, but not necessarily in other forms, approximately 68% of the area under the curve lies between two ordinates, one s units above, and one s units below the mean.

Figures 21 (p. 128), 23 (p. 161), and 24 (p. 161) show distributions of a variety of shapes in each of which the standard deviation has been marked off on the base line. Examination of these will afford some little familiarity with the relation between shape of distribution and size of standard deviation, but real clarification of this concept can come only through experience in the use of the standard deviation, which succeeding sections will provide. In Figure 11 (p. 69), the position of the mean has been indicated by a large arrow, and the points one standard deviation above or below the mean by small arrows. Note the relation of these points to the deciles, and thus convince yourself that the proportion of area included between the ordinates at $\pm s$ is dependent upon the shape of the curve.

Exercise 14*

1. The set of verbal statements presented below may be used as a dictation exercise, one person reading the phrases aloud slowly while another writes down the corresponding symbols just as a stenographer writes shorthand. While the statements are true, some of them are intentionally complicated, and no attempt should be made to remember them. It is not necessary that the student recognize the meaning of a statement in order to record it correctly. Ten or fifteen minutes of such dictation at the beginning of several class periods should help a class learn to use symbolism as a means of conveying ideas, and should greatly increase the ability to read all subsequent material.

Illustrations:

One person reads slowly	While another writes
If every score in a distribution is squared and the sum of all these squares is obtained and from this sum there is subtracted N times the square of the mean of the scores	ΣX^2
	$-$
	$N(\overline{X})^2$
the result will be	$=$
N times the variance	Ns^2

The equation which translates this long sentence is therefore:

$$\Sigma X^2 - N(\overline{X})^2 = Ns^2$$

a. If the mean is subtracted from each of the scores in a distribution, the sum of the remainders will be zero.

b. If the mean is subtracted from each of the scores in a distribution, and the remainder is squared, the sum of all such squares will be N times the variance.

c. If the number 50 is subtracted from each score in a distribution, the mean of these remainders will be 50 less than the mean of the original scores.

d. If the square of the mean of a distribution is subtracted from the mean of the squares of the scores, the result will be the square of the standard deviation.

e. The number of cases in a distribution can be found by adding together all the frequencies in the intervals.

f. If each score in a distribution is increased by 1 and the result squared, the sum of these squares will be equal to the sum of three terms, namely, the sum of the squares of the original scores, twice the sum of the original scores, and the number of the cases in the distribution.

g. The sum of the squares of the deviations around the mean is smaller than the sum of the squares of the deviations around any other point. (Let P represent "any point other than the mean.")

h. Choose any arbitrary origin and subtract the score corresponding to that origin from each score in the distribution; take the mean of all the resulting deviations; add this mean to the value of the origin selected. The result will be the mean of the distribution.

i. If the variance is subtracted from the mean of the squares of the scores, and this remainder is decreased by the square of the mean, the result will be equal to the sum of the deviations from the mean.

j. The square of the mean of the deviations of the scores from the mean of the distribution is zero.

k. If every score in a distribution is increased by 5, the mean of the new set of scores will be equal to the original mean plus 5.

l. Let every score in a distribution be increased by 2. If the mean of the squares of the increased scores is reduced by the square of the mean of the increased scores, the remainder will be the variance of the original scores.

m. The mean of the deviations of the scores from a given reference point A plus the mean of the deviations of the scores from the mean is equal to the amount by which the mean exceeds A.

2. Below is a set of phrases and a set of symbols. Look among the phrases to find all those which properly translate the first symbol, the second symbol, etc. Some of the phrases apply to more than one symbol, some of the symbols are described by several phrases.

Symbol	Phrase
1. Σf	a. A class frequency
2. $\overline{Y}$	b. A mean
3. $y + \overline{Y}$	c. A variance
4. $\dfrac{\Sigma f(Y - \overline{Y})^2}{N}$	d. Zero
	e. The sum of the squared deviations from the mean
5. Ns^2	f. The number of cases
6. $\Sigma(Y - \overline{Y})$	g. A gross score
7. f	h. The square root of the variance
8. $\dfrac{\Sigma f Y^2}{N} - \left(\dfrac{\Sigma f Y}{N}\right)^2$	i. A deviation from the mean

Symbol | Phrase

$\mathbb{X}$ 9. $\dfrac{\Sigma fY}{N}$ j. The square of the standard deviation

10. s

11. $\dfrac{\Sigma fy^2}{N}$

12. $Y - \overline{Y}$

3. Compute the standard deviation for each of the three distributions in Table XXIII.

(Practice in computing the standard deviation is provided in Chapter IX.)

Use of the Standard Deviation for Comparison of Groups. Variability is an important group character and it may often be desirable to know whether one group is more or less variable than another. Suppose, for example, that several nursery schools, each enrolling 40 children, had age distributions as shown in Table XXVII.

TABLE XXVII

Four Distributions with the Same Mean and Same Number of Cases, but Different Variability: Age in Months of Children in Four Nursery Schools (Fictitious Data)

Age at Last Birthday	Number of Cases				
	School A	School B	School C	School D	All Schools
37–38			2		2
35–36					
33–34			1	1	2
31–32		3	3	2	8
29–30	7	5	3	6	21
27–28	7	8	6	6	27
25–26	10	9	7	8	34
23–24	11	7	8	8	34
21–22	5	5	5	7	22
19–20		2	2	2	6
17–18		1	2		3
15–16			1		1
Total	40	40	40	40	160
Mean	25.5	25.5	25.5	25.5	25.5
s^2	6.6	11.6	23.6	11.8	13.4
s	2.6	3.4	4.9	3.4	3.7

The four distributions have the same central tendency, so one cannot say that any one school has children who are, on the whole, older or younger than the others, but it is apparent that school A is much more homogeneous with respect to age and school C much more heterogeneous than the other schools. Obviously the problems of administering these schools would be different, not because of a difference in age level but because of a difference in spread. To reach this conclusion it would not be necessary to see the distributions themselves. The same conclusions could have been obtained from an examination of some measure of variability computed for each group. The standard deviations in the last row of Table XXVII would be enough evidence to permit a comparison of the relative homogeneity of the various groups. The values of the variance in the preceding row serve a similar purpose.

Both variance and standard deviation are expressed in the units of the original distribution. The standard deviation of the weights of a group of 12-year-old children from underprivileged homes might be compared with the standard deviation of the weights of a group from privileged homes because both standard deviations are in terms of weight units and the means are not very disparate. One could not, in the same way, ask whether a group of children are more variable in weight than in height, because one standard deviation is expressed in weight units and one in height units, and there is no basis for comparison. Nor would it be reasonable to say that adults are more variable in weight than babies merely because the standard deviation of adult weights is larger than that of infant weights. The means of the two groups would be so diverse that one feels inclined to inquire how large is the variability relative to the average.

Caution. At this stage there is a great temptation for the beginning student to run ahead of his information. He has, let us say, found that a group of 150 girls had a higher mean score and a larger variability than a group of 120 boys on a test of art appreciation. That is an observation, true for these particular cases. But the research worker is tempted to go further and to say, not that "these girls had a higher mean than these boys and were more variable" but that "girls have a higher mean than boys," making a generalization from the particular cases observed to boys and girls at large. Such generalization is known as a statistical inference, being an inference from an observed sample to the unknown population from which that sample is drawn. The more extended analysis on which such inferences must be based will be introduced in Chapter XV of this text and developed more fully in Book II, soon to be published. For the present, the student would be well advised not to generalize on his data, and to report his conclusions in the past tense so that his readers will understand that they apply specifically to the groups studied.

Measuring Relative Variation of Groups. Suppose you wish to know whether in a large district food prices are more uniform from store to store than are the prices of some other commodity, say gasoline. A committee conducts a survey of grocery stores and finds that the mean price for a dozen strictly fresh eggs is 31.5 cents and standard deviation .82. A similar survey reveals that the mean price for a gallon of regular gasoline, excluding tax, is 13.8 cents with standard deviation .76. Both standard deviations are measured in units of 1 cent. The committee is about to decide that the two sets of prices are almost equally variable when someone recognizes that the measure of variability depends in part upon the unit for which price was obtained. Had the gasoline prices been taken for 2-gallon lots instead of one gallon, the mean price would have been 27.6 and standard deviation 1.52, both being doubled. Who is to say whether a dozen eggs is comparable to one gallon of gasoline or to two gallons, or to what?

A useful expedient in such situations is to divide the standard deviation by the mean, obtaining a measure of variability known as the *coefficient of variation*, and defined as

$$V = \frac{100s}{\overline{X}} \tag{16}$$

This coefficient of variation is independent of the size of unit in which measurement is made. For gasoline prices

$$\frac{100s}{\overline{X}} = \frac{76}{13.8} = 5.5$$

and for eggs

$$\frac{100s}{\overline{X}} = \frac{82}{31.5} = 2.6$$

Thus the price of gasoline varied more than the price of eggs *in relation to the mean*.

The use of a coefficient of variability cannot be defended when the scores in question have no zero point. Unless a true zero can be found, ratios are meaningless because they can be manipulated by a change in the origin from which scores are measured. Most psychological data have no true zero point, and therefore the coefficient of variation should not be used.

Use of the Standard Deviation as Measure of Relative Position of an Individual. To say that a child is "two pounds underweight" is not meaningful unless we know the variability to be expected among children of his age. At 3 months this would be serious; at 15 years, negligible. A pound seems to be an unsatisfactory unit in which to measure deviations from the norm of weight.

The two chief methods of showing the position of an individual in his group are by the use of percentile ranks and of standard scores.

Suppose, for example, a child aged 30 months is enrolled in school C. What is his relative position in the age distribution of that school? By reference to Table XXVII, we can ascertain that he has a *percentile rank* of 83 in that school. If he should be transferred to school A, his percentile rank in age within school A would be 95. No one can doubt that this change in percentile rank as the child transfers from one school to another reflects a change in something which to the child is a very real aspect of his environment. His age does not change, but the relationship of his age to that of his associates does, and that change is shown in the changed percentile rank.

Referring again to Table XXVII, we see that the child of 30 months is 4.5 months above the mean age of school C, and this is .92 standard deviations. In school A, he would be 4.5 months older than the mean, but here this would be 1.73 standard deviations. The standard deviation may be used as a unit of measure intrinsic to the group for which it is obtained. Deviations expressed in terms of the standard deviation thus take on more meaning. The standard deviation is a kind of average of all the deviations in a distribution, being the square root of the mean of the squared deviations. Arbitrary units such as pounds, feet, months, dollars, and the like, may need additional interpretation when used to measure deviation, but, as we shall see, a standard deviation carries its own interpretation. "Two pounds underweight" may be an ambiguous expression, meaning one thing at one age and something else at another, but "one standard deviation underweight for his age" tells fairly clearly the status of the child, no matter what his age.

In order to develop a feeling as to how extraordinary a deviation of a given size may be, in terms of the number of persons who depart from the mean by at least that amount, we shall now compute the percentage of cases falling in a specified range for each of the schools in Table XXVII. First let us concentrate attention upon one of the schools, say, B. Figure 21 shows the frequency distribution of the age scores for this group with the base line scaled in standard deviation units. This distribution extends somewhat less than three standard deviations from the mean in each direction. Since $\overline{X} = 25.5$ and $s = 3.4$, the seven points marked on the base line have score values respectively of 15.3, 18.7, 22.1, 25.5, 28.9, 32.3, and 35.7.

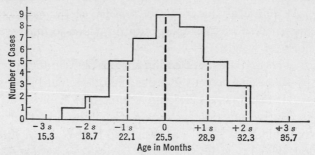

Fig. 21. Histogram with scale of scores laid off in standard deviation units. (Age data for school B from Table XXVII.)

What proportion of all the cases fall above 32.3, that is, what proportion exceed the mean by at least $2s$? The point 32.3 is in the upper interval 31–32 and the proportion of the area of that interval above the point 32.3 is $\dfrac{32.5 - 32.3}{32.5 - 30.5} = \dfrac{0.2}{2} = 0.1$. Since there are 3 cases in this interval, $0.1 \times 3 = 0.3$ of a case may be considered to occupy the narrow strip above the ordinate at 32.3 or $2s$. But $\dfrac{0.3}{N} = \dfrac{0.3}{40} = 0.0075$ or 0.75% of the total area. Therefore 0.75% of all the cases may be said to exceed the mean by at least $2s$ in this distribution.

What proportion of the cases exceed the mean by at least $1s$? The score value of a point 1 standard deviation above the mean has been already found to be 28.9. Above this point are all of the 3 cases in the top interval plus $\dfrac{30.5 - 28.9}{30.5 - 28.5} = 80\%$ of the 5 cases in the interval 29–30. Thus $3 + 0.8(5) = 7$ cases or $\tfrac{7}{40} = 17.5\%$ of all 40 cases may be considered to be at least one standard deviation above the mean.

By computation verify the following statements for school B:

3% of cases lie at least $2s$ units below the mean.

17.5% of cases lie at least s units below the mean.

3.75% of cases depart from the mean by at least $2s$ units.

35% of cases depart from the mean by at least s units.

65% of cases lie within the range from $-s$ to $+s$.

96.25% of cases lie within the range from $-2s$ to $+2s$.

100% of cases lie within the range from $-3s$ to $+3s$.

Comparable figures for each of the four schools and for the combined group are shown in Table XXVIII. It is to be noted that while the percentages are not completely uniform from school to school, yet they are not dissimilar. The last column of the table shows the percentage of area under a "normal" curve which would fall in the same range.

TABLE XXVIII

Percentage of Cases Falling in a Given Standard Deviation Range for Four Sets of Data and for a Normal Curve

(*Data from Table XXVII*)

Range	Percentage of Cases Included in Range					
	School A	School B	School C	School D	All Schools	Normal Distribution
Above 3s	0%	0%	0%	0%	1.2%	0.13%
Below −3s	0	0	0	0	0	0.13
−3s to +3s	100	100	100	100	98.8	99.73
Above 2s	0	0.75	5.0	3.0	2.35	2.28
Below −2s	0	3.00	1.5	0.5	2.1	2.28
−2s to +2s	100	96.25	93.5	96.5	95.6	95.45
Above s	21	17.50	15.4	19.5	16.0	15.87
Below −s	18	17.50	13.1	19.0	15.2	15.87
−s to +s	61	65.00	71.5	61.5	68.8	68.27

The skeptical reader (would that he were more numerous!) may say that, inasmuch as these were fictitious data, the areas may have been intentionally arranged to correspond to the areas of the normal curve, and other distributions would show no such similarity. It is recommended that this reader collect data from many sources and treat them in the manner of Table XXVIII. He will find that the percentage of cases in a given standard deviation range varies somewhat from one distribution to another, departing more widely the more the shape of the distribution departs from "the normal" form. Nevertheless, to say that a score is 2.5s above the mean ought to convey a fairly clear idea that the score is near the top of the group; to say that a score is −.2s from the mean ought to convey the idea that it is very near and slightly below the middle of the group.

The variance and the standard deviation are both measures of variability, and the variance has some properties which make it more valuable than the standard deviation in certain situations which will be discussed later on. The standard deviation is a linear unit, the variance is the square of a linear unit. Therefore, the variance cannot be used to lay off a linear distance on the scale of scores, as the standard deviation was used in the preceding paragraphs.

BIBLIOGRAPHY ON MEAN DEVIATION

Garrett, H. E., *Statistics in Psychology and Education*, second edition. New York, Longmans Green & Co., 1937, pp. 38–41.

Holzinger, K. J., *Statistical Methods for Students in Education*. Boston, Ginn & Co., 1928, pp. 102–107.

Kelley, T. L., *Statistical Method*. New York, The Macmillan Co., 1923, pp. 70–75.

Kenney, J. F., *Mathematics of Statistics*. New York, D. Van Nostrand Co., 1939, Part I, pp. 81–83.

Lindquist, E. F., *A First Course in Statistics*. Boston, Houghton Mifflin Co., 1942, pp. 71–74.

Mills, F. C., *Statistical Methods*, revised edition. New York, Henry Holt & Co., 1938, pp. 139–145.

Peters, C. C., and Van Voorhis, W. R., *Statistical Procedures and Their Mathematical Bases*. New York, McGraw-Hill Book Co., 1940, pp. 63–67.

Rietz, H. L., *Handbook of Mathematical Statistics*. Boston, Houghton Mifflin Co., 1924, pp. 29–31.

Sorenson, H., *Statistics for Students of Psychology and Education*. New York, McGraw-Hill Book Co., 1936, pp. 134–138.

Waugh, A. E., *Elements of Statistical Method*. New York, McGraw-Hill Book Co., 1938, pp. 63–68.

Yule, G. V., and Kendall, M. G., *An Introduction to the Theory of Statistics*, eleventh edition. London, Charles Griffin & Co., Ltd., 1937, pp. 144–146.

CHAPTER IX

THE MEAN AND STANDARD DEVIATION UNDER VARIOUS CIRCUMSTANCES

"He that seeketh findeth"—he finds what he seeks, as we know from the use of quotations and statistics.   T. R. Glover

The public generally . . . are in the habit of seeing public men making use of the most opposite statistical results with equal assurance in support of the most opposite arguments. . . . If the same ingenuity and enthusiasm . . . should have tempted . . . historians to group facts also, it would be no more reasonable to make the historical facts answerable for the use made of them than it would be to make statistical science responsible for many an ingenious financial statement.

> Prince Albert, in his presidential address at the opening of the International Statistical Congress, London, 1860

It has been stated several times that the mean and standard deviation are algebraic functions of all the scores in a distribution and that this fact confers upon them a certain superiority over the other measures of central position and variability. The nature of this advantage will now be examined further.

Purpose of the Chapter. The problems presented in this chapter have been designed to serve several purposes simultaneously. The main purpose is to develop certain important relationships of immediate value, and to promote a better understanding of the standard deviation by seeing how it is affected by various changes in the scores of a distribution. The material has also been planned to provide a kind of preview of the concepts of correlation, reliability of measurement, and analysis of variance which will be studied later. Only such aspects of these topics as can be easily suggested without distracting attention from the main purpose of the chapter will be discussed now. A third purpose of the chapter is to provide computational experience without resorting to pure drill. The computations called for in this chapter are incidental to the exploration of new ideas, but they can take the place of practice exercises for the preceding chapter.

Ways of Seeking Information. No matter on what level he works, the statistical worker is certain, sooner or later, to encounter a problem for which his previous study has not prepared him. By what method can he obtain help? Various methods of attack will be illustrated in the paragraphs which follow, but will first be considered in general.

1. *Intuition*. A great many persons tend to argue that "it must be this way" or "how could it be otherwise?" often basing their argument on some mental, geometric picture of a set of data. As a foundation for a rule or procedure or formula, intuitions are quite undependable. When employed as a teaching device by a person who already knows the correct answer, they can provide very helpful illustrations. In this text, appeal to intuition is made continually in order that some process, which the writer can justify by a mathematical argument beyond the scope of this text, may appear reasonable to the reader. This does not mean that the unguided intuition of either reader or writer could be trusted.

2. *Appeal to Authority*. The success of this expedient depends largely upon the quality of the authority available. It also depends upon the degree of understanding which can be achieved between the person asking and the person answering a question. In many cases, the only authority known to the seeker after information is a textbook. No textbook can possibly deal with all the quirks and variations which arise in practical research. The particular issue discussed in the text may differ in some apparently minor but actually very important respect from the practical situation. The text may not state clearly the limitations of the procedures described, or the reader may not note the limitations which are stated. The original articles on which all texts are based are much more likely to contain the information needed, but the statistical literature is voluminous and the more scholarly articles are beyond the ability of the non-mathematical reader.

3. *Empirical Evidence*. Suppose one wants to know how the standard deviation of a sum compares with the standard deviations of its component parts, how a correlation coefficient is affected by eliminating extreme cases from the data, or what is the shape of the distribution of a set of 100 means obtained for 100 samples from a particular kind of universe. A particular experiment providing numerical data would throw some light on the question, but would not furnish conclusive evidence. The peculiar circumstances under which the data are gathered may cause an exceptional result, from which no generalization can be made. A long series of experiments, set up to explore many kinds of situations, may be very enlightening either as an illustration of a relationship already known or as an approach to the discovery of a generalization which has not yet been established. Table XXX of this chapter is an instance of the use of empirical data to illustrate and clarify a relation-

ship for the benefit of persons to whom it is not yet familiar. Such data could neither provide the law nor prove it.

4. *Mathematical Solution.* The only method by which the correctness of a formula can be established is by mathematical analysis. Some of the simpler derivations involving only elementary algebra are shown in Appendix B of this text. However, most of the important relationships require a knowledge of the calculus at least, and the person who has no mathematical background must take them on authority. This is undeniably a serious handicap for which nothing can compensate. The man who cannot follow the derivation of a formula is never quite sure that he knows all the assumptions which are implicit therein. He cannot adapt his formulas to changes in the data, so must compel his data to conform to the formulas he happens to know. Because this text is written for the person without mathematical training, many statements must be made more or less arbitrarily.

Effect of Adding a Constant to Each Score in a Distribution. In the small distribution shown here, each score has been augmented by 5 points. What effect should this have on the mean? On the standard deviation? Does it affect the shape of the distribution to add the same amount to every score? To subtract the same amount from every score? Does it move the frequency distribution along on the scale of scores to add the same amount to every score? To subtract the same amount from every score?

Score	Augmented Score	f
15	20	4
14	19	5
13	18	6
12	17	6
11	16	10
10	15	7
9	14	6
8	13	4
7	12	2

By computation, verify the statement that the addition of 5 points to each score has not changed the standard deviation at all, but has increased the mean 5 points. Try subtracting 2 points from each score; adding 10 points.

To see the general relationship, let us add a to each score in a distribution, understanding, of course, that since a may be negative, algebraic addition will include arithmetic subtraction.

Then instead of X_1 we shall have $X_1 + a$
instead of X_2 we shall have $X_2 + a$

. . . .

instead of X_N we shall have $X_N + a$
and instead of ΣX we shall have $\Sigma X + Na$
also instead of $\overline{X}$ we shall have $\overline{X} + a$

Therefore $\overline{X + a} = \overline{X} + a$
or $\overline{X - a} = \overline{X} - a$ (17)

In general, if each score in a distribution is increased (or decreased) by a constant amount a, *the mean is increased (or decreased) by that same amount.* A similar statement holds for the median, for the mode, and for all the percentiles.

This clearly is the principle by which it is possible to compute a mean from an arbitrary origin other than zero. Suppose we place the origin at score 35 and take x' deviations in score units from 35 instead of from zero. Then we have subtracted 35 from each score, and the mean of the deviations from 35 will be 35 points smaller than the mean, so $\overline{X} = \overline{x}' + 35$.

What happens to measures of variability under these circumstances? If Q_3 and Q_1 are each increased by a, the distance between them is unchanged. Computing the standard deviation of the original distribution and of some new distribution obtained by adding the same amount to each score, you find them identical. Let us examine the algebraic reason.

In the original distribution, the ith individual's score X_i deviated from the mean by $x_i = X_i - \overline{X}$. After X_i was increased to $X_i + a$ and the mean was increased to $\overline{X} + a$, the deviation of the score of this same individual from the new mean was $(X_i + a) - (\overline{X} + a) = X_i - \overline{X}$. Therefore, if all the scores are changed by the same amount, the deviation of each of those scores from the mean is not changed at all, and $\frac{\Sigma x^2}{N} = s^2$ is also unchanged. *In general, measures of variability are not affected by the increase or (decrease) of every score by a constant amount.* They are *invariant* under this particular transformation. The fact that the standard deviation is not affected by the addition of the same amount to every score or by the subtraction of the same amount from every score, may be stated symbolically as

$$s_{x+a} = s_x \qquad (18)$$

The coefficient of variation ceases to have any meaning when scores are manipulated in this fashion, its numerator being invariant and its denominator changing.

Effect of Multiplying Each Score in a Distribution by the Same Number. In the illustrative distribution of the preceding section multiply each score by 2, compute the mean, the variance, and the standard deviation. The mean and the standard deviation of the new set of scores should be twice as large, and the variance four times as large as the corresponding values of the original set of scores. Try multiplying each score by 3, multiplying each score by $\frac{1}{2}$, multiplying each score by 0.1. For each set of transformed scores compute the mean, median, variance, interquartile range, standard deviation. If you make no computational errors, you should find that measures of central tendency and linear measures of variability have been multiplied by the same number which was used to multiply the scores and the variance has been multiplied by the square of that number.

Again let us look at this matter algebraically. If each score is multiplied by a,

Instead of X_1 we shall have aX_1
instead of X_2 we shall have aX_2

. . . .

instead of X_i we shall have aX_i

. . . .

instead of X_N we shall have aX_N
instead of ΣX we shall have $a\Sigma X$

and instead of $\overline{X} = \dfrac{\Sigma X}{N}$ we shall have $\overline{aX} = \dfrac{\Sigma aX}{N} = \dfrac{a\Sigma X}{N}$

Therefore $\overline{aX} = a \cdot \overline{X}$ $\hspace{3cm}$ (19)

In the original distribution, the deviation of the score of the ith individual from mean was $x_i = X_i - \overline{X}$. In the new distribution his deviation from the new mean will be $aX_i - a\overline{X} = a(X_i - \overline{X})$. Thus the deviation of each score from the mean is multiplied by a when the scores are multiplied by a. Each squared deviation is multiplied by a^2. The sum of the squared deviations is

$$a^2x_1{}^2 + a^2x_2{}^2 + \cdots + a^2x_i{}^2 + \cdots + a^2x_N{}^2 = a^2\Sigma x^2$$

and the new variance is $\dfrac{a^2\Sigma x^2}{N}$ which is $a^2s_x{}^2$.

The standard deviation is $\sqrt{a^2s_x{}^2} = as_x$.

Symbolically stated,

$$s_{ax}{}^2 = a^2s_x{}^2 \hspace{3cm} (20)$$

or

$$s_{ax} = as_x \hspace{3cm} (21)$$

Inasmuch as a may be a fraction, this same argument holds for division as well as multiplication.

In general, if every score is multiplied (or divided) by the same number, the mean, median, mode, any percentile, any interpercentile range, and the standard deviation are also multiplied (or divided) by that number. The variance is multiplied (or divided) by the square of that number. The coefficient of variation is invariant under this transformation.

It is because of this principle that reduced scores can be used in computing mean and standard deviation. Suppose the step interval contains i score units. To change a deviation from score form to interval form is to divide it by i. The mean of all these deviations has therefore been divided by i, and must be multiplied by i again to obtain the corresponding value in score units. Likewise the standard deviation of these reduced scores expressed in interval units is $1/i$ times as large as it would be if deviations were in score units.

An important characteristic of the coefficient of variation is the fact that it is not affected by a change in the unit of measurement because that change merely multiplies both its numerator and its denominator by the same number. Symbolically stated,

$$V = 100\,\frac{s}{\overline{X}} = 100\,\frac{as}{a\overline{X}} = 100\,\frac{s_{ax}}{a\overline{X}} \tag{22}$$

The coefficient of variation is called a *pure number* because it is independent of the unit of measure. It is *invariant* under transformations of the scores caused by changing the unit of measure.*

Standard Scores. The deviation of a score from its mean, expressed as a multiple of the standard deviation, is called a *standard score*. The letter z is commonly used to indicate a standard score, which is sometimes called a z-score. (The letter z, however, is also used for three or

---

* A certain vocabulary difficulty, created by similarity in the sound of certain words, can be relieved by a little attention to their meaning;

variable,   noun or adjective, meaning that which varies;

variate,   noun sometimes used synonymously with variable, but more often used to mean a particular set of values of a variable;

variation,   noun, naming an abstract characteristic of a frequency distribution, and meaning fluctuation, scattering, spread;

variance,   noun, a technical term applied to one particular measure of variation.

variant,   adjective, meaning not constant;

invariant,   adjective, used to describe something which, in the midst of change, remains unchanged;

invariance,   noun, meaning constancy in the midst of change. This is not so much a statistical idea as a philosophical and mathematical idea. "Change and decay, in all around I see, Oh, Thou who changest not, abide with me." It is of great value to understand the situations under which a particular statistical measure is invariant.

four other important and quite different concepts, some of which are listed in the glossary of symbols in Appendix E. The alphabet is not long enough to provide a unique letter for every statistical measure!) For a score exactly at the mean, $z = 0$. Scores larger than $z = +3$ or smaller than $z = -3$ would be very unusual.

$$z = \frac{X - \overline{X}}{s} \tag{23}$$

Often it is inconvenient to use negative numbers, and decimal points are sometimes in danger of being overlooked. To mistake -1.20 for $+1.20$ or for -0.12 would be seriously to misjudge the position of an individual in his group. Therefore it is a common practice to multiply standard scores by 10, thus expanding the scale, and to add the results to 50, thus moving the mean of the distribution 50 points along the scale. The result, usually also called a standard score, will be:

$$Z = 10z + 50 \text{ or } Z = \frac{10(X - \overline{X})}{s} + 50 \tag{24}$$

Suppose now that the mean of a distribution has been found to be 39.4 and its standard deviation to be 2.5. We want to make a conversion table to transform raw scores into scores of the form $Z = \frac{10x}{s} + 50$. Assume that the mean and the standard deviation have been previously found by the usual procedures. Write down in a column all the individual scores which might occur, say from 31 to 45. If this range is not wide enough it can be extended later. Two methods of conversion are about equally easy, and can be used as a check on each other.

Method 1. a. Subtract the mean from each score, obtaining values of $X - \overline{X}$ shown in the second column of Table XXIX.

b. Divide each value of $(X - \overline{X})$ by s, giving the z values in the third column. Note that successive values in this column are equally spaced, and use this as a check on accuracy.

c. Multiply each value of z by 10 and add to 50.

The first two rows shown in Table XXIX were found by this method.

Method 2. a. Find the value of $X - \overline{X}$ for one or two entries only, probably for an entry near the mean and for one at each extreme.

b. Find the value of $1/s$, and multiply the obtained values of $X - \overline{X}$ by this to obtain corresponding values in column 3.

c. Add $1/s$ to, or subtract it from, these values in column 3, to obtain the other values of z in that column.

d. When $1/s$ does not come out exactly, there may be a cumulative error, which should be checked by direct division for a few extreme scores.

e. Multiply each value of z by 10 and add 50.

The four values near the middle of the table were obtained thus.

TABLE XXIX

Conversion of Raw Scores to Z-Scores
$(\overline{X} = 39.4$ and $s = 2.5)$

X Raw Score, or Deviation from Zero in Units of Original Distribution	$x = X - \overline{X}$ Deviation Score, or Deviation from Mean in Units of Original Distribution	$z = x/s$ Standard Score, or Deviation from Mean in Standard Deviation Units	$Z = 10z + 50$ Converted Score in Units of 0.1 of the Standard Deviation
45	5.6	2.24	72
44	4.6	1.84	68
43			
42			
41		0.64	56
40	0.6	0.24	52
39	−0.4	−0.16	48
38		−0.56	44
37			
36			
35			
34			
33			
32			
31			

Earlier in this chapter there was a discussion of the effect upon the mean and the standard deviation of multiplying every score in a distribution by the same number and of adding the same number to every score. The principles there developed can now be used to show that the measure

$$Z = 50 + 10\frac{X - \overline{X}}{s}$$

has a mean value of 50 and a standard deviation of 10. Study carefully the following schedule to see how each row is obtained from the preceding row.

Measure	How Obtained	Mean	Standard Deviation
X	Original score	$\overline{X}$	s
$x = X - \overline{X}$	Subtracting $\overline{X}$ from score	$\overline{X} - \overline{X} = 0$	s
$z = \dfrac{x}{s}$	Dividing by s	$\dfrac{0}{s} = 0$	$\dfrac{s}{s} = 1$
$10z$	Multiplying by 10	$10(0) = 0$	$10(1) = 10$
$Z = 10z + 50$	Adding 50	$0 + 50 = 50$	10

Combining Scores on Different Tests. Suppose that a class has taken two tests on the same subject, the means being $\overline{X}_1 = 42.3$ and $\overline{X}_2 = 64.1$, the two standard deviations being $s_1 = 12.4$ and $s_2 = 3.1$. The instructor feels that the tests are about equally valid and wishes to give them equal weight in a composite score. If he combines them by averaging the raw scores, Test 1 will have much greater influence on the composite score because of its larger standard deviation. After correlation has been studied, the reason for this statement will be clearer.

To give equal weight to the two test scores, they may be transformed to standard scores before combination. Thus if student A has a score of 40 on the first test and of 67 on the second, his composite score would be

$$\frac{1}{2}\left[\frac{40 - 42.3}{12.4} + \frac{67 - 64.1}{3.1}\right] = \frac{-0.185 + 0.935}{2} = \frac{0.75}{2} = 0.375.$$

By formula 24 this number is converted to a score * of 54.

Exercise 15

1. If the mean and standard deviation of a distribution are respectively 18.5 and 2.1, what is the z-score value of these raw scores? (a) 23, (b) 19, (c) 16, (d) 12. What value would each of these scores have if transformed by the formula $Z = 10z + 50$?

2. Make a table of z-score equivalents for the data of Table III.

3. Below are listed the scores of 5 pupils on three tests. Note that they have been so selected that the sum of the raw scores is 144 for each of the 5. Reduce each score to a z-score, using the information provided as to the mean and standard deviation of the entire group of which these 5 cases are a part.

---

* The set of scores obtained by averaging, for each member of the class, his standard scores on two tests, as 0.375 was obtained above, will have a mean value of 0 but the standard deviation will usually be larger than 1, and so the scores are not really standard scores. $s_{x_1+x_2} = \sqrt{s_1{}^2 + s_2{}^2 + 2rs_1s_2}$. If $s_1 = s_2 = 1$, then $s_{x_1+x_2} = \sqrt{2 + 2r}$ where r is the correlation coefficient between the test scores added. In such situations, r is usually positive. Therefore the scores converted by formula 24 have a mean of 50 and standard deviation which is usually larger than 10.

Find the mean z-score for each pupil, and transform to Z to obtain the composite scores listed on the right.

Selected Pupil	Raw Score			Composite Z
	Test I	Test II	Test III	
A	42	92	10	52
B	40	90	14	55
C	35	93	16	59
D	45	81	18	54
E	52	75	17	49
Class Value				
$\overline{X}$	31.2	86.5	14.7	
s	11.5	3.6	2.4	

Effect of Variable Errors of Measurement. Variable errors of measurement infest most of our concrete data. Usually actual *bias* can be avoided and errors of measurement can be held to a minimum but they can never be entirely avoided. It is important to know what effect they have on the statistics computed. Careless, random errors of measurement may affect the mean slightly in one direction or the other, but the cumulative effect of a large number of such random errors on the mean is negligible, because positive and negative errors tend to offset each other. On the standard deviation, however, the effect of such random errors is cumulative, tending to increase it oftener than to decrease it. The algebraic proof of this statement belongs to the study of the reliability of measurement, which must wait for the development of correlation. However, an illustration can be given now.

Every measurement may be considered as consisting of a true measurement of the trait in question plus a variable error, and sometimes plus a constant error or a biased error. It is the business of the investigator to eliminate the biased error, and to hold the variable error to a minimum. Suppose, for example, children are weighed in the school medical office in their ordinary clothing, at whatever time happens to suit their schedule of classes. The weight of clothing will vary from child to child, creating an error of measurement. Another error arises because of the lack of uniformity in the recency and amount of intake of food and water. Therefore the recorded weight is the child's real weight plus a variable error.

To illustrate the effect of purely random errors of measurement,

TABLE XXX

Scores to Which Random Errors of Measurement Have Been Attached

Case	Language Score	Intelligence Quotient	Case	Language Score	Intelligence Quotient
1	$17 + 6 = 23$	$99 - 11 = 88$	56	$22 - 4 = 18$	$108 - 7 = 101$
2	$15 - 3 = 12$	$83 - 1 = 82$	57	$14 - 12 = 2$	$112 + 5 = 117$
3	$26 - 6 = 20$	$117 - 6 = 111$	58	$21 + 8 = 29$	$98 + 11 = 109$
4	$12 + 5 = 17$	$83 + 10 = 93$	59	$22 + 11 = 33$	$105 - 12 = 93$
5	$27 - 3 = 24$	$109 + 9 = 118$	60	$24 + 12 = 36$	$123 + 4 = 127$
6	$21 + 5 = 26$	$111 - 4 = 107$	61	$32 - 5 = 27$	$148 + 9 = 157$
7	$30 + 1 = 31$	$92 - 13 = 79$	62	$17 - 2 = 15$	$93 + 3 = 96$
8	$12 + 4 = 16$	$95 + 12 = 107$	63	$25 - 12 = 13$	$129 + 13 = 142$
9	$23 + 13 = 36$	$79 - 1 = 78$	64	$26 - 3 = 23$	$106 - 2 = 104$
10	$26 - 8 = 18$	$115 - 7 = 108$	65	$17 + 6 = 23$	$111 - 1 = 110$
11	$19 - 8 = 11$	$120 - 7 = 113$	66	$25 + 4 = 29$	$121 + 8 = 129$
12	$14 + 9 = 23$	$101 - 11 = 90$	67	$20 - 7 = 13$	$115 - 12 = 103$
13	$14 - 4 = 10$	$87 + 4 = 91$	68	$29 - 13 = 16$	$130 + 1 = 131$
14	$16 - 13 = 3$	$106 + 9 = 115$	69	$30 - 12 = 18$	$114 - 5 = 109$
15	$20 - 4 = 16$	$100 - 5 = 95$	70	$39 - 9 = 30$	$118 - 4 = 114$
16	$19 - 2 = 17$	$120 - 6 = 114$	71	$30 + 8 = 38$	$103 - 9 = 94$
17	$16 + 6 = 22$	$99 + 6 = 105$	72	$12 + 11 = 23$	$108 - 4 = 104$
18	$17 - 7 = 10$	$119 - 2 = 117$	73	$31 - 12 = 19$	$123 + 1 = 124$
19	$11 + 9 = 20$	$66 - 1 = 65$	74	$30 - 4 = 26$	$142 + 11 = 153$
20	$19 - 10 = 9$	$77 - 4 = 73$	75	$25 + 4 = 29$	$120 - 12 = 108$
21	$29 + 13 = 42$	$124 + 3 = 127$	76	$29 - 2 = 27$	$136 + 12 = 148$
22	$18 - 9 = 9$	$125 - 3 = 122$	77	$28 - 10 = 18$	$131 - 8 = 123$
23	$23 - 2 = 21$	$104 - 1 = 103$	78	$24 - 11 = 13$	$141 - 8 = 133$
24	$19 + 11 = 30$	$89 - 8 = 81$	79	$22 + 8 = 30$	$106 - 1 = 105$
25	$26 - 12 = 14$	$97 + 6 = 103$	80	$19 + 5 = 24$	$126 + 9 = 135$
26	$30 - 6 = 24$	$126 - 6 = 120$	81	$23 - 11 = 12$	$125 + 8 = 133$
27	$17 + 12 = 29$	$68 + 6 = 74$	82	$36 - 3 = 33$	$131 + 4 = 135$
28	$23 + 6 = 29$	$83 + 11 = 94$	83	$29 + 11 = 40$	$104 + 4 = 108$
29	$7 - 2 = 5$	$64 + 5 = 69$	84	$30 + 10 = 40$	$128 + 8 = 136$
30	$26 + 13 = 39$	$96 - 10 = 86$	85	$26 + 9 = 35$	$133 - 8 = 125$
31	$19 - 12 = 7$	$91 + 5 = 96$	86	$24 + 6 = 30$	$127 - 12 = 115$
32	$18 + 4 = 22$	$75 - 5 = 70$	87	$36 - 4 = 32$	$138 - 3 = 135$
33	$22 + 12 = 34$	$103 + 4 = 107$	88	$31 + 2 = 33$	$132 + 2 = 134$
34	$14 - 5 = 9$	$86 + 3 = 89$	89	$32 + 4 = 36$	$136 - 3 = 133$
35	$19 + 13 = 32$	$118 - 1 = 117$	90	$22 + 10 = 32$	$119 - 9 = 110$
36	$31 + 12 = 43$	$140 - 2 = 138$	91	$17 - 10 = 7$	$106 - 8 = 98$
37	$21 - 4 = 17$	$120 + 6 = 126$	92	$29 + 7 = 36$	$124 - 1 = 123$
38	$24 - 11 = 13$	$93 - 10 = 83$	93	$14 + 10 = 24$	$124 + 5 = 129$
39	$24 + 5 = 29$	$112 + 5 = 117$	94	$20 - 12 = 8$	$102 + 9 = 111$
40	$33 + 12 = 45$	$116 - 7 = 109$	95	$15 - 3 = 12$	$83 - 9 = 74$
41	$24 + 11 = 35$	$123 - 7 = 116$	96	$26 + 7 = 33$	$93 - 6 = 87$
42	$25 + 13 = 38$	$105 - 1 = 104$	97	$23 - 11 = 12$	$113 + 4 = 117$
43	$28 - 6 = 22$	$121 + 12 = 133$	98	$18 - 13 = 5$	$90 - 13 = 77$
44	$16 - 1 = 15$	$114 + 13 = 127$	99	$17 - 7 = 10$	$103 - 7 = 96$
45	$20 + 13 = 33$	$113 - 4 = 109$	100	$11 + 6 = 17$	$88 - 2 = 86$
46	$19 - 12 = 7$	$111 + 11 = 122$	101	$17 + 9 = 26$	$111 + 6 = 117$
47	$23 + 8 = 31$	$114 - 11 = 103$	102	$25 - 1 = 24$	$130 + 5 = 135$
48	$15 + 6 = 21$	$99 - 12 = 87$	103	$9 + 10 = 19$	$91 - 6 = 85$
49	$16 + 10 = 26$	$101 + 4 = 105$	104	$10 - 6 = 4$	$106 + 12 = 118$
50	$15 - 2 = 13$	$112 - 6 = 106$	105	$28 - 7 = 21$	$115 - 4 = 111$
51	$16 - 2 = 14$	$125 + 12 = 137$	106	$26 - 8 = 18$	$120 + 8 = 128$
52	$20 + 11 = 31$	$105 + 9 = 114$	107	$19 - 11 = 8$	$116 - 7 = 109$
53	$18 + 12 = 30$	$100 + 1 = 101$	108	$35 + 1 = 36$	$120 + 12 = 132$
54	$28 + 13 = 41$	$144 - 5 = 139$	109	$18 + 7 = 25$	$123 + 7 = 130$
55	$17 + 1 = 18$	$101 + 12 = 113$			

Table **XXX** has been constructed from the language scores and the intelligence quotients of the 109 children in Appendix A. A variable error was attached to each score in this way. Two decks of cards were shuffled together and a card drawn. The number on the first drawn card was taken as the error to be added to the score of the first child, the number on the second card drawn as the error for the second child, etc. Red cards were considered to indicate positive errors, black cards, negative. After each tenth drawing the cards were reshuffled. For case 1, the original language score was 17, the first card drawn was a six of hearts, and so the score plus error is $17 + 6 = 23$. (It must not be supposed that the original scores were free from measurement error!)

By computation from the set of intelligence quotients in Appendix A and from the set with errors attached in Table **XXX** verify the figures in Table **XXXI**.

Note how they conform to the generalization that *random errors of measurement have a negligible effect upon the mean, but tend to increase the variance and the standard deviation.*

If two investigators take measurements of the same set of individuals on some trait, say chest girth, but investigator A is very careful and accurate, while B is careless in placing the tape and careless in reading results, the means they obtain may agree closely, but the standard deviation of the records obtained by B is almost certain to be larger than that obtained by A.

TABLE XXXI

Illustration of the Effects of Random Errors of Measurement upon Mean and Standard Deviation

(Based upon Figures of Table XXX)

Measure	Value for Original Set of Intelligence Quotients	Value for Set of Intelligence Quotients with Error Attached
Sum of the scores	11,994	11,992
Mean	110.04	110.02
Sum of squares of scores	1,353,268	1,361,170
Variance	306.50	383.4
Standard deviation	17.51	19.58

Finding the Mean and Standard Deviation of a Total Group when the Means, Standard Deviations, and Frequencies of Subgroups Are Known. In a statistical study it often happens that the data are not all gathered at one time, and that after the mean and the standard deviation have been computed for part of the data, additional measures are obtained which must be included in the study. It would be a great loss of time to have to start again from the beginning with a new tabulation of all the measures. Therefore a formula which enables the student to obtain the mean and standard deviation of the combined group from the computations which have already been made for the component groups effects great saving of time.

Table XXXII shows the frequency distribution for 50 boys and 40 girls on a test, and the combined distribution for boys and girls together.

Rows (a) to (h) in the section of the table immediately below the frequency distribution present the computation of the three means and three standard deviations. Here an arbitrary origin was taken at the midpoint of the interval 58–62. To assure yourself that you understand the procedure, carry through these same steps working from some other origin.

Rows (i) to (l) in the next section of the table are set down for the sake of obtaining a check on the computations of mean and standard deviation. Aside from the effect of rounding errors in the outcome of earlier computations, the checks in the last section of the table should be perfect. As there are 4 significant digits in the values of d and of s^2, the final check cannot be expected to hold for more than four places, and there might be an error in the fourth. It happens here that the sum of the two entries in row (l) is 6894.7 while the last entry in row (k), which should check with this, is 6894.75, a more accurate check than the number of significant digits in d and s^2 would have led us to expect.

The general relations back of these check formulas are:

$$N_c = N_1 + N_2 \tag{25}$$
$$N_c \overline{X}_c = N_1 \overline{X}_1 + N_2 \overline{X}_2 \tag{26}$$
$$N_c s_c^2 = N_1(s_1^2 + d_1^2) + N_2(s_2^2 + d_2^2) \tag{27}$$

Here the subscript c refers to the combined group and the numerical subscripts to the component groups, or subgroups; d_1 is $\overline{X}_1 - \overline{X}_c$, and d_2 is $\overline{X}_2 - \overline{X}_c$.

These formulas are particularly useful when the original distributions are not available, but the values of N, $\overline{X}$, and s are known for the

TABLE XXXII

Computation Illustrating the Relation of the Mean of Combined Group to Means of the Component Groups and Variance of Combined Group to Variances of the Component Groups

Class Sort	Frequency		
	Boys	Girls	Both
73–77	3		3
68–72	7	2	9
63–67	8	5	13
58–62	12	6	18
53–57	9	11	20
48–52	6	6	12
43–47	5	6	11
38–42		4	4
(a) N = Number of cases	50	40	90
(b) $\Sigma fx'$ = Sum of deviations in interval units from an arbitrary origin at $A = 60$	−5	−48	−53
(c) $\overline{X}$ = Mean = $A + i\left(\dfrac{\Sigma fx'}{N}\right)$	59.5	54.0	57.055
(d) $\Sigma f(x')^2$ = Sum of squares of deviations in interval units from arbitrary origin at $A = 60$	141	166	307
(e) $\dfrac{(\Sigma fx')^2}{N}$ = Square of (b) divided by the number of cases	0.5	57.6	31.21
(f) $Ns^2 = \Sigma fx^2 = \Sigma f(x')^2 - \dfrac{(\Sigma fx')^2}{N}$ = Sum of squares of deviations in interval units from mean, obtained by subtracting (e) from (d)	140.5	108.4	275.79
(g) s^2 = Variance in interval units, obtained by dividing (f) by N	2.81	2.71	3.064
(h) s = Standard deviation in score units, obtained by taking square root of (g) and multiplying it by width of interval	8.38	8.23	8.75
(i) d = Difference between mean of component group and mean of combined group	+2.445	−3.055	
(j) Nd^2	298.9	373.3	
(k) Ns^2 = Sum of squares of deviations in *score* units, from the mean, obtained by multiplying (f) by square of width of interval	3512.5	2710.0	6894.75
(l) $Nd^2 + Ns^2$ = sum of (j) and (k)	3811.4	3083.3	

Checks:
From row (a) $50 + 40 = 90$
From row (b) $-5 - 48 = -53$
From row (d) $141 + 166 = 307$
From rows (l) and (k) $3811.4 + 3083.3 \doteq 6894.75$

subgroups, and the corresponding values are sought for the combined group. Suppose, for example, that the only data available were as follows, the original distributions being inaccessible:

	Boys	Girls
Number of cases	50	40
Mean	59.5	54.0
Standard deviation	8.38	8.23

The number of cases in the combined group is 90, found by the formula $N_c = N_1 + N_2$. The mean of the combined group can be found by the formula

$$N_c \overline{X}_c = N_1 \overline{X}_1 + N_2 \overline{X}_2 = 50(59.5) + 40(54.0)$$
$$90 \overline{X}_c = 5135$$
$$\overline{X}_c = 57.055$$

Having obtained the mean of the combined group, we obtain

$$d_1 = \overline{X}_1 - \overline{X}_c = 59.5 - 57.055 = 2.455$$

and

$$d_2 = \overline{X}_2 - \overline{X}_c = 54.0 - 57.055 = -3.055.$$

Then we use the formula

$$N_c s_c^2 = N_1(s_1^2 + d_1^2) + N_2(s_2^2 + d_2^2)$$
$$= 50[(8.38)^2 + (2.455)^2] + 40[(8.23)^2 + (-3.055)^2]$$
$$= 6895$$
$$s_c^2 = 76.6$$

and

$$s_c = 8.75$$

The agreement of these values with the values of $\overline{X}_c$, s_c^2, and s_c computed directly from the combined frequency distribution is as good as could be expected. We were working from values of the mean and standard deviation expressed with three digits, and no subsequent computations could have more than three-place precision.

When more than two groups are to be combined, formulas (25), (26), and (27) may be generalized as follows:

$$N_c = N_1 + N_2 + \cdots + N_k \tag{28}$$
$$N_c \overline{X}_c = N_1 \overline{X}_1 + N_2 \overline{X}_2 + \cdots + N_k \overline{X}_k \tag{29}$$
$$N_c s_c^2 = N_1(s_1^2 + d_1^2) + N_2(s_2^2 + d_2^2) + \cdots + N_k(s_k^2 + d_k^2) \tag{30a}$$
$$N_c s_c^2 = (N_1 s_1^2 + N_2 s_2^2 + \cdots + N_k s_k^2)$$
$$+ (N_1 d_1^2 + N_2 d_2^2 + \cdots + N_k d_k^2) \tag{30b}$$

A proof of formula (30) has been placed in Appendix B for those who care to examine it.

Because the mean and the standard deviation are algebraic functions of all the scores in the distribution, it is possible to obtain for them the preceding formulas. Because the percentiles are not algebraic, there is no way to obtain the median or a percentile for the combined group in any other way than to go back to the original scores, forming a combined frequency distribution, and computing directly from that.

Table XXXIII shows the height distribution for boys at ages 11–15 in the 7th grade of a given city. Experience tells us that boys who are of the same age will vary less in their height than boys whose ages range from 11 to 15. Thus we expect the variance of the total group to be larger than the mean of the variances of the subgroups, as it is. The formula also tells us that s^2 is larger than the mean of the variances of the subgroups by the amount

$$\frac{N_1 d_1{}^2 + \cdots + N_k d_k{}^2}{N_1 + \cdots + N_k}$$

If the means of the five age-groups were all equal, this amount would be zero, but since the mean height changes from age to age, it is not zero. In other words, age and height are correlated traits. One characteristic of a correlation table is that the mean changes from column to column. Another characteristic of a correlation table is that the standard devia-

TABLE XXXIII

Frequency Distribution Formed from Five Component Distributions
Height of Boys at Ages 11 to 15

Height to Nearest Inch	Number of Boys at Age					
	11	12	13	14	15	All Ages
69–71					1	1
66–68				1	1	2
63–65			1	1	4	6
60–62	1	1	2	7	6	17
57–59	2	3	13	17	3	38
54–56	9	13	26	20	2	70
51–53	12	16	16	8	1	53
48–50	4	5	3	1		13
45–47	1	1	1			3
42–44		1				1
Total	29	40	62	55	18	204

tions of the separate columns tend to be less than of the whole group. If correlation were perfect, the intraclass variation would disappear entirely, and all the scores in one column would be placed exactly at the mean of that column. This idea will become clear when correlation is studied in later chapters of the text.

Relation of Technique for Obtaining Variance of Combined Groups to Analysis of Variance. Formula (30b) is merely a rearrangement of (30a), but it shows clearly that the variance of the combined groups, s_c^2, has been broken into two portions. If the means of all the subgroups were exactly the same, all the d's would be zero, and the second portion would disappear. This second portion, then, reflects the amount of variation among the means of the component groups, and is related to the *interclass variation*. If all the members of group 1 were exactly alike, $N_1 s_1^2$ would be zero, and similarly for the other groups. The first portion, then, reflects the amount of variation among the individuals within their own groups, and is related to the *intraclass variation*. When the second portion is very small in relation to the first, the means of the subgroups do not differ among themselves more than one might expect from the means of random samples drawn from the same population, and they are said not to be significantly different from each other. When the interclass variation is large in relation to the intraclass, it is not reasonable to believe that all the subgroups are random samples out of one population, and they are said to be significantly different.

This paragraph and the formulas stated above provide a preliminary glimpse at the very important topic of *analysis of variance* which will be treated at some length in the second book of this series.

Effect of Adding to or Removing from a Distribution Certain Selected Scores. It is easy to see that the addition (or the removal) of scores exactly at the mean will not affect the mean; that addition (or removal) of two scores at equal distances from the mean but on opposite sides thereof will not affect the mean; that the addition of a single score greater than the mean will raise the mean and the removal of such a score will lower it, and inversely for scores below the mean.

To understand the effect of a single score on the variance and the standard deviation, we must remember that the variance is the average of the squared deviations of scores from the mean of the distribution. A score which is just one standard deviation from the mean is thus contributing just the average amount to $s^2 = \dfrac{\Sigma x^2}{N}$, and its removal will not affect that average. Any score which lies closer to the mean than one standard deviation in either direction contributes less than the average amount to the variance, and therefore the addition of such a score will decrease variance and standard deviation, while its removal will increase them. Addition of a score outside the range from $-s$ to $+s$ will increase variance and standard deviation; its removal will decrease them. These relationships often become quite important in matching up two groups for experimental purposes. Sometimes a research worker wants to use two groups with approximately the same mean and same standard deviation, but not necessarily the same number of cases. The empirical process of discarding cases from one or the other group until the groups are equated is a tedious one at best, but is rendered somewhat less haphazard by knowing in advance the general effect that eliminating a certain kind of score will have.

Effect of Grouping Measures into Broad Categories. Such grouping errors have a negligible effect upon the mean, because some scores are increased and some decreased, and the positive and negative errors tend to balance each other. However, they tend to increase the variance and the standard deviation. This phenomenon was first observed by W. H. Sheppard, who developed a formula to estimate the variance of the ungrouped distribution from the variance of the grouped distribution. (The proof can be followed only by persons with a fairly good knowledge of mathematics. References are given at the end of the chapter.)

Exercise 16

1.* Suppose the lowest interval in a distribution is marked 37–39, and one computer interprets this to mean that the real limits of this interval are 36.5–39.5, while another interprets it to mean real limits 37–40. If neither one makes computational errors, how will their results compare as to the mean? As to the standard deviation?

2.* If the mean and standard deviation of a set of measurements are 44.4 inches and 3.6 inches, what would they be if all the measurements had been taken in feet?

3. Compute the mean and standard deviation of each column and of the totals in Table XXXIII and verify your computation by substitution in the formulas, following the computational pattern displayed in Table XXXII.

4.* Indicate which of the following changes you think will necessarily affect the values named below:

No change of any sort
An increase
A decrease
A change which might be in either direction
A probable increase
A probable decrease
A probable change which may be in either direction

a. The mean and standard deviation of a class on Form B of a standardized test have been obtained. This class is to be combined with several other classes which have been tested on Form A, and the mean of Form A is known to run on the average 1.5 points lower than the mean for Form B when both are administered to the same group. Therefore it is proposed to subtract 1.5 points from the Form B score of each pupil. How will this affect the following statistics of this class obtained on the original Form B scores?

(1) The mean
(2) The standard deviation
(3) The variance
(4) The difference between the quartiles
(5) The percentile rank of Mary Brown
(6) The deviation of Mary Brown from the group mean
(7) The 40th percentile of the group
(8) The mode

b. The mean and standard deviation of the intelligence quotients of a class of 20 fifth-grade children are 104.5 and 5.4 respectively. A child of IQ 117 drops out. How will this affect

(1) The mean?
(2) The standard deviation?
(3) The range?

c. In the same class, instead of the child mentioned above, 4 children with IQ's 100, 104, 105, and 109 drop out. How will this affect the following?

(1) The mean
(2) The standard deviation
(3) The range.

d. The mean and standard deviation of 63 children on an arithmetic test are respectively 27.6 and 7.1. To them are added a new group of 26 who have had less training and whose mean is 19.2 and standard deviation 6.2. How will the values of the combined group differ from those of the original 63 children as to the following:

(1) The mean
(2) The standard deviation
(3) The range
(4) The percentile rank of a score of 20.

5.* A research worker needs to eliminate cases from one or the other of two groups, A and B, in order that they may have approximately the same mean and standard deviation. He wants to lose as few cases as possible. For each of the situations described below, suggest from what part of the distribution of group B he should remove one or more cases in order to have the desired effect.

a. The two groups have approximately the same mean, but *B* is considerably more variable.

b. The two groups have approximately the same standard deviation, but *B* has the larger mean.

c. *B* has a larger mean than *A* and is less variable.

d. *B* has a smaller mean than *A* and a larger standard deviation.

6. Compute the mean and standard deviation of the language scores as they are listed in Appendix A and also of the language scores affected with variable error in Table XXX. Does the relation between these means and the relation between these standard deviations agree with the general principle stated on page 142?

7. The new Stanford Achievement Test—Form V was given to all the 8B pupils of the elementary schools of the Board of Education, City of New York, on December 21 and 22, 1938. The distribution of scores on the sub-test "Paragraph Meaning" by boroughs is given below. Compute the mean and standard deviation for each borough.

Class Sort	Manhattan	Bronx	Brooklyn	Queens	Richmond
130–134				1	
125–129	2	3	6	8	
120–124	19	21	87	62	4
115–119	56	103	214	177	30
110–114	159	343	625	504	78
105–109	214	495	944	756	97
100–104	293	734	1389	1106	191
95– 99	256	558	1177	799	170
90– 94	235	522	1087	698	167
85– 89	177	287	761	452	84
80– 84	243	324	1038	578	128
75– 79	127	185	627	288	62
70– 74	102	93	442	179	51
65– 69	63	50	335	96	15
60– 64	34	24	166	50	7
55– 59	17	4	61	16	3
50– 54	4	3	36	4	
45– 49	3	5	10	4	1
40– 44	4		8	1	
35– 39	1	1	5	1	1
30– 34	1	4	2		
25– 29			1		
N	2010	3759	9021	5780	1089

8. Knowing only the mean and standard deviation and *N* for each borough, show how you compute the mean and standard deviation for the city.

BIBLIOGRAPHY ON SHEPPARD'S CORRECTIONS

Camp, B., *Mathematical Part of Elementary Statistics*. D. C. Heath & Co., 1931, p. 220.

Carver, H. C., "The fundamental nature and proof of Sheppard's adjustments," *Annals of Mathematical Statistics*, 7 (Sept., 1936), 154–163.

Elderton, W. P., *Frequency Curves and Correlation*. Charles & Edwin Layton, London, 1927, pp. 24–29.

Kullback, Solomon, "A note on Sheppard's corrections," *Annals of Mathematical Statistics*, 6 (Sept., 1936), 158–159.

Lewis, W. T., "A reconsideration of Sheppard's corrections," *Annals of Mathematical Statistics*, 6 (March, 1935), 11–20.

Sheppard, W. F., "On the calculation of the most probable values of frequency constants for data arranged according to equidistant divisions of a scale," *Proceedings of the London Mathematical Society*, 29 (1898), 353–380.

—— "The calculation of moments of a frequency distribution," *Biometrika*, 5 (1907), 450–459.

CHAPTER X

FURTHER CHARACTERISTICS OF A FREQUENCY DISTRIBUTION *

Symmetry and Skewness. Without reproducing the entire data, it is often necessary to describe a frequency distribution as accurately as possible through the use of certain summary measures. Two characteristics of a distribution, its central position and its variability, have already been discussed. These, however, give no clue as to the extent to which a distribution may be asymmetrical, or skewed, or the extent to which it may be flat-topped, peaked, or even U-shaped.

In a *symmetrical distribution*, if the frequency curve or the histogram is folded on the ordinate at the mean, the two halves of the curve coincide. In such a distribution, the mean and the median are identical. If the curve has a single mode, it coincides with the mean; if it has more than one mode, these are symmetrically placed on each side of the mean. Equal positive and negative deviations from the mean occur with equal frequency. All the distributions in Table XXXVI and Figure 23 are symmetrical. Any distribution which is not symmetrical is asymmetrical or skewed. Different degrees of asymmetry are represented by the distributions in Table XXXVII and Figure 24.

Measure of Skewness Based on Percentiles. When the median is used as the measure of central position, the appropriate measure of variability is some interpercentile range such as Q_U–Q_L or P_{90}–P_{10}. A measure of skewness appropriate to use with these measures of central position and variability might be based on a comparison of the amounts by which the two quartile points deviate from the median. In a symmetrical distribution $Q_U - Md = Md - Q_L$. Thus a crude measure of skewness is provided by $(Q_U - Md) - (Md - Q_L) = Q_U + Q_L - 2Md$. This expression, however, is affected not only by the asymmetry of a distribution but also by its variability, and therefore it is customary to divide $Q_U + Q_L - 2Md$ by the semi-interquartile range, $\frac{1}{2}(Q_U - Q_L)$, obtaining

$$Sk_Q = \frac{Q_U + Q_L - 2Md}{\frac{1}{2}(Q_U - Q_L)} = \frac{2(Q_U + Q_L - 2Md)}{Q_U - Q_L} \tag{31}$$

as a quartile coefficient of skewness. This coefficient is not appropriate to

* This chapter may be omitted in a minimum course.

152

use in connection with the mean and standard deviation, but only with the median and interpercentile range.

Measure of Skewness Based on Mean and Median. A measure of skewness, which is valuable in theoretical studies in which the mathematical equation of a curve is known, is the difference between mean and mode divided by the standard deviation, $\dfrac{\overline{X} - \breve{X}}{s}$. For concrete data, however, the mode is so unreliable, and so greatly affected by grouping errors, that this formula is of little value as a description of observed data. For smooth curves with a single mode in the middle of the distribution, the mean tends to be about 3 times as far from the mode as from the median. Therefore

$$Sk = \frac{3(\text{Mean} - \text{median})}{s} \tag{32}$$

is commonly used instead. A distribution in which the mean is larger than the median, such as the upper sketch in Figure 19, has *positive* skewness. The longer tail of the frequency curve of a positively skewed distribution extends to the right.

Concrete Illustration of a Skewed Distribution. The figures in Table XXXIV were obtained by Willeford in a study of 400 families in Leslie County, Kentucky.* The skewness of these distributions is even more clearly indicated by the derived data of Table XXXV. For each district, the mean is considerably larger than the median, indicating positive skewness. Also the median is closer to the lower quartile than to the upper, which indicates positive skewness. The fact that the standard deviation is nearly as large as the mean, in a distribution that has no negative scores, is also an indication that the scores must be bunched together between zero and the mean, and stretched out over a wide range above the mean.

To present only the mean as evidence of the central tendency of these data would grossly mislead the reader, for nearly three-fourths of the families have incomes lower than the mean income. The elimination of the four families with incomes of over a thousand dollars would lower the mean of the combined districts by 16.87. The total range is misleading as a measure of spread. Note how strikingly the range shrinks if eight families at each end are excluded. The resulting range, $P_{98}-P_{02}$, in which the middle 96% of the cases fall, is, for the combined districts, less than one-third as great as the total range. The two measures of skewness

---

* *Income and Health in Remote Rural Areas.* Teachers College, Columbia University, Bureau of Publications, 1932, p. 23.

TABLE XXXIV

Skewed Frequency Distribution: Number of Families Having a Given Money Income per Family in Dollars in Two Magisterial Districts

(*Adapted from Mary B. Willeford*, Income and Health in Remote Rural Areas)

Income in Dollars *	Number of Families		
	District A	District B	Both Districts
2975	1		1
1325		1	1
1275		1	1
1175		1	1
975	1		1
925		1	1
875	1	2	3
825			
775	3	2	5
725	2		2
675	3		3
625	2	1	3
575	4		4
525		2	2
475	2	2	4
425	7	1	8
375	2	7	9
325	10	5	15
275	15	14	29
225	48	62	110
175	57	67	124
125	30	24	54
75	5	3	8
25	7	4	11
Total	200	200	400

* Each entry represents the midpoint of an interval $50 wide.

TABLE XXXV

Characteristics of a Skewed Distribution: Money Income per Family in Dollars for 400 Families in Two Magisterial Districts

(Computed from Original Data on Which Table XXXIV Is Based)

Measure	District A	District B	Both Districts
Mean	256.5	240.8	248.6
Median	201.0	201.6	201.4
Standard Deviation	215.4	181.1	199.1
Upper Quartile	260.0	242.0	246.8
Lower Quartile	157.0	164.2	160.9
Total Range	0 — 2959.3	0 — 1311.0	0 — 2959.3
Range of Middle 96% of Families	34 — 754	50 — 890	43 — 870
$\dfrac{3(\text{Mean} - \text{Median})}{s}$	0.77	0.65	0.71
$\dfrac{2(Q_U + Q_L - 2Md)}{Q_U - Q_L}$	0.29	0.08	0.11

reported in the last two lines of the table are not connected in any particular way, except that each would be zero if the distribution were symmetrical, and that both are almost certain to have the same sign. The measure which involves the mean is more greatly affected by one or two extreme cases than is the other. The quartile coefficient is nearly zero for the data from district B, because the quartile points are almost equally distant from the median, although beyond these points the scores stretch out unequally and produce an asymmetry in the extremities of the distribution which is reflected by the measure that involves the mean.

Moment. The percentiles, deciles, median, and quartiles belong to one family, all members of which are measures obtained by finding a score which corresponds to a given proportion of frequency. The mean and standard deviation belong to a different family, the members of which are measures based on deviations from some origin. These two groups of measures constitute two systems, the *percentile system* and the *moment system*. The moment system is so named because of certain analogies to physics such as the relationship of a mean to the center of equilibrium of a distribution, discussed in Chapter VII. There is no great advantage in understanding these analogies, and the term *moment* may be accepted as defined in the next paragraph, without any attempt to understand why this particular term came into use instead of some other.

In general, an expression of the form $\dfrac{\Sigma f X^r}{N}$ is called the rth moment around zero; $\dfrac{\Sigma f(X - A)^r}{N}$, the rth moment around an arbitrary origin A; and $\dfrac{\Sigma f x^r}{N}$, the rth moment around the mean.* We shall use the Greek letter μ (mu) to represent a moment, giving it a subscript to indicate the power to which the variable is to be raised, and giving it a prime when deviations are taken from any origin other than the mean.

Thus the rth moment around any arbitrary origin A is

$$\mu_r' = \frac{\Sigma f(X - A)^r}{N} = \frac{\Sigma f(x')^r}{N} \tag{33}$$

When the arbitrary origin is taken at zero, that is, when $A = 0$, we have the following special case of (33),

$$\mu_r' = \frac{\Sigma f(X - 0)^r}{N} = \frac{\Sigma f X^r}{N} \tag{34}$$

Another special and very important case of (33) arises when the arbitrary origin is taken at the mean, that is when $A = \overline{X}$. This special case is written without the prime, as

$$\mu_r = \frac{\Sigma f(X - \overline{X})^r}{N} = \frac{\Sigma f x^r}{N} \tag{35}$$

Study the following schedule:

Moments about any arbitrary origin	Moments about zero	Moments about the mean
$\mu_1' = \dfrac{\Sigma f x'}{N} = a$	$\mu_1' = \dfrac{\Sigma f X}{N} = \overline{X}$	$\mu_1 = \dfrac{\Sigma f x}{N} = 0$
$\mu_2' = \dfrac{\Sigma f(x')^2}{N}$	$\mu_2' = \dfrac{\Sigma f X^2}{N}$	$\mu_2 = \dfrac{\Sigma f x^2}{N} = s^2$
$\mu_3' = \dfrac{\Sigma f(x')^3}{N}$	$\mu_3' = \dfrac{\Sigma f X^3}{N}$	$\mu_3 = \dfrac{\Sigma f x^3}{N}$
$\mu_4' = \dfrac{\Sigma f(x')^4}{N}$	$\mu_4' = \dfrac{\Sigma f X^4}{N}$	$\mu_4 = \dfrac{\Sigma f x^4}{N}$

The familiar equation $s^2 = \dfrac{\Sigma f(x')^2}{N} - \left(\dfrac{\Sigma f x'}{N}\right)^2$, when translated into the moment symbolism becomes $\mu_2 = \mu_2' - (\mu_1')^2$.

* Originally the term *moment* was applied to $\Sigma f X^r$ and *moment coefficient* to $\dfrac{\Sigma f X^r}{N}$.

The term *higher moments* is customarily applied to moments higher than the second. The first four moments of a frequency distribution are capable of providing a description of its dispersion, its skewness, and its peakedness or flatness. Before these measures are studied, it will be helpful to read pages 184–187 of *Mathematics Essential for Elementary Statistics* and to answer the questions in Exercise 17.

Exercise 17

1. a. Write out in full the expression represented by the symbol μ_3.

Ans. $\frac{1}{N}(x_1{}^3 + x_2{}^3 + x_3{}^3 + \cdots + x_N{}^3)$

b. Write out in full the expression represented by the symbol $\mu_3{}^2$.

Ans. $\left[\frac{1}{N}(x_1{}^3 + x_2{}^3 + \cdots + x_N{}^3)\right]^2 = \frac{1}{N^2}[x_1{}^6 + x_2{}^6 + \cdots$

$+ x_N{}^6 + 2(x_1{}^3x_2{}^3 + x_1{}^3x_3{}^3 + \cdots + x_1{}^3x_N{}^3 + \cdots + x_{N-1}{}^3x_N{}^3)]$

c. Of what degree is the term $\mu_3{}^2$? Ans. Of sixth degree.

2. Write out in full the expression represented by

    a. μ_5 b. $\mu_2\mu_3$ c. $\mu_3\mu_4$

3. Translate into moment symbolism

    a. $\dfrac{\Sigma fx^5}{N}$ c. s^2 e. $\dfrac{\Sigma fX^6}{N}$

    b. $\dfrac{\Sigma fX^2}{N} - \left(\dfrac{\Sigma fX}{N}\right)^2$ d. $\dfrac{\Sigma f(x')^7}{N}$ f. $\left(\dfrac{\Sigma fx^3}{N}\right)^2$

4. Express the following in terms previously familiar

    a. μ_2 c. $\mu_2' - (\mu_1')^2$ e. $\mu_2{}^2$ g. μ_1

    b. $\sqrt{\mu_2}$ d. $\dfrac{\mu_2' - (\mu_1')^2}{\mu_2}$ f. $\mu_2{}^{3/2}$

5. What is the degree of each of the following expressions?

    a. μ_5 d. $\mu_4/(\mu_2)^2$ g. $\mu_3{}^2/\mu_2{}^3$

    b. $\mu_3{}^2$ e. $\mu_3\mu_2$ h. $\sqrt{\mu_4}$

    c. μ_4/μ_2 f. $\mu_3\mu_1$ i. $\mu_3{}^2 \div \mu_2{}^3$

6. Express in moment notation:

    a. The sum of the squares of deviations from the mean

    b. The mean of the squares of deviations from any arbitrary origin

    c. The sum of the cubes of the deviations from zero

    d. The mean of the deviations from zero

    e. The mean of the squares of the deviations from zero minus the square of the mean of the deviations from zero

    f. The variance

    g. The standard deviation

    h. The mean

    i. The variance plus the square of the mean

Measure of Skewness Based on Moments. In a symmetrical distribution, all the odd moments, i.e., μ_1, μ_3, μ_5, etc., are equal to zero. Because the first moment around the mean is always zero for every distribution, since $\mu_1 = \dfrac{\Sigma x}{N} = 0$, it is useless as a test of skewness. The third is preferable to any higher moment because it is easier to compute and because the higher the moment the more it varies from sample to sample, and consequently the less reliable it is. But μ_3 alone is not a satisfactory measure of skewness because it is affected by the size of the step interval. Karl Pearson introduced the use of a measure which he called *beta one*,

$$\beta_1 = \frac{\mu_3{}^2}{\mu_2{}^3} \tag{36}$$

This ratio is a pure number, being uninfluenced by the size of the unit in which measurements have been made. The size of β_1 indicates the amount

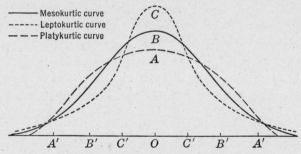

Fig. 22. Three frequency curves with different degrees of kurtosis. (Points of inflection are marked on horizontal axis.)

of skewness. The direction of skewness is shown by the sign of μ_3, which, however, is lost in the process of squaring, and must be restored to β_1, if the latter is used as a measure of skewness. A more satisfactory measure in this respect is

$$\alpha_3 = \frac{\mu_3}{\mu_2{}^{3/2}} \tag{37}$$

in which the sign of the μ_3 is preserved. Both β_1 and α_3 are zero for all symmetrical distributions, and in general positive when the two previously discussed measures of skewness are positive, negative when they are negative. For a smooth frequency distribution with a single mode, the measure

$$\frac{3(\text{Mean} - \text{Median})}{s} \quad \text{approximates} \quad \frac{\alpha_3.}{2}$$

Measure of Kurtosis Based on Moments. The distributions in Figure 23 differ chiefly in regard to convexity, a characteristic to which Karl Pearson gave the name *kurtosis*. A normal curve, or a skewed curve that has the same degree of convexity as the normal curve, he called a *mesokurtic*, or moderately arched curve. In Figure 22 the curve drawn with unbroken line is a mesokurtic curve. If some of the cases near the middle of this curve should move out a little to each side, rounding out the shoulders of the curve, and some of the cases at the ends draw in, depleting the tails, the result would be a flat-topped, or *platykurtic* curve such as *A* in Figure 22. If the reverse should take place, and some of the cases about one standard deviation from the mean move in toward the center and others move out toward the tails, the result would be a *leptokurtic* curve such as *C*. The abscissa of the point of inflection for each curve, that is, the point where the curve crosses its own tangent, is marked on the base line. Clearly these are changes in form, and not merely in scale. The terms platykurtic, leptokurtic, mesokurtic, mesokurtosis, are not particularly important, but they are rather interesting, and roll pleasantly under one's tongue. "Student" once suggested that the platykurtic curves, like the platypus, are squat with short tails, while leptokurtic curves are high with long tails like the kangaroo which "leps." * Karl Pearson proposed a measure for kurtosis which he called *beta two*,

$$\beta_2 = \frac{\mu_4}{\mu_2{}^2} \tag{38}$$

Since this is derived from the fourth moment, μ_4, in the same way that the measure of skewness is derived from the third moment, μ_3, it is also called α_4.

$$\alpha_4 = \beta_2 = \frac{\mu_4}{\mu_2{}^2} \tag{39}$$

For a normal curve, α_4 is exactly 3; for more peaked curves it is larger than 3; for flatter curves less. For a rectangular curve it is approximately 1.8. For a U-shaped curve it is less than 1.8. The *excess* of α_4 over 3,

* "Student" was a well-known British statistician named William Sealy Gosset (1876–1937) who was adviser to the Guinness brewery in Dublin. A ruling of that firm forbidding their employees to publish the results of research was relaxed to allow him to publish mathematical and statistical research under a pseudonym. His paper on "The probable error of a mean," published in *Biometrika* in 1908, which first called attention to the fact that the normal curve does not properly describe the distribution of the means of small samples, is now a classic. Information about Gosset's life and work may be found in the following papers: Fisher, R. A., "'Student'," *Annals of Eugenics*, IX (1939), 1–9; McMullen, L., "'Student' as a Man," *Biometrika*, XXX (Jan., 1939), 205–210; Pearson, E. S., "'Student' as Statistician," *Biometrika*, XXX (1939), 210–250.

TABLE XXXVI

Symmetrical Distributions Illustrating Different Degrees of Kurtosis

Score	A	B	C	D	E	F
13	1					
12	1	2	1		4	16
11	3	3	5	10	8	12
10	5	6	8	10	10	9
9	8	10	11	10	13	6
8	12	13	12	10	9	4
7	20	16	13	10	6	3
6	20	16	13	10	6	3
5	12	13	12	10	9	4
4	8	10	11	10	13	6
3	5	6	8	10	10	9
2	3	3	5	10	8	12
1	1	2	1		4	16
0	1					
Total	100	100	100	100	100	100
Central Position						
Mean	6.5	6.5	6.5	6.5	6.5	6.5
Median	6.5	6.5	6.5	6.5	6.5	6.5
Crude Mode	6.5	6.5	6.5	None	4 and 9	0 and 13
Variability						
Range	13	11	11	9	11	11
$Q_U - Q_L$	2.83	3.38	4.0	5.0	5.54	8.5
s	2.35	2.41	2.56	2.87	3.19	4.21
Moments About Mean						
μ_2	5.53	5.81	6.57	8.25	10.17	17.69
μ_3	0	0	0	0	0	0
μ_4	101.10	88.36	93.14	120.86	179.90	423.34
Skewness						
$\dfrac{2(Q_U + Q_L - 2Md)}{Q_U - Q_L}$	0	0	0	0	0	0
$3(M - Md)/s$	0	0	0	0	0	0
α_3	0	0	0	0	0	0
Kurtosis						
α_4	3.31	2.62	2.16	1.78	1.74	1.35
$\alpha_4 - 3$	0.31	-0.38	-0.84	-1.22	-1.26	-1.65

i.e., $\alpha_4 - 3$, is a measure of kurtosis which gives a value of zero for any mesokurtic curve, a positive value for more peaked curves, and a negative value for flatter curves.

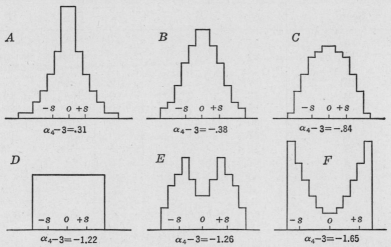

Fig. 23. Symmetrical histograms illustrating different degrees of kurtosis. (From data of Table XXXVI.)

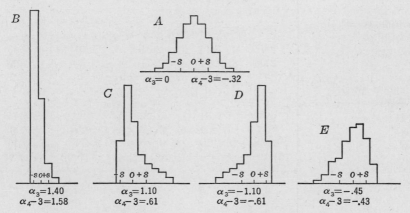

Fig. 24. Histograms illustrating different degrees of skewness and kurtosis. (From data of Table XXXVII.)

Computation of Moments. As in the computation of a standard deviation, it is easier to take deviations from an arbitrary origin and to make corrections afterward by the formulas:

$$\mu_2 = \mu_2' - (\mu_1')^2 \tag{40}$$
$$\mu_3 = \mu_3' - 3\mu_2'\mu_1' + 2(\mu_1')^3 \tag{41}$$
$$\mu_4 = \mu_4' - 4\mu_3'\mu_1' + 6\mu_2'(\mu_1')^2 - 3(\mu_1')^4 \tag{42}$$

TABLE XXXVII

Distributions Illustrating Different Degrees of Skewness and Kurtosis

Score	A	B	C	D	E
13					
12	1		2		
11	3		4		
10	7		5		7
9	12	2	7	15	16
8	17	7	10	35	21
7	20	30	22	22	20
6	17	61	35	10	15
5	12		15	7	9
4	7			5	8
3	3			4	3
2	1			2	1
Total	100	100	100	100	100
Central Position					
Mean	7	6.5	7	7	7
Median	7	6.32	6.5	7.5	7.2
Crude mode	7	6	6	8	8
Variability					
Range	10	3	7	7	8
$Q_U - Q_L$	2.76	1.06	2.01	2.01	2.63
s	2.00	.71	1.71	1.71	1.85
Moments About Mean					
μ_2	4.02	.51	2.92	2.92	3.44
μ_3	0	.51	5.52	−5.52	−2.82
μ_4	43.38	1.19	30.76	30.76	30.44
Skewness					
$\dfrac{2(Q_U + Q_L - 2Md)}{Q_U - Q_L}$	0	.45	.54	−.54	−.17
$3(M - Md)/s$	0	.76	.88	−.88	−.32
α_3	0	1.40	1.10	−1.10	−.45
Kurtosis					
α_4	2.68	4.58	3.61	3.61	2.57
$\alpha_4 - 3$	−.32	1.58	.61	.61	−.43

These formulas apply no matter where the arbitrary origin is taken. When a computing machine is available, it is preferable to take deviations from zero.

For proof of these formulas, see Appendix B.

TABLE XXXVIII

Computation of Measures of Skewness and Kurtosis for Distribution B in Table XXXVI

Score	f	x'	fx'	$f(x')^2$	$f(x')^3$	$f(x')^4$
12	2	5	10	50	250	1250
11	3	4	12	48	192	768
10	6	3	18	54	162	486
9	10	2	20	40	80	160
8	13	1	13	13	13	13
7	16	0	0	0	0	0
6	16	−1	−16	16	−16	16
5	13	−2	−26	52	−104	208
4	10	−3	−30	90	−270	810
3	6	−4	−24	96	−384	1536
2	3	−5	−15	75	−375	1875
1	2	−6	−12	72	−432	2592
Total	100		−50	606	−884	9714

$$\Sigma fx' = -50 \qquad \mu_1' = -50/100 = -0.50$$
$$\Sigma f(x')^2 = 606 \qquad \mu_2' = 606/100 = 6.06$$
$$\Sigma f(x')^3 = -884 \qquad \mu_3' = -884/100 = -8.84$$
$$\Sigma f(x')^4 = 9714 \qquad \mu_4' = 9714/100 = 97.14$$

$$\mu_1 = 0$$
$$\mu_2 = \mu_2' - (\mu_1')^2 = 6.06 - 0.25 = 5.81$$
$$\mu_3 = \mu_3' - 3\mu_2'\mu_1' + 2(\mu_1')^3 = -8.84 - 3(6.06)(-0.5) + 2(-0.125)$$
$$= -8.84 \qquad + 9.09 \qquad - 0.25 = 0$$
$$\mu_4 = \mu_4' - 4\mu_3'\mu_1' + 6\mu_2'(\mu_1')^2 - 3(\mu_1')^4 = 97.14 - 17.68 + 9.09 - 0.19$$
$$= 88.36$$
$$\alpha_3 = \frac{\mu_3}{\mu_2^{3/2}} = 0 \qquad \alpha_4 = \frac{\mu_4}{\mu_2^2} = \frac{88.36}{(5.81)^2} = 2.62 \qquad \alpha_4 - 3 = -0.38$$

Exercise 18

1. Verify by computation the measures of skewness and kurtosis in Tables XXXVI and XXXVII, following the pattern of computation shown in Table XXXVIII.

2. Examine Figures 23 and 24 to obtain an understanding of what is meant by positive, zero, and negative skewness; by positive, zero, and negative excess.

3. Specify the type of curve for which each of the statements below would necessarily be true. Use the most general description applicable.

N normal curve $\qquad\qquad$ P platykurtic curve
S any symmetrical curve $\qquad$ L leptokurtic curve
R rectangular curve $\qquad\quad$ M mesokurtic curve
O no curve named here $\qquad$ X any curve whatever

a. The mean and median coincide.

b. One-fourth of the area under the curve lies between the ordinates erected at the median and the lower quartile.

c. The mean is larger than the mode.

d. All the odd moments are zero.

e. The fourth moment is equal to 3 times the square of the second.

f. The fourth moment is equal to 4 times the square of the second.

g. The fourth moment is equal to twice the square of the second.

h. The difference between the 1st and 2nd deciles is the same as the difference between the 2nd and 3rd or between the 3rd and 4th.

i. The median is equal to half the sum of the 30th and 70th percentiles.

j. The ordinate at the mean bisects the area.

k. The mode lies between the mean and the median.

l. The proportion of area lying between the ordinates at the 1st and 2nd deciles is the same as the proportion lying between the 2nd and 3rd or between the 3rd and 4th.

m. The difference between the 1st and 2nd deciles is the same as the difference between the 8th and 9th.

n. The median is the 5th decile.

o. The mean is larger than the median.

p. 68% of the area under the curve lies between the ordinates at Q_U and Q_L.

q. The first moment around the mean is positive.

r. The third moment is zero and the square of the second moment is one-third as large as the fourth moment.

s. Ten persons have been ranked by the same rater from 1 to 10 on some trait, and the curve of distribution of the ranks is drawn. There are no ties in rank.

4. Estimate roughly the direction of skewness to be found in each of these distributions and indicate those you think would be approximately symmetrical by 0, those positively skewed by +, those negatively skewed by −.

a. The incomes of 10,000 persons drawn at random from the population of the United States.

b. The strength of grip in pounds of 500 unselected male students in colleges and universities.

c. Scores on a test which has a low ceiling and a large percentage of perfect scores.

d. The number of errors in an arithmetic test given after very thorough drill, when the material has been well learned.

e. The age of a sample of 100 cars parked in a parking lot in downtown New York.

CHAPTER XI

THE NORMAL DISTRIBUTION

I know of scarcely anything so apt to impress the imagination as the wonderful form of cosmic order expressed by the "Law of Frequency of Error." The law would have been personified by the Greeks and deified, if they had known it. It reigns with serenity and in complete self-effacement amidst the wildest confusion. The huger the mob and the greater the apparent anarchy, the more perfect is its sway. It is the supreme law of Unreason. Whenever a large sample of chaotic elements are taken in hand and marshalled in the order of their magnitude, an unsuspected and most beautiful form of regularity proves to have been latent all along. Sir Francis Galton

Frequency distributions so often have a symmetrical bell-shaped form, with most of the cases near the mean of the distribution, that it is easy to understand why this form has come to be called the "normal" curve. Our previous study of frequency curves has, however, showed clearly that there exist many traits whose distributions are typically more skewed and more or less peaked, than the so-called "normal curve." The name is an unfortunate one, in that it encourages a mistaken assumption that all distribution curves should conform to this shape as to a universal pattern.

Discovery of the Normal Curve.* The curve which we now call "normal" is the curve of normal probability or curve of error which attracted the interest of most of the great mathematicians and astronomers of the first half of the nineteenth century. More than two centuries ago, Abraham De Moivre (1667–1754), a refugee mathematician living in London, making his living partly by solving problems for wealthy gamblers, recognized that the random variation in the number of heads appearing on throws of n coins corresponds to the terms of the binomial expansion of $(.5 + .5)^n$, and that as n becomes larger this distribution approaches a definite form. In 1733 De Moivre derived the equation for this curve and presented it privately to some friends. To him it was only a mathematical exercise, utterly unconnected with any sort of application to empirical data.

* For a more extended treatment, see Walker, H. M., *Studies in the History of Statistical Method*, Baltimore, The Williams & Wilkins Co., 1929, Chapter II; "Bi-centenary of the normal curve," *Journal of the American Statistical Association*, 29 (1934), 72–75; "Abraham de Moivre," *Scripta Mathematica*, 2 (1934), 316–333.

At that time there were no collections of empirical data at hand for study. As yet no one had made any measurements of any large number of individuals. A Swiss mathematician named Jacques (or James) Bernoulli (1654–1705, eldest of the very remarkable family of mathematicians by that name) had suggested that the theory of probability might have useful applications in economic and moral affairs, but he, himself, was too near death to investigate the applications, and, moreover, he had no numerical data which he could have used for that purpose. The idea must have seemed fantastic to his contemporaries. In 1713, his great book on probability, *Ars Conjectandi*,* was published posthumously under the editorship of his nephew Nicolas, who seems to have tried in vain to induce other mathematicians to develop the argument further. Nearly a century passed before any scientific worker began to gather large masses of concrete data and to study the properties of distributions. The application of the normal curve in studies of concrete data begins with the work of the great mathematical astronomers who lived at the beginning of the nineteenth century, chiefly Laplace (1749–1827) in France, and Gauss (1777–1855) in Germany, each of whom derived the law independently and presumably without any knowledge of De Moivre's derivation.

The probability curve is often called the Gaussian curve, because until recently it was supposed that Gauss had been the first person to make use of its properties. However, in 1924, Karl Pearson discovered a hitherto unknown derivation by Abraham De Moivre.†

The idea that this curve could be used to describe data other than errors of observation in the physical sciences seems to have originated with the great Belgian statistician, Adolphe Quetelet (1796–1874), who first popularized the idea that statistical method was a fundamental discipline adaptable to any field of human interest in which mass data were to be found. He was convinced that the measurement of mental and moral traits waited only for the collection of sufficient and trustworthy data, and was so sure that when such measurement was feasible, the distribution of these traits would be found to be in accordance with the "law of error" that he talked about "the *normal* curve of error."

General Form of the Curve. Several sketches of a normal curve have already been presented (see Figure 20, page 121; Figure 11A, page 69; and Figure 22B, page 158). Most people are familiar in a general way with this bell-shaped, symmetrical frequency distribution which has an unlimited

* Conjecto = to throw together, therefore to gamble, therefore to guess at or surmise.

† Pearson, K., "Historical note on the origin of the normal curve of error," *Biometrika*, XVI (1924), 402–404.

range and which approaches the base line more and more closely as the absolute value of the abscissa becomes larger. Most people have heard so much about this curve that they have an exaggerated idea of its universality, and imagine that every distribution which has a peak near the center is normal. Actually the normal curve is a mathematical abstraction, a sort of mathematical model. Some concrete data have distributions which approximate this form, but it is not in any sense the expected pattern to which observed distributions conform.

Variables Known to Have a Distribution Approximately Normal. A variable which is the resultant of several independent, equally potent causes, each as likely to be present as absent in any given instance, has a binomial distribution. This binomial distribution is discrete, but may be represented by a histogram. If the number of independent, equally potent causes increases, the number of intervals in the histogram increases. When the number of intervals becomes very great, the histogram begins to suggest a smooth curve. The limiting form of this histogram as the number of these independent, equally potent causes becomes infinitely great, is the normal curve.

Thus if several unbiased pennies are tossed simultaneously, the number of heads appearing on a single throw is a variable which depends upon the way each of the several coins falls. These coins are independent; each is, presumably, as likely to fall one way as to fall the other; and each has the same effect upon the total. In the long run, the proportion of N throws which would be expected to show no heads, 1 head, 2 heads, etc., is as follows:

Number of pennies tossed	0	1	2	3	4	5
		Proportion expected to show given number of heads				
1	$\frac{1}{2}$	$\frac{1}{2}$				
2	$\frac{1}{4}$	$\frac{2}{4}$	$\frac{1}{4}$			
3	$\frac{1}{8}$	$\frac{3}{8}$	$\frac{3}{8}$	$\frac{1}{8}$		
4	$\frac{1}{16}$	$\frac{4}{16}$	$\frac{6}{16}$	$\frac{4}{16}$	$\frac{1}{16}$	
5	$\frac{1}{32}$	$\frac{5}{32}$	$\frac{10}{32}$	$\frac{10}{32}$	$\frac{5}{32}$	$\frac{1}{32}$

Such percentages are shown graphically in Figure 25, where the sequence has been extended to suggest how the binomial approaches the normal distribution as the number of causes (here number of coins) becomes very large. *The normal curve is a continuous distribution which is the limiting form of the discrete binomial distribution $(.5 + .5)^n$ as n is made to increase without limit.*

Random errors of measurement and observation in the physical

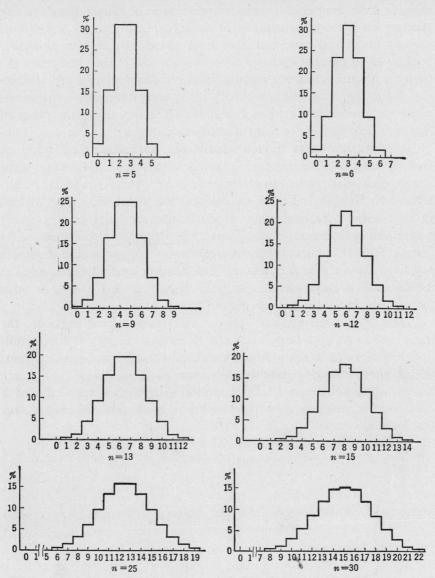

Fig. 25. Binomial distribution: percentage of heads appearing when n "perfect" coins are spun.

sciences have long been known to show normal distributions. Early treatises on the normal curve were almost entirely due to astronomers and surveyors, and somewhat later to physicists, geographers, and other workers in physical science.

That stature and other anthropometric measurements had a normal distribution for a random sample of a population homogeneous as to age, race, sex, and other important conditioning factors was the belief of Quetelet. His data were scant and he imputed to the normal distribution a universality it does not possess. In general we may, however, expect a normal distribution in hereditary traits of the Mendelian type unless some selective factor, or some conditioning environmental factor, interferes. Weight, which is subject to a degree of voluntary control, would not be expected to show a distribution as nearly normal as the distribution of measures of bony structure. The voluntary control may become prepotent, destroying the condition of "a large number of independent, equally potent causes, each of which is as likely to be present as absent in a given case." Similarly, in an unselected group, one is more likely to find a normal distribution in innate capacities than to find a normal distribution in traits dependent on the structure of the social order, such as income, extent of education, age of automobile, length of working day, length of vacation enjoyed by workers in a given industry, age at marriage, and so on.

Measures which might show a normal distribution in an unselected group from a homogeneous population may depart widely from normality under certain conditions. (1) If a particular selective factor is operating the resulting curve will probably not be normal. For example, the distribution of intelligence quotients for college graduates is affected by the elimination of more dull than bright students. (2) If a limit is imposed at one end of the distribution, either by necessity or by fiat, a normal distribution cannot be expected. For example, if an institution for the feeble-minded sets a maximum limit to the intelligence quotients of the inmates it will receive, the distribution of intelligence quotients of the inmates of that institution cannot be expected to resemble the normal curve. (3) If a distribution of a trait is made for a group composed of subgroups which do not belong together, it is not usually normal. Anthropometric measures in composite groups are often not normal, as cranial measurements of a group in which there are distinct subgroups of widely differing ethnic strains, or as pelvic measurements of a group including both sexes, or as height in a group including varying proportions of different age groups. (4) If a composite group is formed from a number of subgroups, each of about the same size, each normally distributed, and differing considerably among themselves as to their mean score, the composite is likely to be more flat-topped than a normal curve. This situation would occur if a test maker selected, for the purposes of standardizing a test, a normally distributed group of 200 children in each school grade from the 4th through the 9th, and then combined all 1200 in one distribution.

The most important applications of the normal curve are in connection with sampling studies such as those discussed in Chapter XV. Suppose, for example, that an investigator has given an audiometer test to 150 ten-year-old boys, and has obtained their mean score. If he should repeat the experiment with another set of 150 ten-year-old boys, no one would expect that the means obtained in the two studies would be identical. Imagine that the investigation is repeated, say, 1000 times, with 150 different subjects each time, so that 1000 different means are obtained. Now even if the audiometer readings of individual boys do not show a normal distribution, the 1000 mean readings will have a distribution approximately normal if the samples are chosen at random * from the same population. (If the distribution of individual readings is extremely skewed, the distribution of means may not be strictly normal, but will be more nearly normal than the original distribution of individual scores.) The fact that the means of successive random samples tend to have a normal distribution makes the tables of that distribution very important for studies in which facts about a sample are generalized to the population from which the sample is drawn.

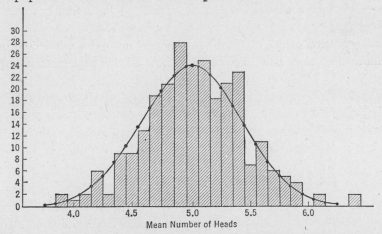

Fig. 26. Normal curve fitted to histogram: mean number of heads appearing in 260 samples of 16 throws of 10 pennies each. (From data of Table XXXIX.)

$$\overline{X} = 5.0 \qquad s = 0.43$$

* See Chapter XV for a discussion of what is meant by "choosing at random."

Figure 26 illustrates the approach to normality of the frequency distribution of means presented in Table **XXXIX**.

To obtain the data for this figure, several classes of statistics students threw pennies, ten at a time, recording the number of heads. When a student had made 16 such throws, he computed the mean, the variance, and the standard deviation of the sample of 16 throws. Figure 26 shows the histogram representing means of 260 such samples. On this histogram there has been drawn, by a procedure to be explained presently, a normal curve with the same mean, standard deviation, and area, as the histogram. The irregularities of the histogram are accidental, and it would undoubtedly become smoother if many more means were added.

Mathematical Equation. The equation of the normal curve is

$$y = \frac{Ni}{\sigma\sqrt{2\pi}} e^{-\frac{x^2}{2\sigma^2}} \tag{43}$$

where x is any abscissa
    y is the corresponding ordinate
    σ is the standard deviation of the distribution
    π is the mathematical constant which gives the ratio of any circle to its diameter, and whose approximate value is 3.1416
    e is another mathematical constant whose approximate value is 2.71828
    N is the number of cases in the distribution and therefore also the number of area units under the curve when it has been drawn.

As we are now discussing a mathematical ideal rather than a set of observed data, we shall use σ rather than s as the symbol for the standard deviation of this ideal curve.

For any given curve, N, σ, π, and e are all constant, while x and y are variables. However, these constants are not all quite alike. The letters π

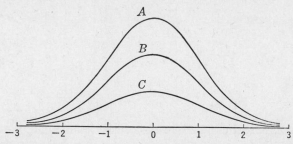

Fig. 27. Three normal curves all having the same mean and standard deviation but different total frequencies.

For curve A, $N = 300$, $\sigma = 1$
For curve B, $N = 200$, $\sigma = 1$
For curve C, $N = 100$, $\sigma = 1$

and e represent numbers which are absolute constants; they have exactly the same values wherever they occur, no matter what the type of problem; whereas N and σ are constant within one situation, but may change from one situation to another. Such "variable constants" are called parameters. The normal curve has two parameters, N and σ. Examine Figures 27 and 28 to see how the shape of the curve appears to change as N or σ is

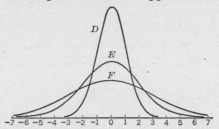

Fig. 28. Three normal curves all having the same total frequency but different standard deviations.

For curve D, $N = 300$, $\sigma = 1$
For curve E, $N = 300$, $\sigma = 2$
For curve F, $N = 300$, $\sigma = 3$

changed. The scales of these curves can be so converted that they would all have the same shape.

Plotting a Normal Curve. To get a feeling of the shape of this very interesting curve, every student should plot at least one. This is not difficult, and for most people it involves a distinct esthetic enjoyment.

The first problem is to determine how high the ordinate at the mean should be made in order to have the area under the curve contain as many area units as there are cases in a given distribution.

The ordinate at the mean is the ordinate for which $x = 0$. Therefore $\frac{-x^2}{2\sigma^2} = 0$, and therefore $e^{-\frac{x^2}{2\sigma^2}} = e^0$. It is a mathematical definition that any number raised to the zero power is equal to 1. Therefore $e^0 = 1$. Consequently, when $x = 0$,

$$y_0 = \frac{N}{\sigma\sqrt{2\pi}}(1) = \frac{N}{\sigma\sqrt{6.2832}} = 0.399\frac{N}{\sigma}$$

Now consider Figure 26. The number of cases being 260, both histogram and normal curve must contain 260 area units. An area unit here is a little rectangle whose base is one step interval or 0.1 score unit on the horizontal scale, and whose altitude is one unit on the vertical scale. (The vertical scale is merely the scale used in plotting the histogram and does not directly represent any physical property of the distribution.

Score is represented on the horizontal scale. Frequency is represented by area.) The observed standard deviation of these data is 0.43 score unit. Each interval on the horizontal scale is 0.1 score unit. Hence one standard deviation contains 4.3 of the linear interval units in which the horizontal scale is laid off. We shall make σ of the theoretical curve equal to s of the observed data. As N is represented by 260 area units and σ by 4.3 linear units on the horizontal scale, $\dfrac{N}{\sigma}$ will be represented by $\dfrac{260}{4.3} = 60.5$ linear units on the vertical scale, and

$$y_0 = 0.399 \, \frac{N}{\sigma} = 0.399(60.5) = 24.1$$

units on the vertical scale with which the histogram is plotted. If we make the maximum ordinate 24.1 units, the normal curve will contain the same area as the histogram.

Study Figure 26 to see that the areas of the curve and histogram are equivalent.

To clarify these relationships further, study the following sets of data:

N	σ in scores	Width of interval	Height of maximum ordinate in units of vertical scale
1200	7.5	3	$(0.399)\,\dfrac{1200}{2.5} = 191.5$
420	12.4	5	$(0.399)\,\dfrac{420}{2.48} = 67.6$
1000	10	1	$(0.399)\,\dfrac{1000}{10} = 39.9$
986	15.6	3	$(0.399)\,\dfrac{986}{5.2} = 75.7$

Having found the height of the maximum ordinate, it is easy to sketch in the rest of the curve, because the heights of ordinates at selected points can be read from the Table of Ordinates of the Normal Probability Curve in Appendix D.

Before we attempt to superimpose a normal curve on a particular histogram, it will be helpful to draw a large-scale chart of a normal curve which can later be used to clarify certain area relationships. Suppose we wish to have $N = 1000$, $\sigma = 10$, and $i = 1$. Then the ordinate at the mean should be $(0.399)\,\frac{1000}{10} = 39.9$ and each of the other ordinates should be $\frac{1000}{10} = 100$ times as large as the appropriate number given in the Table of Ordinates.

Exercise 19

1. On graph paper, lay off a horizontal scale such that each linear division represents 0.1σ. The scale should extend to about 2.5σ or perhaps 3σ on each side of the origin. Lay off a vertical scale of convenient dimensions, remembering that your maximum ordinate will be approximately 40 on that scale if the area is to be $N = 1000$ and $\sigma = 10$. Above each of the division points on the horizontal scale plot a point whose ordinate is $\dfrac{N}{\sigma} = \dfrac{1000}{10} = 100$ times as great as the corresponding entry in the Table of Ordinates of the Normal Curve in Appendix D. The curve is symmetrical about $x = 0$, so that the ordinate for a negative value of x is exactly the same as the ordinate for the corresponding positive value. Draw a smooth curve through the points you have plotted.

2. If you drew your curve to the specifications given, the area under it is the equivalent of 1000 area units. Count the squares between the ordinate at $\dfrac{x}{\sigma} = 0$ and the ordinate at $\dfrac{x}{\sigma} = 1$, estimating as best you can the area in the broken squares along the curve. Your estimate should be somewhere near 340, and this would be $\frac{340}{1000} = 34\%$ of the entire area under the curve. This estimate will vary a little from person to person, as it depends upon the accuracy of the drawing and the accuracy of the counting.

Draw up a table format in which the stub has the heading "$\dfrac{x}{\sigma}$ values of points at which ordinates are drawn," and the other two columns have the headings "Number of area units between the ordinates" and "Proportion of area between the ordinates." In the stub make entries as follows: 0 and 1; 1 and 2; 2 and 2.5; 0 and 2; 0 and 2.5; -1 and $+1$; -2 and $+2$; -2.5 and $+2.5$. Now, by counting squares in your diagram, find the appropriate entries for the other two columns. It should be clear that after squares have been counted to obtain the number of area units between the ordinates at $\dfrac{x}{\sigma} = 0$ and at $\dfrac{x}{\sigma} = 1$; the number of area units between the ordinates at $\dfrac{x}{\sigma} = 1$ and at $\dfrac{x}{\sigma} = 2$; and the number of area units between the ordinates at $\dfrac{x}{\sigma} = 2$ and at $\dfrac{x}{\sigma} = 2.5$; then all the other blanks in the same column can be filled by addition of these values without further counting of squares. The *proportion* of area is obtained from the corresponding *number of area units* by dividing the number of counted units by the total number of area units under the entire curve, that is, by 1000.

3. Compare these values with the corresponding entries in Table XXVIII, where the proportions of cases falling within a given standard deviation range is shown for several groups. Compare them also with the corresponding entries in the Table of Areas of the Normal Curve of Appendix D.

Unit Normal Curve. If the entries in the Table of Ordinates are plotted exactly as they stand, without multiplying them by $\dfrac{N}{\sigma}$, the result is the same as if it had been agreed to let $N = 1$ and $\sigma = 1$. The resulting curve is called the _unit normal curve_ because its area is one unit; in other words, $N = 1$.

The formula for the unit normal curve is obtained by setting $N = 1$ and $\sigma = 1$ in formula (43). The letter z is often used to represent the ordinate of a unit normal curve, but because we have employed that letter consistently to mean $\dfrac{x}{s}$, or now $\dfrac{x}{\sigma}$, we shall use the letter u instead.

$$u = \frac{1}{\sqrt{2\pi}} e^{-\frac{x^2}{2}} \tag{44}$$

Superimposing a Normal Curve on a Given Histogram. The procedure for doing this is only slightly different from the procedure for drawing a normal curve as followed in Exercise 19. It involves two additional steps: (1) the horizontal scale must be adjusted by finding the $\dfrac{x}{s}$ or $\dfrac{X - \overline{X}}{s}$ values of selected points, and (2) the area must be adjusted by multiplying tabled ordinates by $\dfrac{N}{s}$. The process will be illustrated with data presented in Table XL. Each of the cases in this table represents one variance

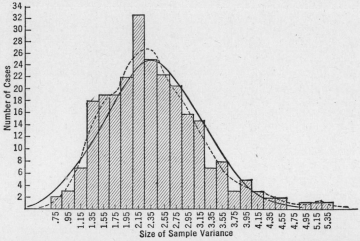

Fig. 29. Frequency distribution of 256 sample variances, same distribution smoothed by taking a running average of three consecutive frequencies, and fitted normal curve.

$$\overline{X} = 2.39 \qquad s = 0.82$$

TABLE XXXIX

Mean Number of Heads Appearing in Successive Random Samples of 16 Throws of Ten Pennies Each

Size of Mean	f
6.4	2
6.3	
6.2	
6.1	2
6.0	
5.9	4
5.8	5
5.7	6
5.6	11
5.5	7
5.4	23
5.3	21
5.2	18
5.1	25
5.0	24
4.9	28
4.8	21
4.7	19
4.6	13
4.5	9
4.4	9
4.3	2
4.2	6
4.1	2
4.0	1
3.9	2

Number of Samples   260
Mean of Means   5.036
Standard Deviation
of Means   0.43

TABLE XL

Variance of Number of Heads Appearing in Successive Random Samples of Sixteen Throws of Ten Pennies Each

Variance	f
5.3–5.4	1
5.1–5.2	1
4.9–5.0	1
4.7–4.8	
4.5–4.6	2
4.3–4.4	2
4.1–4.2	3
3.9–4.0	5
3.7–3.8	3
3.5–3.6	8
3.3–3.4	7
3.1–3.2	15
2.9–3.0	16
2.7–2.8	21
2.5–2.6	23
2.3–2.4	25
2.1–2.2	33
1.9–2.0	22
1.7–1.8	19
1.5–1.6	19
1.3–1.4	18
1.1–1.2	7
.9–1.0	3
.7– .8	2

Number of Samples   256
Mean of Variances   2.39
Standard Deviation
of Variances   0.82

computed by a student who threw 10 pennies 16 times and recorded the number of heads on each of the 16 throws. Figure 29 presents a histogram based on the data of Table XL. The data have been smoothed with a running average of 3 consecutive frequencies to reduce the chance irregularities and to show that a normal curve really does not fit these data very well. See page 195. A normal curve has been superimposed. We shall now examine the steps in the latter operation.

Steps in Superimposing a Normal Curve on a Histogram

1. Compute the mean. In the illustrative problem $\overline{X} = 2.39$.

2. Compute the standard deviation. $s = 0.82$.

3. Write down the score values of the division points between successive intervals as in column X of Table XLI.

4. Obtain the entries in column x by subtracting the mean from each value of X.

5. Divide each value of x by s to obtain the values in the column headed $\frac{x}{s}$.

6. From a table of ordinates of the normal probability curve, read the ordinate corresponding to each $\frac{x}{s}$. (The s of the observed distribution now becomes the σ of the normal curve.) Enter these in the column headed u. They are the ordinates of a unit normal distribution.

7. Multiply each value of u by $\frac{N}{s/i} = \frac{Ni}{s}$. (In the illustration $\frac{s}{i} = \frac{0.82}{0.2}$ $= 4.1$ and $\frac{N}{s/i} = \frac{256}{4.1} = 62.4$.) Enter these values in the column headed y.

8. Plot the values of y against the values of x.

In this transformation, the total area, the mean, the standard deviation, and the scale of measurement remain invariant, while the proportion of area in any given interval may be altered. This procedure is an excellent exercise for familiarizing the student with the use of tables of the normal curve.

Tables of Normal Probability Curve. In almost every text in statistical method, a table of areas of the normal curve is now to be found. The tables found in texts are usually abridgments of longer tables specially designed for computers. A list of sources in which these more extended tables are available and the name of the person who computed each table, will be found in the special bibliography at the end of this chapter.

Such tables are always made up for the unit normal curve, and consequently are applicable to any normal distribution, no matter what

TABLE XLI

Procedure for Finding the Ordinates of a Normal Curve to Be Superimposed on an Observed Distribution

Observed Distribution Shown in Table XL

$$\overline{X} = 2.39$$
$$s = 0.82$$
$$N = 256$$

X	x $(x-\overline{x})$	$\dfrac{x}{s}$	u	y
5.25	2.86	3.49	.0009	
5.05	2.66	3.24	.0021	0.1
4.85	2.46	3.00	.0044	0.3
4.65	2.26	2.76	.0088	0.5
4.45	2.06	2.51	.0171	1.1
4.25	1.86	2.27	.0303	1.9
4.05	1.66	2.02	.0519	3.2
3.85	1.46	1.78	.0818	5.1
3.65	1.26	1.54	.1219	7.6
3.45	1.06	1.29	.1736	10.8
3.25	.86	1.05	.2299	14.4
3.05	.66	.80	.2897	18.1
2.85	.46	.56	.3410	21.3
2.65	.26	.32	.3790	23.6
2.45	.06	.07	.3980	24.8
2.25	−.14	−.17	.3932	24.5
2.05	−.34	−.41	.3668	22.9
1.85	−.54	−.66	.3209	20.0
1.65	−.74	−.90	.2661	16.6
1.45	−.94	−1.15	.2059	12.8
1.25	−1.14	−1.39	.1518	9.5
1.05	−1.34	−1.63	.1057	6.6
.85	−1.54	−1.88	.0681	4.2
.65	−1.74	−2.12	.0422	2.6

values N and σ may have. The values tabled are the abscissa, or x/σ, the ordinate erected at x/σ, and some corresponding area value. All these may be in one table, or abscissa and ordinate in one table, abscissa and area in another. The ordinate is less frequently needed than the others, and is sometimes omitted.

Exercise 20

Each question in the following list relates to a normal distribution.

1. What proportion of the area lies between the mean and 1.38σ?
In the Table of Areas and Ordinates in Appendix D locate the number 1.38 in the column headed x/σ. The corresponding number in the Area column, which is .4162, is the number sought. The answer is 41.6%.

2. *In a normal distribution*, what proportion of the cases are more extreme than 2.05σ?
The entry in the Area column corresponding to the number 2.05 in the x/σ column is .4798. If 47.98% of the cases lie between the mean and 2.05σ, then 2.02% exceed the mean by 2.05σ or more. Similarly 2.02% fall short of the mean by the same amount, and 4.04% deviate from the mean by at least 2.05σ in one direction or the other.

3. What proportion of the area lies between -1.27σ and $+.64\sigma$?
From the table we learn that

.3980 of the area lies between the mean and -1.27σ

.2389 of the area lies between the mean and $+.64\sigma$

.6369 or 64% of the area lies between -1.27σ and $+.64\sigma$

4. What proportion of the cases would lie between -2.56σ and -1.19σ?
From the table we learn that

.4948 of the area lies between the mean and -2.56σ

.3830 of the area lies between the mean and -1.19σ

Therefore .1118 or 11% of the area lies between -2.56σ and -1.19σ

5. What range includes the middle 99% of the area under a normal curve?
In this case 49.5% must lie between the mean and $+x/\sigma$ and 49.5% between the mean and $-x/\sigma$. In the table we look among the tabular entries for that entry which most closely approximates 49.5. We find that 49.49% of the area lies between the mean and 2.57σ and that 49.51% lies between the mean and 2.58σ. The point we seek is about halfway between 2.58σ and 2.57σ. (Actually, more extensive tables show it to be 2.5758.) The range which includes the middle 99% of the area extends from -2.575σ to $+2.575\sigma$, approximately.

6. What is the percentile rank of a point $.52\sigma$ below the mean? As 19.8% of the area lies between $-.52\sigma$ and the mean, 50% $-$ 19.8% $=$ 30.2% of the area lies below the point $-.52\sigma$. The percentile rank of this point is 30.

7. What standard score corresponds to the 73rd percentile? As 73% of the area lies below P_{73}, 73% $-$ 50% $=$ 23% lies between the mean (or median) and P_{73}. In the table we find that 22.9% lies between the mean and $.61\sigma$ and 23.2% lies between the mean and $.62\sigma$. Therefore P_{73} corresponds to a standard score between .61 and .62, and somewhat nearer to .61. This is a z-score, in deviation form and standard deviation units. The corresponding Z-score is $50 + 6.1 = 56$.

8. If the mean is 26.2 and the standard deviation is 4.8, what percentage of the cases in a distribution would be expected to have scores larger than 30?

The given score, 30, lies $30 - 26.2 = 3.8$ score units above the mean. This is $\frac{3.8}{4.8} = 0.79$ standard units above the mean. The table indicates that 28.5% of the cases lie less than 0.79 standard units above the mean, and that therefore $50\% - 28.5\% = 21.5\%$, would exceed the mean by $0.79\frac{x}{\sigma}$ or more. Thus 21.5% would have scores at least as large as 30.

9. What is the value of the 82nd percentile in a distribution in which the mean is 61.3 and standard deviation is 3.5?

32% of the area lies between the mean and P_{82}.

According to the table, 31.9% of the area lies between the mean and the point for which $\frac{x}{\sigma} = 0.91$, and 32.1% between the mean and the point for which $\frac{x}{\sigma} = 0.92$. If $\frac{x}{\sigma} = 0.915$, $x = (0.915)(3.5) = 3.2$. If $\frac{x}{\sigma} = 0.91$, $x = 0.91(3.5) = 3.185$

$X = 61.3 + 3.2 = 64.5 = P_{82}$

10. If the mean is 16.7 and standard deviation is 4.1, between what score points would the middle 90% of the cases fall?

45% of the area lies between the mean and the point for which $\frac{x}{\sigma} = 1.645$.

If $\frac{x}{\sigma} = 1.645$, $x = 1.645(4.1) = 6.74$.

$X_1 = 16.7 - 6.7 = 10.0$ The score points between which 90% of
$X_2 = 16.7 + 6.7 = 23.4$ the cases fall are 10.0 and 23.4.

11. What percentile rank corresponds to these values of $\frac{x}{\sigma}$?

a. -2.13 d. $+1.58$
b. $+.22$ e. -2.41
c. $-.67$ f. -3.00

12. What percentage of area lies between these values of x?

a. 1.15σ and 2.15σ c. $\pm.85\sigma$
b. $-.47\sigma$ and $+1.53\sigma$ d. -1.07σ and 1.52σ

13. If the mean is 62.5 and the standard deviation is 3.6, what scores correspond to these percentiles?

a. P_{25} c. P_{10} e. P_{50}
b. P_{75} d. P_{80} f. P_{92}

14. If the mean is 79.2 and standard deviation is 6.5, what proportion of all the cases would have scores at least 10 points from the mean in either direction?

Transforming Categorical Ratings into Numerical Scores. It has already been seen that few traits with which the research worker is concerned have units whose equality can be determined directly. Linear measurements, weight, all statistics obtained by direct enumeration such as daily attendance, number of persons possessing a particular trait, costs, income and the like, and some other traits, yield units which can be directly compared. Other traits such as mental age, measures of capacity, the underlying ability "measured" by a paper and pencil test, etc., have units "equal by definition." In still other situations individuals can be placed in an ordered series but establishing the equality of units even by definition appears dubious.

If it seems reasonable to postulate a normal distribution of an underlying trait, as "teaching skill" in the illustration which follows, and to assume that the ordered categories represent unequal intervals on the scale of that trait, we may utilize the relationship between area and deviation for the normal curve to find numerical equivalents for the categories. Many persons justify the assumption that mental characteristics are normally distributed on the ground that certain physical characteristics are known to be normally distributed and that mental traits are probably inherited in much the same way as physical. It has been pointed out, however, that traits subject to environmental influence or conscious control are less likely to have a normal distribution than traits which cannot be thus controlled, and that the manner of selecting data often affects the shape of the distribution. These two limitations should be borne in mind by anyone making the assumption of normality for a particular set of data.

Suppose, for example, that a supervisor has placed a group of 300 teachers in 6 qualitative categories of descending order of excellence, as shown in Table XLII.

It would be easy enough to raise questions as to the validity of such ratings, but at the moment that is not the point under consideration, and we should not allow ourselves to be distracted by it. The question facing us now is whether we can say that the distribution of ratings is or is not normal.

Certainly we can make neither statement, unless we are willing to assume that A, B, C, D, E, and F represent equally spaced intervals on a scale of merit. Few persons would be inclined to consider the equality of these intervals to be a reasonable assumption. Let us make the assumption that the trait rated by the supervisor for these 300 teachers has a normal distribution, that the supervisor has made his records in large and unequal intervals. The 12 persons rated unsatisfactory are not all equally poor, but the only information we have is that they constitute the lowest 4% of the group. By consulting a table of the normal curve, we learn that the lowest 4% of the frequency lies beyond a point which is 1.75 standard deviations below the mean. Consult tables to verify the values of the division points between each pair of adjacent categories in Figure 30.

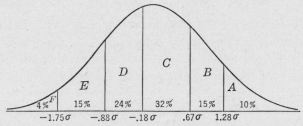

Fig. 30. Normal curve showing division points between the categories. (Data from Table XLII.)

TABLE XLII

Distribution in Ordered but Non-Scaled Categories: Classification of 300 Teachers in Order of Excellence

Key	Interpretation of Key	Teachers in Given Category		Teachers in Lower Category $+ \frac{1}{2}$ Those in Given Categories	
		N	$\%$	N	$\%$
1	*2*	*3*	*4*	*5*	*6*
A	Excellent in every way	30	10%	285	95%
B	Superior in most traits	45	15	247.5	82.5
C	Very good, above average	96	32	177	59
D	Fair	72	24	93	31
E	Poor, but not subject to dismissal	45	15	34.5	11.5
F	Unsatisfactory, subject to dismissal	12	4	6	2

Obviously, however, it is not these division points which are needed to represent the typical positions of the various subgroups, but some average measure. The 45 teachers marked "superior" may be considered to be distributed along a range from 0.67σ to 1.28σ, more of them being near the lower end of this range than near the upper end. The problem now is to find some satisfactory average value which can represent each subgroup. Several possibilities will be discussed.

1. The Middle of the Range. This would be only moderately satisfactory for categories in the middle of the distribution, and quite meaningless for the two categories at the ends. If we should use $\dfrac{.67 + 1.28}{2}\sigma = .975\sigma$ as the central position of the superior group, it is clear that this would overestimate the standing of more than half of the group. This method would always give an estimate too far from the mean of the total no matter whether the category was above or below that mean. The middle of the range cannot be found for the two most extreme categories.

2. The Median of the Subclass. This is easy to find and easy to interpret. An ordinate which bisects the area in any one of the categories must be located at the median of that category. The figures in column 5 of Table XLII show the number of teachers, and the figures in column 6 show the percentage of teachers below the median of each category. Note that the latter are the *percentile ranks* of the medians of the categories, computed exactly as percentile ranks were computed in Chapter V. These percentile ranks are now transmuted into x/σ values on the assumption that the trait is normally distributed.

What is the point below which 95% of the area under the normal curve lies? It is a point such that $95\% - 50\% = 45\%$ of the area lies between it and the mean. Reference to the Table of Areas and Ordinates in Appendix D shows this to be the point for which $x/\sigma = 1.645$, and accordingly that is the amount by which the median of the 30 teachers rated A departs from the mean of the entire group.

In Figure 31 the medians of the categories have been indicated. Examine this figure to assure yourself that ordinates drawn at these median values bisect the areas in their respective categories. These category areas are bounded by ordinates as in Figure 30. Verify the numerical values of the medians.

Multiplying these median values by 10 and adding 50 produces what W. A. McCall has named *T-scores.**

3. The Mean of the Subclass. The size of a subclass mean will not be very different from that of the median, but it is found by an algebraic method and theoretical statisticians always prefer algebraic methods. This solution and the mathematical justification for it will be found in Appendix B.

Combining Letter Grades. The transformation described in the preceding section is very useful when it is necessary to average letter

* He gave them this name in honor of Thorndike and Terman, pioneers in the measurement movement. Each "T" unit is one-tenth of a standard deviation, the mean of a set of T-scores being 50 and standard deviation 10.

grades given to the same student by teachers who have assigned very
different proportions of grades in each category.

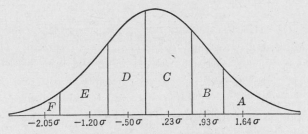

Fig. 31. Normal curve showing median values of categories. (Data from
Table XLII.)

Let us suppose that letter grades have been assigned as follows by
three teachers to their classes in three different subjects:

Mark	Latin Teacher	History Teacher	Mathematics Teacher
A	12	8	9
B	26	26	30
C	22	35	51
D	16	25	33
E	4	5	21
F		1	6
	80	100	150

Either the three groups differ in achievement or the same mark has a
different meaning when used by the various teachers.

To assign a constant weight to each letter grade, for example $A = 5$,
$B = 4$, $C = 3$, $D = 2$, $E = 1$, $F = 0$, and to use these equivalents in
obtaining averages is to assume implicitly that the classes have unequal
achievement. The use of these weights would give a mean of 3.325 to the
Latin class, 3.04 to history, and 2.7 to mathematics. Perhaps this truly
represents the situation. Perhaps, on the other hand, the teachers have
different standards of marking and an A given by the mathematics teacher
represents a higher level of achievement than an A given by the Latin
teacher. If it seems wise to postulate equality of work and ability from
class to class, we may transform the letter marks into numerical scores
separately for each teacher by one of the methods just described.

Exercise 21

1. Verify the following sets of equivalent scores computed from the data in the preceding section:

Mark	T-Score Equivalent to Median of Category		
	Latin	History	Mathematics
A	64	68	69
B	55	58	60
C	47	50	52
D	40	41	44
E	30	32	38
F		24	29

2. What average score should be accorded to each of these students from the classes yielding the data of the preceding question?

Student	Latin Mark	History Mark	Mathematics Mark
V	C = 47	B = 58	A = 69
W	A = 64	B = 58	B = 60
X	B = 55	A = 68	C = 52
Y	D = 40	A = 68	C = 52
Z	A = 64	C = 50	B = 60

$\bar{X} = \dfrac{\Sigma X}{N}$

Shape of Distribution Dependent Upon Choice of Items and of Units. When we are dealing with a single unitary trait such as height or weight or money income or number of children per family or age at which death occurs or the like, the shape of a frequency distribution is not difficult to discover. However, most of the measurements with which a research worker is concerned are composite scores representing measurement by definition, and the choice of the items which make up those composite scores determines the apparent shape of the distribution. Shape of distribution in such situations is an artifact. Not only *can* the research worker manipulate it, but he cannot escape from manipulating it.

For example, suppose a research worker is trying to make an instrument for "measuring" socio-economic status, and he decides to use such questions as "Do you have a telephone?" "Do you have an automobile?" The significance of each question may be different in different regions and at different periods of time, but that matter is outside the scope of the present discussion. Suppose this research worker has a number of items some of which are answered affirmatively by very few of his respondents, some by about 50%, and some by nearly all. He is forced to decide which of these items shall go into his instrument. If he uses chiefly items each of which is answered affirmatively by about 50% of the group, his distribution of composite scores is likely to look something like normal. If he uses only the items which have a very large affirmative response (or only those with very small response), the distribution will probably be skewed and may have a large number of scores clustering at one end. If he makes up an instrument in which about half of the items have a very large and half a very small affirmative response, the distribution may be bimodal.

The choice of unit in which a distribution is scaled is also often necessarily arbitrary. The research worker must face the question as to whether units which he assumes to be equal are really equal all along his scale. An inch is an inch, but does it require the same increment of skill for an amateur pole vaulter to raise his record by one inch as for the world's champion to raise his by one inch? A dollar is a dollar, but does a salary increase of $100 a year mean the same to a man earning $1000 and to a man earning $10,000? A year is a year, but does one additional year's schooling mean the same thing in terms of professional training and competence when it is taken by a student in the 10th grade and by one who has already had 2 years of graduate work in a university? A year is a year, but does the passage of one year produce comparable changes in the physical characteristics of a five-year-old child and of an adult?

When the research worker is dealing with some composites such as test scores, he can often feel even less confidence about the equality of his units. In terms of raw scores on some test he has constructed, there is little reason to be sure that the difference between scores of, say, 11 and 12 represents the same difference in skill, or ability, or information, as the difference between scores of, say, 51 and 52.

If a research worker knows that his units are uniform in all parts of his scale, he can draw conclusions about the shape of a distribution. If he knows, or will make assumptions about, the shape of the distribution, he can arrive at a definition of his units. If he knows neither one and will make no assumptions about either, he is at an impasse. Usually the less dangerous procedure seems to be to base the scaling of the trait upon an assumption as to shape of distribution it is desired to achieve.

Transforming Scores to Achieve Symmetry of Distribution.* The apparent nature of the distribution of a trait often depends largely upon

---

* Several statistics recently devised by the mathematical statisticians and studied in more advanced courses can be justified partly on the ground that they have a symmetrical, or perhaps even a normal, sampling distribution. The statistic $z = \frac{1}{2}\log_e\left(\frac{1-r}{1+r}\right)$ is an illustration. Suppose that in a large population there is a high correlation between two traits, and suppose that 1000 samples of 50 cases each are drawn from that population, and for each the choice of the unit in which measurement is made. Lack of wisdom in the selection of such units may interfere seriously with interpretation of the data.

As an example, let us consider the problem of handedness. No one knows exactly what the distribution of native handedness is in the population, or to what extent the shape of the curve of distribution of relative efficiency of the right and the left hand changes with age. Suppose an investigator has constructed a scale on which to measure the product produced by each hand separately, the scores for the two hands being designated as R and L. If now he takes R/L as a measure of handedness, the ambidextrous person will have a score of 1, the completely left-handed person a score of $0/L = 0$, and the completely right-handed a score of $R/0$ which is large without bound. The entire range for the left-handed is compressed into the interval from 0 to 1, while the range for the right-handed stretches out indefinitely from 1 toward infinity. Under such a scheme, it is futile to discuss the shape of the distribution of handedness. A similar distortion, but in the opposite direction, would result from using L/R as a measure of handedness. Such distortion affects not only the shape of the distribution itself, but the correlation between handedness and any other trait. The measure should be so defined that two scores equally distant from the mean indicate equally strong preferences for the right and left hands. If $\dfrac{R - L}{R + L}$ is used as a measure, this desirable condition will be met without sacrificing anything else.

Rectangular Distribution Produced by Transforming Scores to Ranks. At the close of Chapter V one use of ranks was briefly presented. Many such situations arise in which a small number of individuals, whom it would be impossible or at least very difficult to score on some trait, can be satisfactorily placed in order with respect to the amount of that trait they are considered to possess. Sometimes it is also useful to assign rank order to individuals who have already been given numerical scores, as, for example, when a relationship is to be found between a ranked trait and a scored trait. The topic of rank order correlation will be taken up again in Chapter XIII. At present, our chief interest in the matter of ranks is in the shape of the distribution of a set of ranks.

Suppose a group of 20 tennis players has gone through a series of

---

sample a correlation coefficient, r, is obtained. From these 1000 values of r a frequency distribution can be formed, which will be a skewed distribution. If, instead of r, we compute $z = \frac{1}{2} \log_e \left(\dfrac{1 - r}{1 + r} \right)$, the distribution of z will be symmetrical. It will even be nearly normal. The subject of sampling distribution will be discussed in Chapter XV.

matches on the basis of which it is possible to place them in an order of merit, no two being tied for the same place. Let these 20 ranks be represented by intervals on a horizontal scale. Then each rank has a frequency of one, and therefore the frequency distribution of the ranks is a rectangle, as in the adjacent sketch. The underlying skill of the players is, however, not likely to be of this form at all. More likely there are a number with

very nearly the same skill, so that a distribution of some other measure of skill would show a concentration of scores on some part of the scale, with low frequencies at one or both ends.

Normalizing a Set of Numerical Scores. Suppose that a man who is standardizing a new test has administered it to a group of unselected twelve-year-olds in the public schools. Examination of the resulting distribution of raw scores shows it to be considerably skewed, with a long tail at the left and the mode very near to the highest score. Does this mean that the trait measured by the test is not normally distributed for twelve-year-olds? That question cannot be answered from these data, for any one of several possible causes might have produced the asymmetry. Among such possible causes are the following:

1. The group was not really a random sample of twelve-year-olds but a selection had actually taken place of such a nature that the brightest children were missing.

2. The trait is really not normally distributed among unselected twelve-year-olds.

3. The test was too easy for the brightest pupils, causing their scores to pile up around the maximum score.

4. The questions were not properly scaled, and an increment of one point at one part of the scale is not equal to an increment of one at another part.

Since any one of these causes—and perhaps others—acting alone could produce a skewed distribution, it is not possible to tell which of the causes, either alone or in combination, may be at work. The causes are all sufficient but none of them can be proved necessary. Therefore the testmaker decides that he will assume that the true distribution of the trait in question would be normal if he had a satisfactory measure of it, and that he will readjust his scores to make them conform to the normal distribution.

If scores are transformed to standard scores by the formula $Z = 10\dfrac{(X - \overline{X})}{s} + 50$ they are *not* normalized. This transformation

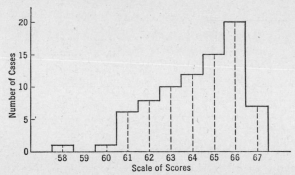

Fig. 32. Distribution of 80 scores from Table XLIII.

affects the scale of the distribution and its central position, but not its shape. The problem now under consideration is how to change the shape

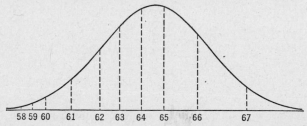

Fig. 33. Distribution of Fig. 32 normalized by T-score transformation.

of the distribution by stretching the scale of scores at some points and squeezing it at others.

Transforming Numerical Scores into T-Scores. Consider the 80 scores in Table XLIII, and their histogram in Figure 32 based on the assumption that the scores 60, 61, 62, · · · 67 are equally spaced along a scale of scores. When these are transformed into T-scores by the method described earlier in this chapter, the distribution is transformed into that of Figure 33. In this transformation the total area and the area in each subclass remain invariant, but the scale of measurement is altered by being stretched at certain places. The mean and standard deviation are likely to be altered, but all the percentile values are invariant. The procedure for this transformation is described verbally in the accompanying schedule, and is carried out in columns 3 to 7 of Table XLIII.

TABLE XLIII

Conversion of Raw Scores to T-Scores and Comparison of These T-Scores with Standard Scores $\left(\overline{X} = 64.3, s = 1.9, Z = \dfrac{10x}{s} + 50\right)$

Raw Score	f	Cases below Given Score $+ \frac{1}{2}$ Those at That Score		$\% - 50\%$	Value of x/σ in a Normal Curve Corresponding to Given $\%$	*T*-Score	*Z*-Score
		N	$\%$				
1	2	3	4	5	6	7	8
67	7	76.5	95.6	45.6	1.71	67	64
66	20	63	78.8	28.8	.80	58	59
65	15	45.5	56.9	6.9	.17	52	54
64	12	32	40.0	−10.0	−.25	48	48
63	10	21	26.2	−23.8	−.64	44	43
62	8	12	15.0	−35	−1.04	40	38
61	6	5	6.2	−43.8	−1.54	35	33
60	1	1.5	1.9	−48.1	−2.07	29	27
59		1.0	1.2	−48.8	−2.26	27	22
58	1	0.5	0.6	−49.4	−2.51	25	17
	80						

The cumulative frequency here is slightly different from the method used in Tables X of Chapter III and XII of Chapter V. There the entries in the cumulative frequency distribution were made to correspond to the *division points between intervals*. Here we are taking cumulative frequencies at the *midpoints of intervals*, and we treat each interval as though one-half the frequency in the interval were above and one-half below that midpoint. The two methods produce the same cumulative frequency curve, but do not produce the same set of points on that curve. When the cumulative curve is actually drawn, one method is as satisfactory as the other, because if the percentile ranks for the tops of the intervals are computed, the percentile ranks for the midpoints can be read from the graph, and vice versa. The method of Table X requires slightly less computation than that of Table XLIII, and therefore is usually preferred when the graph is to be drawn. However, for computing *T*-scores, the graph need not be drawn. Inasmuch as the observed scores we want to transform to *T*-scores are located at the midpoints of intervals, we must take cumulative frequencies at the midpoints rather than at the tops of the intervals.

In column 8, the original scores have been transformed to standard scores by the formula $Z = \dfrac{10x}{s} + 50$. These standard score values are placed here for comparison with the T-scores. The more nearly normal the original distribution is when raw scores are assumed to be equally spaced, the more closely will the T- and Z-scores correspond. The alteration of scale involved in the T-score transformation and the uniform stretching (or squeezing) of the scale involved in the Z-score transformation are illustrated in Figure 34, where the original scores in the first column of Table XLIII are shown moving over into the positions indicated by the corresponding values in columns 7 and 8. Had the Z-scores in column 8 been carried out to more decimal places, the differences between successive scores would have been constant. The inequality of increments observed here is entirely due to rounding errors.

These data, with one or two very low scores, are typical of scores often obtained from class tests in academic subjects. The Z-score method

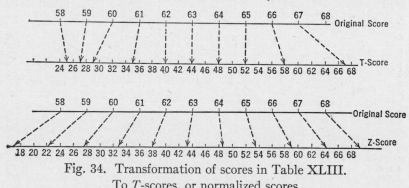

Fig. 34. Transformation of scores in Table XLIII.
To T-scores, or normalized scores.
To standard scores, or Z-scores.

here has produced one very low score, and no comparably high scores. This seems undesirable and suggests that normalizing the scores by the T-score method before entering them as a class record might be a much wiser practice.

Various tables are available, though not presented in this text, which permit the T-score to be read at once from the cumulative percentage.

Procedure for Computing T-Scores

1. Set up a frequency distribution in the usual fashion (columns 1 and 2 in Table XLIII).

2. Make a cumulative frequency distribution, adding all the cases below a

given score and half of those at the score (column 3). Note that cumulation is to midpoint of interval.

3. Divide each cumulative frequency by N to produce a cumulative percentage (column 4).

4. Subtract 50% from each cumulative percentage. The result is the percentage of cases between ordinates at the given score and at the median (column 5).

5. Turn to a table of areas and abscissas of the normal curve and read from it the abscissa value of a point such that the given percentage of area lies between an ordinate at that point and an ordinate at the mean (column 6).

6. Multiply each abscissa value by 10 and add 50 to obtain the T-score (column 7).

The Normal Percentile Chart. A special kind of graph paper called probability paper is so constructed that when the cumulative percent-

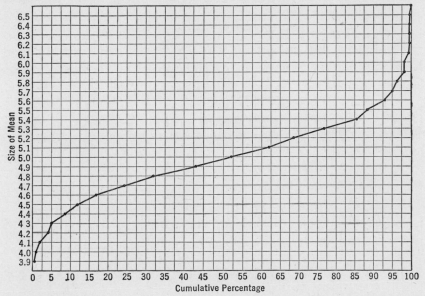

Fig. 35. Cumulative percentage chart of an approximately normal distribution plotted on ordinary grid: distribution of means of 260 samples of 26 throws of 10 pennies each. (From data of Table XLIV.)

age distribution of a normal distribution is plotted on it, the result is a straight line. The distribution of means of random samples shown in Table XXXIX and Figure 26 is approximately normal. Figure 35 shows the cumulative percentage distribution for these data. (The cumulative distributions drawn in Chapter V have scores on the horizontal axis and frequency or percentage on the vertical. Here the scales have been reversed to correspond with the scales on the probability paper.)

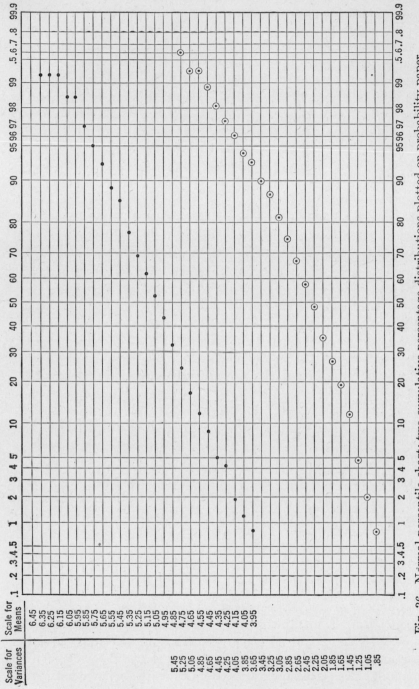

Fig. 36. Normal percentile chart: two cumulative percentage distributions plotted on probability paper.

• • • • • Set of 260 means of random samples with approximately normal distribution.

⊙ ⊙ ⊙ ⊙ Set of 256 variances of random samples with asymmetric distribution.

194

Imagine that the grid of Figure 35 is elastic and that you stretch it horizontally in such a way that the ogive is drawn out into a straight line. To do this would require distorting the horizontal scale, making its intervals increasingly larger as they are farther from the mean. The percentage scale is placed on the horizontal axis; the scale of scores for any given set of data may be placed on the vertical. Figure 36 shows the outcome of plotting, on such probability paper, the distribution of 260 means of random samples and the distribution of 256 variances. Look again at Figure 26, which shows a normal distribution superimposed on the distribution of these means, Figure 35, which shows their cumulative percentage distribution, and Figure 36 (upper curve), which shows that latter distribution looking like a straight line when placed on probability paper. Now look again at Figure 29, which shows a normal distribution superimposed on the distribution of variances and not fitting it quite as well as the other normal distribution fits the means, and at Figure 36 (lower curve) which shows the cumulative percentage distribution of variances not making a very straight line when drawn on probability paper. If on the basis of these figures a student should be tempted to generalize, saying that the means of a large number of random samples all of the same size out of the same population have a normal distribution while the variances of those samples do not have a normal distribution, he would be arriving empirically at an important idea which can be proved by mathematical reasoning.

Procedure for Plotting a Frequency Distribution on a Normal Percentile Chart

1. Set up a frequency distribution in the usual fashion (see columns headed "f" in Table XLIV).

2. Obtain the cumulative frequency distribution by the method described on page 43. Cumulation is to *top* of the respective interval (see columns headed "cum. *f*").

3. Divide each cumulative frequency by N to obtain a cumulative percentage (see columns headed "cum. %").

4. Lay off the scale of the distribution on the vertical axis of a sheet of probability paper, as in Figure 36. Let the division points between intervals be placed opposite the horizontal rulings on the graph paper.

5. Plot one point corresponding to the upper limit of each interval. The point will lie on the horizontal line corresponding to that upper limit and on the vertical line corresponding to the cumulative percentage; that is, the percentage of cases falling below that upper limit.

6. If the plotted points appear to lie along a straight line, that line may be drawn. If it does not seem appropriate to draw a straight line, draw a smooth curve.

TABLE XLIV

Cumulative Percentage Distributions for the Data of Tables XXXIX and XL: Mean and Variance of Number of Heads Appearing on Successive Samples of Sixteen Throws of Ten Pennies Each

Mean Number of Heads				Variance of Number of Heads			
Upper limit of interval	f	cum. f	cum. %	Upper limit of interval	f	cum. f	cum. %
6.45	2	260	100%	5.45	1	256	100%
6.35	—	258	99.2	5.25	1	255	99.6
6.25	—	258	99.2	5.05	1	254	99.2
6.15	2	258	99.2	4.85	—	253	98.8
6.05	—	256	98.5	4.65	2	253	98.8
5.95	4	256	98.5	4.45	2	251	98.0
5.85	5	252	96.9	4.25	3	249	97.3
5.75	6	247	95.0	4.05	5	246	96.1
5.65	11	241	92.7	3.85	3	241	94.1
5.55	7	230	88.5	3.65	8	238	93.0
5.45	23	223	85.8	3.45	7	230	89.8
5.35	21	200	76.9	3.25	15	223	87.1
5.25	18	179	68.8	3.05	16	208	81.3
5.15	25	161	61.9	2.85	21	192	75.0
5.05	24	136	52.3	2.65	23	171	66.8
4.95	28	112	43.1	2.45	25	148	57.8
4.85	21	84	32.3	2.25	33	123	48.0
4.75	19	63	24.2	2.05	22	90	35.2
4.65	13	44	16.9	1.85	19	68	26.6
4.55	9	31	11.9	1.65	19	49	19.1
4 45	9	22	8.5	1.45	18	30	11.7
4.35	2	13	5.0	1.25	7	12	4.7
4 25	6	11	4.2	1.05	3	5	2.0
4.15	2	5	1.9	.85	2	2	0.8
4.05	1	3	1.2				
3.95	2	2	0.8				

Probability paper, convenient for use in work of the type described on page 195, can be obtained commercially. The Codex Book Co. publishes two forms. In one the vertical scale is ruled in equal intervals, as in Figure 36; in the other it is ruled logarithmically. A very convenient form is the Normal Percentile Chart designed by Arthur S. Otis and published by the World Book Co.

Transforming Ranks to Scores on the Assumption of Normality in the Under-lying Trait. When only rank order is given, the true shape of distribution of the trait is unknown.

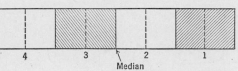

Consider a set of 4 individuals placed in rank order. The median lies halfway between the second and third case, and $\frac{1}{2}$ of $\frac{1}{4}$, or $\frac{1}{8}$, of the total area under the rectangular distribution lies between the point marked 2 and the median. Between the point 1 and the median lies $\frac{1}{4} + \frac{1}{2} \times \frac{1}{4} = \frac{3}{8}$ of the area. If these area relation-

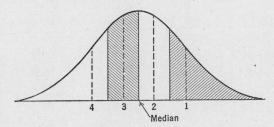

ships are preserved and the points assumed to lie on the horizontal scale of a normal curve, they will occupy such positions as will be defined by the values of $\frac{x}{\sigma}$ for which $\frac{3}{8}$ and $\frac{1}{8}$ of the areas respectively are contained between ordinates at those points and the ordinate at the median.*

Rank	Proportion of Cases between Given Case and Median	$\frac{x}{\sigma}$ Value Read from Normal Probability Table	$T = \frac{10x}{\sigma} + 50$
1	$\frac{3}{8} = 0.375$	1.15	62
2	$\frac{1}{8} = 0.125$	0.32	53
3	$\frac{1}{8} = 0.125$	−0.32	47
4	$\frac{3}{8} = 0.375$	−1.15	38

As the number of cases to be ranked changes, the $\frac{x}{\sigma}$ values corresponding to the rank changes. Note the following computation for a set of 9 ranks.

---

* This very easy method of converting ranks to standardized scores is appropriate for most problems. The method used by Hull, Symonds, and others, employs the mean of the category rather than the median, and so produces slightly different results. The method employed by Fisher and Yates in computing Table XX "Scores for Ordinal (or Ranked) Data" in their *Statistical Tables for Biological, Agricultural and Medical Research* (Oliver & Boyd, 1938) is more highly mathematical and gives results only approximately equal to those obtained by the method described here.

Rank	Proportion of Cases between Given Case and Median	$\frac{x}{\sigma}$ Value Read from Normal Probability Table	$T = \frac{10}{\sigma} x + 50$
1	$\frac{4}{9} = 0.444$	1.59	66
2	$\frac{3}{9} = 0.333$	0.97	60
3	$\frac{2}{9} = 0.222$	0.59	56
4	$\frac{1}{9} = 0.111$	0.28	53
5	0	0	50
6	$\frac{1}{9} = 0.111$	−0.28	47
7	$\frac{2}{9} = 0.222$	−0.59	44
8	$\frac{3}{9} = 0.333$	−0.97	40
9	$\frac{4}{9} = 0.444$	−1.59	34

Exercise 22

1. Draw up a form like the one shown below, in which the number of individuals to be ranked is shown along the horizontal axis and the rank of an individual in his group along the vertical. For each value of N, compute the T-score corresponding to a given rank, and insert the values in the table.

Rank	T-Score Assigned to Rank when N is											
	2	3	4	5	6	7	8	9	10	11	12	13
1	57	60	62	63				66				
2	43	50	53	55				60				
3		40	47	50				56				
4			38	45				53				
5				37				50				
6								47				
7								44				
8								40				
9								34				
10												
11												
12												
13												

BIBLIOGRAPHY ON TABLES OF THE NORMAL CURVE

(This list does not include any tables published in textbooks, or short tables published elsewhere.)

Holzinger, Karl J., *Statistical Tables for Students in Education and Psychology*, Chicago, University of Chicago Press, 1925, 1928, and 1931.

Table XI. Areas and ordinates of the normal probability curve in terms of deviates from the mean. The argument is x/σ from 0 to 3.99 at intervals of

0.1. The tabular entries are area from mean to x/σ, to 4 decimal places, and ordinate to 4 places.

Table XII. Deviates and ordinates of the normal probability curve in terms of area from the mean. The argument is the area between the mean and x/σ extending from 0 to .499, at intervals of .001. The tabular entries are x/σ and the ordinate, each to 4 decimal places.

Table XIV. P.E. deviates of the normal curve in terms of area from the mean. The argument is the area between the mean and $x/$P.E., extending from 0 to .499 at intervals of .001. The tabular entries are the values of the probable error to 4 decimal places.

Kelley, Truman L., *The Kelley Statistical Tables*, New York, The Macmillan Co., 1938.

Table I. Eight-place normal distribution, simple correlation, and probability functions. The table covers 101 pages. The argument is the proportion of area below the given point, and ranges from .5000 to .9999 at intervals of .0001, with a few selected values beyond .9999. The tabular entries are x/σ, the ordinate, and three other values whose importance would not be clear at this time, each carried to 8 decimal places.

Conrad, Herbert S., and Krause, Ruth H., "A seven-decimal table of the area (α) under the unit normal curve, for abscissae expressed in terms of P.E.," *Psychometrika*, II (March, 1937), 55–66.

Table 1. The argument is the abscissa $\frac{x}{\text{P.E.}}$ from .00 to 7.00 at intervals of .01, and the tabular entries are area between $\frac{+x}{\text{P.E.}}$ and $\frac{-x}{\text{P.E.}}$, to seven decimal places.

Conrad, Herbert S., and Krause, Ruth H., "An extension of the Kelley-Wood and Kondo-Elderton tables of abscissae of the unit normal curve for areas ($\frac{1}{2}\alpha$) between .4500 and .49999 99999," *Journal of Experimental Education*, V (March, 1937), 278–285.

Table I gives values, to six decimal places, of $\frac{x}{\sigma}$ corresponding to areas between the mean and the $\frac{x}{\sigma}$. The argument extends from .4500 to .4999 in intervals of .0001, and then by progressively smaller intervals to .49999 99999. The entries beyond $\frac{1}{2}\alpha = .49999$ are given to fewer decimal places, but these are seldom called for in ordinary statistical work.

Conrad, Herbert S., and Krause, Ruth H., "New and extended tables of the unit normal curve: I. Areas ($\frac{1}{2}\alpha$) corresponding to abscissae from .00 to 10.0 P.E.; II. Abscissae $\frac{x}{\text{P.E.}}$ corresponding to areas ($\frac{1}{2}\alpha$) from .000 to .49999 99999 9," *Journal of Psychology*, V (1938), 397–424.

Table 1 gives, for each value of $\frac{x}{\text{P.E.}}$ from .00 to 9.00 in intervals of .01, and from 9.0 to 10.0 in intervals of .1, the corresponding area ($\frac{1}{2}\alpha$), between the mean and the given $\frac{x}{\text{P.E.}}$, to eight or more decimal places.

Table 4 gives the value of $\frac{x}{\text{P.E.}}$ corresponding to each value of the area ($\frac{1}{2}\alpha$) from .000 to .449 in intervals of .001, and from .4500 to .49999 99999 9 in progressively smaller intervals.

Pearson, Karl, *Tables for Statisticians and Biometricians*, Part I, The Biometric Laboratory, University College, London, 1914, 1924.

Table I. Table of deviates of the normal curve for each permille of frequency. Argument is the permille. Tabular entries are values of $\frac{x}{\sigma}$ to four decimal places.

Table II. Area and ordinate in terms of abscissa. Argument is $\frac{x}{\sigma}$. Tabular entries are the area $\frac{1}{2}(1 + \alpha)$ up to the given $\frac{x}{\sigma}$, and the corresponding ordinate z.

Table III. Abscissa and ordinate in terms of difference of areas. The argument is the area (α), from .00 to .80 between two ordinates at $\frac{+x}{\sigma}$ and $\frac{-x}{\sigma}$. The x column gives the abscissa, and the z column the ordinate, corresponding to each value of the area.

Table IV. Extension of table of the probability integral $F = \frac{1}{2}(1 - \alpha)$. Argument is $\frac{x}{\sigma}$ from 5 to 500. The entries are $(-\log F)$ for each value of $\frac{x}{\sigma}$.

$F = \frac{1}{2}(1 - \alpha)$ is the area at one end of the curve beyond the ordinate at $\frac{x}{\sigma}$.

(Tables I to III were calculated by W. F. Sheppard, and originally published in *Biometrika* II, 174–190; V, 405. Table IV was calculated by Julia Bell, and published in *Draper's Research Memoirs*, Biometric Series, VIII, 27.)

Sheppard, William S. *The Probability Integral*, Cambridge, England. The University Press, 1939. This volume of 6 tables which Sheppard had computed was published after his death by the British Association as a tribute to him. The functions tabled are more involved than those which have been explained thus far in this text.

CHAPTER XII

REGRESSION AND CORRELATION—GENERAL CONCEPTS

It is full of interest of its own. It familiarises us with the measurement of variability, and with curious laws of chance that apply to a vast diversity of social subjects. This part of the inquiry may be said to run along a road on a high level, that affords wide views in unexpected directions, and from which easy descents may be made to totally different goals to those we have now to reach. I have a great subject to write upon, but feel keenly my literary incapacity to make it easily intelligible without sacrificing accuracy and thoroughness.

Sir Francis Galton

Thus wrote Francis Galton in 1889 when the significance of correlation and its measurement had impressed themselves upon him. Up to 1889 men of science had thought only in terms of causation; in the future they were to admit another working category, that of correlation, and thus open to quantitative analysis wide fields of medical, psychological, and sociological research. . . . Henceforward the philosophical view of this universe was to be that of a correlated system of variates, approaching but by no means reaching perfect correlation, i.e., absolute causality, even in the group of phenomena termed physical. Biological phenomena in their numerical phases, economic and social, were seen to be only differentiated from the physical by the intensity of their correlations. The idea Galton placed before himself was to represent by a single numerical quantity the degree of relationship, or of partial causality, between the different variables of one ever-changing universe.

Karl Pearson

Relationship. Most of the control man has achieved over his environment has come about because he has observed the relatedness of certain sets of phenomena. The woodsman observes the fur of wild animals and various aspects of their behavior, and makes a prediction concerning the severity of the coming winter. The clues which come to those who live in the open from watching all the minute signs of nature are meaningful only because accumulated experience has made note of the frequency with which the two phenomena occur together, and the rarity with which they occur separately. From the days of Aesculapius, physicians have been trying to determine the nature and probable course of a disease through the observation of related phenomena, or symptoms.

When the relationship is high, prognosis is efficient. How did savage tribes learn to chew certain leaves and barks to cure certain ailments? Did they become gradually aware that there was a strong tendency for the two situations "man ate leaf" and "man died with fever" not to occur together? Many superstitions are nothing but unfounded beliefs that certain events are related. The ignorant man would not dread a black cat if he did not cherish an implicit belief that the occurrence of misfortune and the crossing of one's path by a black cat were more likely to occur together than separately.

Between two measured variates, the relationship may range all the way from no relationship at all to a relationship so close that one speaks of it in terms of cause and effect.

When every change in one variable necessarily produces a corresponding change in the second variable, the second is called a *mathematical function* of the first. The relationship between them is perfect. When the value of the first variable is known, that of the second is inescapably determined. Thus 'the circumference of a circle is completely determined by its diameter. The speed of a body falling freely in a vacuum depends upon the length of time it has been falling; is a function of time. These two are perfect positive relationships, because the two variables increase together, decrease together. The relationship between the volume of a gas and the pressure upon it is a perfect negative relationship if temperature is held constant. This relationship is negative because volume decreases as pressure increases, and vice versa.

One of the striking differences between pure mathematics and statistics now appears. A mathematical law such as $c = 2\pi r$ or $d = \frac{1}{2} gt^2$ holds universally and inescapably. There are no exceptions. A statistical law, on the other hand, is a statement of trend. It is true in general, for the group at large, but not for every individual in the group. For example, Elderton [*] found the equation $W = 1.6H - 25.7$ to express, for six-year-old boys coming from a favorable environment in Scotland, the relationship between height expressed in inches (H) and weight expressed in pounds (W). But some boys are heavier in proportion to their height than others. Suppose one of these boys is known to be 44 inches tall. This equation implies that the *mean weight* of all such boys 44 inches tall is $1.6(44) - 25.7 = 44.7$ pounds, but it does not guarantee that any particular selected boy will weigh exactly 44.7 pounds. In fact, Elderton's data show a standard deviation of 2.8 for the weight in pounds of these boys even when all were the same height.

* Elderton, Ethel M., "Height and weight of school children in Glasgow," *Biometrika*, X (1915), 288–339.

It is common knowledge that height and weight of children are related positively, the taller children at any given age being in general the heavier and vice versa. It is also common knowledge that the relationship is something less than perfect and that of two given children, A and B, it may happen that A is taller while B is heavier. Large numbers of actual measurements exhibit a strong tendency for height and weight to increase together, with some individual variation away from the general trend.

Plan of Presentation. This material is written with the conviction that the subject of correlation will be better comprehended if the acquisition of computational routines is postponed until certain basic ideas have been grasped. Here, more than in any of the topics previously studied, it is a temptation to become so engrossed in the procedures of computation that the meaning of these fundamental ideas is not apprehended. A clerk with no insight into the meaning of correlation can learn to compute a coefficient of correlation quickly and accurately by any one of several efficient routines. On the other hand, the student who hopes to carry out research or to read the reports of research conducted by others will profit by a somewhat leisurely preliminary exploration of the general ideas implied in such terms as regression, residual, correlation, etc. It is the purpose of this chapter to help the student build such concepts and open his mind to questions of implication and interpretation. Chapter XIII will present formulas and computational routines. Chapter XIV will extend the interpretations of correlational studies.

Galton's Discovery of Correlation. Again and again, students of science or mathematics note the extreme clarity of exposition in the writings of the man who discovered some particular idea. With a multitude of more modern presentations available, the best introduction to some topic is often provided by the paper in which it was first discussed. In the matter of correlation, it is doubtful whether any clearer exposition of the elementary concepts has ever been written than the early papers of Sir Francis Galton.* This is due in part to the rare charm of Galton's language which makes everything he wrote a delight to read, and in part to the naturalness of the steps by which his thinking developed. Unfortunately, the original articles are not widely accessible, and many students must forego the piquancy of Galton's language.

---

* "Regression towards mediocrity in hereditary stature," *Journal of the Anthropological Institute*, XV (1885–86), 246–263. "Family likeness in stature," *Proceedings of the Royal Society*, XL (1886), 42–63. "Co-relations and their measurement, chiefly from anthropometric data," *Proceedings of the Royal Society*, XLV (1888), 135–145. *Natural Inheritance*, 1889. See also Galton's *Memories of My Life*, 1908, and Karl Pearson's "Notes on the history of correlation," *Biometrika*, XIII (1920), 25–45.

Galton was profoundly impressed by *Origin of Species*, which his cousin Charles Darwin published in 1859. As he read he pondered why, if each generation of human beings resembles its parents, the human race does not become more and more variable in stature as one generation succeeds another. Suppose that two very tall persons marry and raise a family whose average height is equal to that of the parents, and suppose further that the tallest members of this second generation have children whose average height is the same as the average height of their parents, and so on and on. Soon a race of giants would begin to develop. By a similar process, dwarfs would begin to appear at the other end of the scale. What is it, asked Galton, that hinders this process and *drags the human race back toward mediocrity?* To answer this question he began to collect data. He raised sweet peas and persuaded many of his friends to do the same, he experimented with pedigreed moths, he studied hounds, and finally offered prizes for records of stature in human families.*

After "transmuting" all female statures to male by multiplying them by 1.08, Galton obtained the average height of two parents which he called "height of mid-parent." Then he drew up a table of stature in which height of "mid-parent" was distributed on the vertical axis and height of adult son or "transmuted" adult daughter on the horizontal axis. The result was a bivariate frequency distribution of the general type illustrated in Table XI, on page 48. The entries in any one horizontal row represented the distribution of height for adult offspring of a group of "mid-parents" of uniform height, and these offspring Galton called a "co-fraternity." Galton marked on each row the position of the median height, and found, somewhat to his surprise, that the points thus indicated were very nearly on a straight line. Thus there appeared to be a regular linear increase in the height of offspring as the height of "mid-parent" is increased from row to row. In similar fashion, he marked the median height of each column and found that these points also were very nearly on a straight line—but not the same straight line as that suggested by the medians of the rows. (Galton customarily worked with medians in situations where a modern statistician would be likely to use means.)

From this table and these two lines through medians of rows and of columns, Galton concluded that, "However paradoxical it may appear at first, it is theoretically a necessary fact, and one that is clearly confirmed by observation, that the stature of the adult offspring must on the whole, be more *mediocre* than the stature of the Parents; that is to say, more near to the M [median] of the general Population." In 1885,

* Pearson, Karl, *Life, Letters and Labours of Francis Galton*, Vol. IIIA. Cambridge University Press, 1930. See pp. 1–79.

Galton published his famous paper on "Regression towards Mediocrity in Hereditary Stature" and called the two lines, *lines of regression.*

Galton's own discussion of his data makes interesting and illuminating reading, and the following brief excerpts from *Natural Inheritance* are presented with occasional explanations inserted in square brackets.

Though the Son deviates on the average from P [the population median] only $\frac{2}{3}$ as widely as his Mid-parent, it does not in the least follow that the Mid-parent should deviate on the average from P, $\frac{3}{2}$ or $1\frac{1}{2}$, as widely as the Son. The Mid-Parent is not likely to be more exceptional than the son, but quite the contrary. The number of individuals who are nearly mediocre is so preponderant, that an exceptional man is more frequently found to be the exceptional son of mediocre parents than the average son of very exceptional parents. This is clearly shown by Table 11 [not reproduced here], where the very same observations which give the average value of Filial Regression when it is read in one way, gives [sic] that of the Mid-Parental Regression when it is read in another way, namely down the vertical columns, instead of along the horizontal lines.

Pearson records that Galton carried this table about with him, trying to see its meaning, and that one morning while waiting at a railway station for a train, his shrewd eye detected in it certain patterns that seemed significant. Somehow, from his crude data, he then made these three generalizations:

1. The medians of the successive rows lie very close to a straight line. The medians of the successive columns lie very close to another straight line. (A correlation table in which this situation holds is now said to possess *linearity of regression.*) These two straight lines intersect each other at the point of intersection of the medians of the entire distribution.

2. The various rows are nearly equal as to variability. The various columns are nearly equal as to variability. (A correlation table for which this situation holds is now said to be *homoscedastic*, or to possess *homoscedasticity.* The name was bestowed by Karl Pearson. *Homo* = equal. *Scedasticity* = scattering. Cf. "Skedaddle.")

3. If on each cell of the bivariate frequency distribution a column is built up having a height proportional to the frequency of the cell, and if the resulting solid is cut by planes parallel to the base, the contour lines thus obtained will be a series of concentric ellipses.

Having recognized these relations in his data, Galton wrote:

These and other relations were evidently a subject for mathematical analysis and verification. It seemed clear to me that they all depended on three elementary measures, supposing the law of Frequency of Error to be applicable throughout; namely (1) the value of Q [the semi-interquartile range $= \frac{1}{2}(Q_U - Q_L)$] in the General Population, which was found to be 1.7 inch; (2) the value of Q in any Co-fraternity, which was found to be 1.5 inch; (3) the Average Regression of the Stature of the Son from that of the Mid-Parent, which was found to be $\frac{2}{3}$. I wrote down these values, and phrasing the problem in abstract terms, disentangled from all reference to heredity, submitted it to Mr. J. D. Hamilton Dickson, Tutor of St. Peter's College, Cambridge. . . . I asked him kindly to investigate for me the Surface of Frequency of Error that would result from these three data, and the various shapes and other particulars of its sections that were made by horizontal planes, inasmuch as they ought to form the ellipses of which I spoke.

The problem may not be difficult to an accomplished mathematician, but I certainly never felt such a glow of loyalty and respect towards the sovereignty and wide sway of mathematical analysis as when his answer arrived, confirming, by purely mathematical reasoning, my various and laborious statistical conclusions with far more minuteness than I had dared to hope, because the data ran somewhat roughly and I had to smooth them with tender caution. . . .

I trust it will have become clear even to the most non-mathematical reader, that the law of Regression in Stature refers primarily to Deviations, that is, to measurements from the *level of mediocrity* to the crown of the head, upwards or downwards as the case may be, and not from the *ground* to the crown of the head. . . .

The law of Regression tells heavily against the full hereditary transmission of any gift. Only a few out of many children would be likely to differ as widely as the more exceptional of the two Parents. The more bountifully the Parent is gifted by nature, the more rare will be his good fortune if he begets a son who is as richly endowed as himself, and still more so if he has a son who is endowed yet more largely. But the law is even-handed; it levies an equal succession-tax on the transmission of badness as of goodness. If it discourages the extravagant hopes of a gifted parent that his children will inherit all his powers; it no less discountenances extravagant fears that they will inherit all his weakness and disease.

It must be clearly understood that there is nothing in these statements to invalidate the general doctrine that the children of a gifted pair are much more likely to be gifted than the children of a mediocre pair. They merely express the fact that the ablest of all the children of a few gifted pairs is not likely to be as gifted as the ablest of all the children of a very great many mediocre pairs.

The Correlation Chart. From the data of Appendix A, the joint frequency distribution of intelligence quotients and language scores is to be set up in the manner described for setting up Table XI on page 48. (The student should now reread the paragraph "Bivariate Frequency Distribution" at the close of Chapter III.) Before beginning to plot this chart, the members of a class should decide upon some uniform practice as to width and beginning point of interval in order that they may check the intermediate stages of their work. Should one person use an interval of 7 points for intelligence quotient and another an interval of 5, their computations would, if correct, yield practically the same final results for the coefficients of regression and of correlation. However, if there were serious disagreement in results, it would not be possible to identify the place where the mistake occurred by comparing the two computations.

For the sake of uniformity, then, let us use an interval of 3 units for language score, with 7–9 as the score limits of the lowest interval; and let us use an interval of 7 units for intelligence quotient, with 63–69 as the score limits of the lowest interval.

Steps in Preparing the Correlation Chart

1. Decide upon a convenient step interval for each variate.
2. Lay off two axes at right angles to each other. On one axis lay off the step intervals for one variate (here intelligence quotient) and on the other axis lay off the step intervals for the other variate (here language score). It makes no difference which scale is placed on which axis, but for the sake of avoiding confusion in subsequent discussions, it would be well for all members of the class to follow the same practice. In Figures 37 and 38 of this text, the horizontal scale has been used for language scores, and the explanatory treatment refers to that arrangement. The intervals should be wide enough to accommodate the tally marks which will be placed in them later, certainly not less than $\frac{1}{4}$ inch each on the vertical scale and $\frac{1}{2}$ inch each on the horizontal scale. Mark the scale clearly on the axes.
3. Through the points of division between the intervals, draw horizontal and vertical lines to form a grid. (The use of prepared charts will be discussed later.) Ordinary graph paper may be used.
4. For each pair of scores, enter one tally stroke in the appropriate cell of the table. The first case has an intelligence quotient of 99, which should be located in the interval marked 98–104 on the vertical scale (assuming that the student has followed the recommendations as to axes and intervals in section 2). The same individual has a language score of 17, which should be located in the interval marked 16–18 on the horizontal scale. One tally stroke is therefore entered in the cell which is the intersection of the horizontal row 98–104 and the vertical column 16–18. Make tally strokes small, firm, uniform in length and slope.

5. After each of the scores has been plotted, place an Arabic numeral in each cell to denote how many tallies the cell contains. The use of a colored pencil for this numeral is helpful.

6. Add the frequencies in each horizontal row and enter the results in a column marked f_y at the right of the grid.

7. Add the frequencies in each vertical column and enter the results in a row marked f_x at the bottom of the grid.

8. Add all the frequencies in the f_y column to be sure that their total is 109. Add all the frequencies in the f_x row to be sure that their total is 109. If both add to the same number and that number is not 109, you should check additions and, if it is still not 109, retabulate from the beginning.

9. Compare your marginal frequencies, that is, the f_y column and the f_x row, with the results obtained by some other student or with Figure 37. If the marginal frequencies are in agreement, it is almost certain that no mistake in tabulating has been made. (It would be possible, though highly improbable, to make two or more compensating mistakes which would not show up in the marginal totals.)

Such a chart as you have now made is sometimes called a *bivariate frequency chart* because it presents the joint frequency distribution of two variates; sometimes called a *correlation chart* because such charts provide the basis for computing a correlation coefficient; sometimes called a *scatter diagram*.

Each horizontal array is called a *row* and each vertical array a *column*. In any single column we have a small frequency distribution of the intelligence quotients of a group of children who are fairly homogeneous as to language score. The frequencies in a column represent scores that are relatively constant with respect to the trait plotted on the horizontal axis, which we will call X, but that form a distribution with respect to the trait plotted on the vertical axis, which we will call Y. In any given row we have a frequency distribution of the X-scores of children who are relatively homogeneous with respect to Y. The marginal frequencies at the right of the table form a frequency distribution of the intelligence quotients (Y-scores) of all 109 children, and are therefore designated as f_y. The marginal frequencies across the bottom of the chart form a frequency distribution of language scores (X-scores) of all 109 children and are therefore designated as f_x. It is entirely immaterial whether a capital or small letter be used as subscript, inasmuch as the sole purpose is to distinguish values pertaining to the X-trait (language scores) from values pertaining to the Y-trait (intelligence quotients).

The mean intelligence quotient for all 109 cases may be computed from the frequencies in the f_y column, and is found to be $\overline{Y} = 110.1$. (If computed directly from the ungrouped scores of Appendix A, this mean is 110.02, the discrepancy being due to errors of grouping.) Locate the point 110.1 on the vertical scale of your chart. In Figure 37 this point is marked by a small asterisk *. Draw a horizontal line across the table, through this point, as in Figure 37 and label it $\overline{Y} = 110.1$. All tallies above this line represent individuals with an intelligence quotient above the mean.

The mean language score for all 109 cases may be similarly computed from the frequencies in the f_x row. Verify that $\overline{X} = 22.0$. Locate the

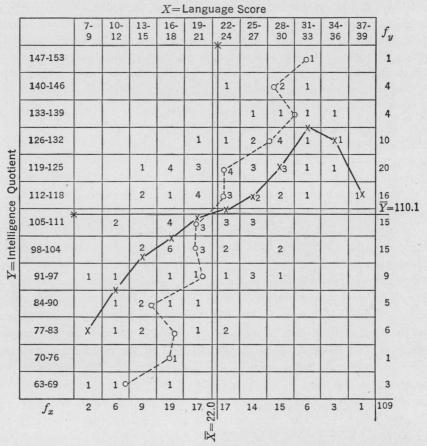

X=Language Score

Y=Intelligence Quotient	7-9	10-12	13-15	16-18	19-21	22-24	25-27	28-30	31-33	34-36	37-39	f_y
147-153									1			1
140-146						1	2	1				4
133-139							1	1	1	1		4
126-132					1	1	2	4	1	1		10
119-125			1	4	3	4	3	3	1	1		20
112-118			2	1	4	3	2	2	1		1	16 $\overline{Y}=110.1$
105-111		2		4		3	3	3				15
98-104			2	6		3	2	2				15
91-97	1	1		1	1	1	3	1				9
84-90		1	2	1	1							5
77-83	X	1	2		1	2						6
70-76			1									1
63-69	1	1		1								3
f_x	2	6	9	19	17	17	14	15	6	3	1	109

$\overline{X}=22.0$

Fig. 37. Bivariate distribution with lines through means of columns and means of rows: intelligence quotients and language scores for 109 fourth-grade children. (From data of Appendix A.)

point 22.0 on the horizontal scale of your chart. In Figure 37 it is indicated by an asterisk. Draw a vertical line across the table through this point and label it $\overline{X} = 22.0$.

These two lines of means will now be considered as a new set of axes for the bivariate distribution. When later we draw regression lines, they will pass through the intersection of these means.

Line Through the Means of the Columns. For each separate column, find the mean intelligence quotient and mark its position with a small cross, as in Figure 37. We shall not need to know the numerical value of this mean, but only its position on the chart. Therefore it is sufficient to choose an arbitrary origin, to count up mentally the weighted sum $\Sigma fy'$, of the positive and negative deviations from that origin and to divide this $\Sigma fy'$ by the number of cases in the column, indicated by the marginal frequency at the bottom of the column. The result will be the *correction in step intervals*, and will indicate how many step intervals to move up or down the column from the midpoint of the interval in which the arbitrary origin lies.

To illustrate how very easy this is to do mentally, let us consider the column 16–18 (Figure 37). Suppose you have decided to take an arbitrary origin at the middle of the interval marked A. You would not need to write anything, but only say to yourself:

16–18	y'	fy'
4	4	16
1	3	3
4	2	8
× 6	1	6
1	0	0
1	−1	−1
	−2	0
1	−3	−3
1	−4	−4
19		

$\overline{Y}\rightarrow$ points to the × row. $A\rightarrow$ points to the row with 6.

$$6 \times 1 = 6$$
$$4 \times 2 = 8 \text{ and } 6 + 8 = 14$$
$$1 \times 3 = 3 \text{ and } 14 + 3 = 17$$
$$4 \times 4 = 16 \text{ and } 17 + 16 = 33$$

. . . .

$$1 \times -1 = -1$$
$$1 \times -3 = -3 \text{ and } -1 - 3 = -4$$
$$1 \times -4 = -4 \text{ and } -4 - 4 = -8$$

. . . .

$$33 - 8 = 25$$

There are 19 cases in the column.

$$\tfrac{25}{19} = 1.3$$

Therefore the column mean is 1.3 intervals above A, and this brings us to the point marked with the little cross.

Draw a broken line connecting the eleven crosses marking the column means. Except for the extreme columns, where cases are few, this line does not exhibit great irregularity, and it seems reasonable to attribute such departure from linearity as is here to chance deviations which might disappear if the size of the group were increased. In order to draw a straight line which will represent the general trend of these crosses, hold a dark thread taut in your fingers and move it among the crosses until they seem to be about evenly balanced around it. Crosses determined by only two or three cases may be disregarded. Find the point where the vertical axis, $\overline{X} = 22.0$, crosses the horizontal axis, $\overline{Y} = 110.1$. Let the thread pass exactly over this intersection point. Draw the straight line which appears to be in the best position to represent the column means.

The line thus drawn is a *regression line*, or more particularly, it is the *line of regression of y on x*, or the line expressing the tendency of *y* to change as *x* changes.

Line Through the Means of the Rows. For each row find the mean language score and mark its position with a small circle. Connect the 13 small circles by a broken line, and then draw the straight line which seems to represent the general trend of these circles in exactly the same way as you drew a straight line through the crosses. This is the line of regression of *x* on *y*, or the line which shows the way in which *x* changes as *y* changes.

A useful device to help you grasp the relationship of each regression line to the various means is to use a red pencil for the line $\overline{Y} = 110.1$, for the points which mark column means, and for the line of regression of *y* on *x* which passes through the column means, and to use a blue pencil for the line $\overline{X} = 22.0$, for the points which mark row means, and for the line of regression of *x* on *y* which passes through the row means.

If each member of a class draws these lines as described here, the position of either line may vary considerably from person to person. A criterion for determining what is the "best" position will be furnished in Chapter XIII. Each line as determined by computing the equation for this "best" position is shown in Figure 38.

Slope of a Line. To understand the subject of regression, one must understand the relationship of equations to their graphs. The reader who has forgotten or has never understood the mathematical graph will need to review the elementary algebra relative to this topic. Chapters XI and XX in *Mathematics Essential for Elementary Statistics* provide a rapid review of the algebraic information which is presupposed in the discussion and the exercises of the present chapter.

Although space does not permit repeating here the elementary algebra essential to understanding regression and correlation, it seems desirable to review briefly one or two points.

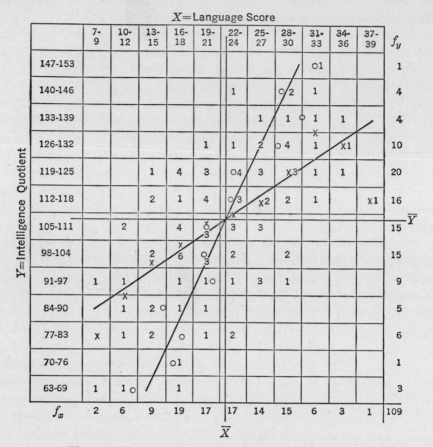

X=Language Score

Y	7-9	10-12	13-15	16-18	19-21	22-24	25-27	28-30	31-33	34-36	37-39	f_y
147-153									o1			1
140-146						1		o/2	1			4
133-139							1	1	o1	1		4
126-132					1	1	2	o4	1	x1		10
119-125			1	4	3	o4	3	x3	1	1		20
112-118			2	1	4	o/3	x2	2	1		x1	16
105-111		2		4	o/3	3	3					15
98-104			2 x	x6	o/3	2		2				15
91-97	1	1		1	1o	1	3	1				9
84-90		1	2 o	1	1							5
77-83	x	1	2	o	1	2						6
70-76				o1								1
63-69	1	1 o		1								3
f_x	2	6	9	19	17	17	14	15	6	3	1	109

Y=Intelligence Quotient

$\overline{Y}$

$\overline{X}$

Fig. 38. Lines of regression. (Compare with Fig. 37.)

The four sections into which a graph is divided by the two axes are called *quadrants* and numbered as in the adjacent sketch.

II	I
III	IV

Distances measured from the origin parallel to the horizontal axis are considered positive when they extend to the right and negative when they extend to the left. Distances measured from the origin parallel to the vertical axis are considered positive when they extend upward and negative when they extend downward.

To measure the slope of the line OA to the horizontal line OX, take any point, P, on OA and from it drop a perpendicular PQ to OX. Measure the length of the line segments OQ and QP and find the ratio of QP to OQ. This ratio is independent of the position of P and of the unit of measurement. This ratio is called the *slope of the line* and is also called the *tangent of angle AOX*.

This ratio is the *coefficient of regression* for the line of regression of y on x. As both QP and OQ are taken in a positive direction, the ratio of QP to OQ is positive and OA has a positive slope. As both $Q'P'$ and OQ' are taken in a

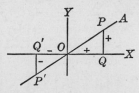

negative direction the ratio of $Q'P'$ to OQ' is positive, and OA has a positive slope. The line OB has a negative slope. The ratio of SR to OS is the ratio of a positive segment to a negative segment, and is therefore negative. The ratio of $S'R'$ to OS' is the ratio of a

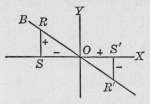

negative segment to a positive segment, and is therefore negative.

To measure the slope of the line OC to the vertical line OY, take any point T on OC and from it drop a perpendicular TU to OY. Measure the length of the line segments UT and OU and find the ratio of UT to OU. This ratio is the slope of OC to OY, or the tangent of the

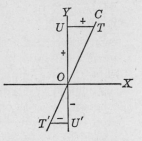

angle COY, and is the coefficient of regression for the line of regression of x on y. For the line OC, the slope is positive, being either the ratio of a positive segment to a positive segment or the ratio of a negative to a negative segment.

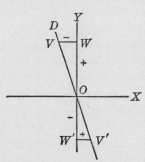

For the line OD the slope is negative, being either the ratio of a negative segment to a positive segment or the ratio of a positive segment to a negative segment.

Exercise 23*

1. As a means of fixing in your mind the underlying ideas, find the words which are needed to complete the following discussion. After you have decided upon the missing words, read the paragraphs over to yourself once or twice until you are sure that you understand them fully. Remember that the axes have been placed at the means of the two traits.

In Figure 37, most of the scores lie in quadrant _____ or in quadrant _____, because as the intelligence quotient increases there is a tendency for language score to _____. This tendency is called a _____ relationship. In this figure, the slope of the line of regression of y on x is positive and the slope of the line of regression of x on y is _____.

In Table XI on page 48, most of the scores lie in quadrant _____ or in quadrant _____, because among these fourth-grade children those who are above average in age tend to be _____ average in reading score, so that as one variable increases the other tends to _____. If the regression lines were drawn, the one through the means of the columns would have a _____ slope and the one through the means of the rows would have a _____ slope. For these children, all of whom are in the same grade, the relationship between age and reading score is negative. This of course does not mean that the relationship between age and reading score would be negative for children unselected as to grade position.

Any selected column in Figure 37 contains a distribution of the _____ of a group of children who are nearly homogeneous with regard to _____. The mean of that column is the best guess which can be made as to the most likely _____ of one of these children if nothing is known about him except his _____. The line which passes among the means of all the columns represents the equation for estimating the most probable _____ when the _____ is known. Any selected row of the table contains the distribution with respect to _____ for a group of children who are nearly homogeneous with respect to _____. The mean of the row in which his score falls provides the best estimate which can be made of the _____ of a child on the basis of information about his _____. The more closely scores in that row cluster around the mean of that row, the _____ this estimate is likely to be.

In terms of x and y, that one of the two regression lines in Figure 38 which lies nearer to the mean of X is the line which represents the trend of the _____ arrays, and which, therefore, furnishes a method of estimating the most probable value of _____ from a known value of _____. That one of the two regression lines which lies nearer to the mean of Y is the line through the _____ means, that is through the means of the _____ arrays. It may be used to obtain an estimate of _____ from a known value of _____. It is called the line of regression of y on x.

When the relationship between the traits is very close, the scores cluster closely around the regression lines and the lines lie _____ each other. When the relationship is positive, no matter what its size, both regression lines lie in quadrants _____ and _____. In this case, high scores in one trait tend to occur in connection with _____ scores in the other. When the relationship is negative, no matter what its size, both regression lines lie in quadrants _____ and _____. In this case, high scores in one trait tend to occur in connection with _____ scores in the other.

A child's language score is known to be 12, but nothing is known about his IQ. From the regression line in Figure 38, the best guess is that his IQ is about _____. A child's IQ is known to be 94 but his language score is not known. The regression line indicates _____ as its most probable value. A child's IQ is 129, and his language score is not known but _____ is the best guess which can be made for it by examining the regression line.

2. Imagine a point moving in such a way that its x value is constantly twice as great as its y value. Sketch the position of its path. Write an equation which will describe that path.

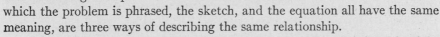

3. Imagine a point moving as described below, sketch the position of its path, and write an equation describing that path. Note that the words in which the problem is phrased, the sketch, and the equation all have the same meaning, are three ways of describing the same relationship.

a. The point is constantly as far above the mean of y as it is to the right of the mean x.

b. The y distance of the point is always 3 times its x distance.

c. The y distance of the point is always $\frac{1}{3}$ as great as its x distance.

d. The sum of its x distance and its y distance remains constantly equal to 3.

e. The sum of its x distance and its y distance remains constantly equal to -2.

f. The sum of its abscissa and ordinate is always zero.

g. Its x and y values have opposite signs, and its x value is numerically $\frac{2}{5}$ as large as its y value.

h. Its x and y values have opposite signs, but its x value is numerically 3 times as large as its y value.

i. Its abscissa is always 2 units larger than its ordinate.

j. Its ordinate is always 4 units larger than its abscissa.

4. The equations $y = 2x + 1$, $y = 2x - 3$, $y = 2x + 5$, $y = 2x$, or in general, $y = 2x + a$, are members of one family of lines. What family characteristic have they in common?

5. The equations $x + y = 5$, $x + y = 1$, $x + y = 0$, $x + y = -3$ or in general, $x + y = c$, are members of one family. What family characteristic have they in common?

6. The equations $y = 3x$, $y = \frac{1}{2}x$, $x + y = 0$, $2x = 3y$, or in general $ay = bx$, are members of one family. What family characteristic have they in common?

7. Think of the general position of the line described by each of these equations. In Position column, write H if the line lies nearer to the horizontal than

Equation	Position	Slope	Equation	Position	Slope
$y = x$			$y - \frac{2}{3}x = 0$		
$y = 3x$	V	$+$	$2x + 5y = 0$		
$x + y = 0$	E	$-$	$7x - 3y = 0$		
$2x = 5y$			$x = 3y$		
$x + 2y = 0$			$y = \frac{1}{2}x$		
$x - y = 0$			$y + \frac{2}{3}x = 0$		

to the vertical axis, write V if it lies nearer to the vertical, and E if it is equally distant from them. In the slope column place a plus sign or a minus sign to indicate whether the slope of the line is positive or negative.

Regression Value and Residual. In Figure 39a, one regression line only has been drawn, the line of regression of y on x. Out of all the many cases which form the correlation table, just one is shown here at P. For this individual, the line segment OA represents his x-score and the line segment AP, his y-score. Had we known his x-score and not his y-score, we should have estimated the latter as AB. This is called the regressed y-score, or the "predicted" y-score. As used by statisticians in this connection, the term "predict" is almost synonymous with "make the best possible estimate of." It implies that some measure, which for the time being is unknown or is treated as unknown, is to be estimated on the basis of some other related known measure or measures. The idea of futurity or sequence of time is not usually involved. The symbol we shall use for this regression value is $\tilde{y}$.

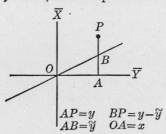

$$AP=y \quad BP=y-\tilde{y}$$
$$AB=\tilde{y} \quad OA=x$$

Fig. 39a. Residual $y - \tilde{y}$ from a regression line.

It may be read "regression y," "regressed y," "estimated y," "predicted y," "regression value of y," or "y tilde." It is sometimes colloquially referred to as "curlicue y" or "y curlicue."

The error made in estimating the y-score for this particular individual is clearly his actual y-score minus the estimated y-score, that is $y - \tilde{y}$. This is represented by the line segment BP, and is called an *error of estimate*, or a *residual error*, or a *residual*. For every individual in a bivariate frequency distribution, there is a residual error in estimating y from x. Look at Figure 38 and imagine that from the center of each cell to the line of regression of y on x (that is, the line through the crosses), a line segment is drawn parallel to the y-axis. These line segments represent residual errors. The smaller such residual errors for the table as a whole, the more successful is the prediction.

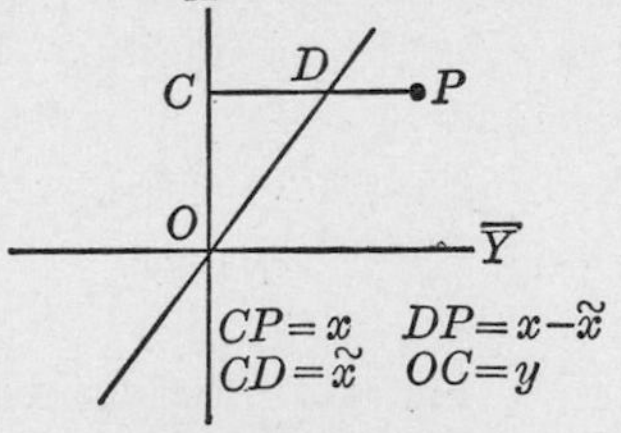

$$CP=x \quad DP=x-\tilde{x}$$
$$CD=\tilde{x} \quad OC=y$$

Fig. 39b. Residual $x - \tilde{x}$ from a regression line.

Residuals in x are measured from the other regression line by segments parallel to the x-axis. In Figure 39b, the segment OC represents the observed y-score and CP the observed x-score of the individual, while CD represents the estimate, $\tilde{x}$, we should have made of his x-score from our knowledge of his y-score, and DP represents the error, $x - \tilde{x}$, we should have incurred in so doing.

The symbols customarily used to indicate the slopes of the regression lines are b_{yx} and b_{xy}. The two equations may thus be written as

$$\tilde{y} = b_{yx}x \qquad \text{and} \qquad \tilde{x} = b_{xy}y \qquad (45)$$

when we wish to speak of them in a general way without giving either a numerical measure of the slope or the formula by which that numerical measure would be computed.

Figure 40 shows the general position of two regression lines, the observed values x_i and y_i for the individual P_i, and the estimated or regressed values $\tilde{y}_i$ and $\tilde{x}_i$. The distance from P to either regression line is a residual.

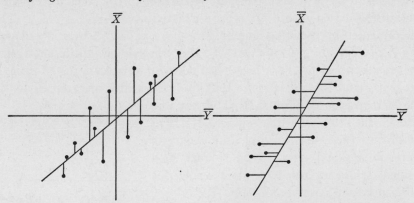

Fig. 40. Lines of regression for predicting x from y and y from x.

Figures 41a and 41b show the paired x- and y-scores of 16 individuals. Figure 41a shows the regression line of y on x and the y-residuals of the 16 individuals from it. Figure 41b shows the regression line of x on y and the x-residuals from it.

The expressions b_{yx} and b_{xy} are called *regression coefficients* or *coefficients of regression*. The symbols may be read "b sub y x" and "b sub x y"

Fig. 41a. Residuals of 16 indi-   Fig. 41b. Residuals of 16 individuals from the regression line.   viduals from the regression line.

$$\tilde{y} = b_{yx}x \qquad\qquad\qquad \tilde{x} = b_{xy}y$$

or merely "b y x" and "b x y." It will be observed that it is the order in which the subscripts are written which distinguishes between them, the order of these subscripts being the same as the order of the variables when the equation is written. The coefficient which expresses the regression of y on x is b_{yx}, while the coefficient which expresses the regression of x on y, or the prediction of x by means of y, is b_{xy}.

Exercise 24*

1. In Figure 38, where does one find those individuals whose y-residuals are very small? Whose y-residuals are positive? Whose y-residuals are negative?

2. Where does one find those individuals whose x-residuals are very small? Whose x-residuals are positive? Whose x-residuals are negative?

3. Locate the cell for which $X = 17$ and $Y = 101$. There are 6 individuals in this cell. The center lies very near to the line $\bar{y} = b_{yx}x$, so that $y \doteq \bar{y}$ and $y - \bar{y} \doteq 0$. (Read "the observed value of y is approximately equal to the regressed value and the error of estimate is approximately equal to zero.") The center of this cell lies about one interval to the left of the line $\bar{x} = b_{xy}y$, so that in interval units $x - \bar{x} = -1$.

4. For each of the following individuals, state whether his y-residual, $y - \bar{y}$, is positive, negative, or approximately zero. His x-residual, $x - \bar{x}$.

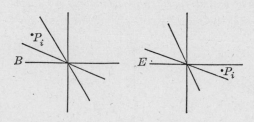

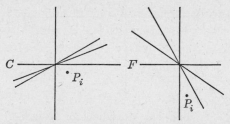

Individual	X-score	Y-score
A	26	94
B	26	112
C	11	108
D	26	129
E	29	129
F	14	87

5. The line $\bar{y} = b_{yx}x$ is the line to predict _____ from _____, and passes through the means of the _____. The line $\bar{x} = b_{xy}y$ is used to predict _____ from _____ and passes through the means of the _____. Of the two lines, the one lying nearer to the vertical axis is _____.

6. In each of the figures above, draw lines to show the values of x_i, y_i, $\bar{x}_i$, $\bar{y}_i$, $x_i - \bar{x}_i$, and $y_i - \bar{y}_i$ for the individual whose paired scores are represented by the point P_i.

7. In one of the sketches on page 219 the regression lines indicate positive and in the other negative correlation. In each shaded area, all the y residuals have the same sign and all the x residuals have the same sign. What are these signs for region A? For region B? For each of the other regions?

Region	Sign of Residual	
	$y - \bar{y}$	$x - \bar{x}$
A		
B		
C		
D		
E		
F		
G		
H		

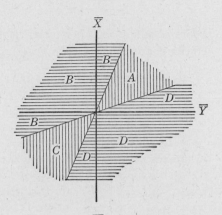

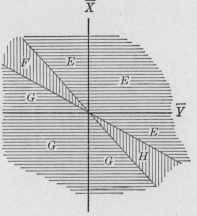

Correlation and Regression. The term correlation literally means *mutual relation;* in fact, Galton once used the spelling "co-relation." While each regression coefficient is a measure of relation, it is not a measure of mutual relation, inasmuch as the numerical value of b_{yx} is not usually the same as that of b_{xy}.

The correlation coefficient is an average of the two regression coefficients, only the average used is not the arithmetic mean but the geometric. The geometric mean of two numbers is called the mean proportional between them. When only two variables are being considered, the correlation coefficient requires no subscript. If subscripts are needed to avoid any possible uncertainty as to what variables have been correlated, the order of subscripts is immaterial, $r_{xy} = r_{yx}$.

$$r_{xy} = \sqrt{b_{yx}\,b_{xy}} \qquad (46)$$

When b_{yx} and b_{xy} are negative, definition (46) makes r negative also, because it is accepted by mathematicians that

$$\sqrt{-a}\,\sqrt{-a} = -a \text{ and not } +a.$$

The relationship between correlation coefficient, the two regression coefficients, and the standard deviations, is

$$b_{yx} = r\frac{s_y}{s_x} \text{ and } b_{xy} = r\frac{s_x}{s_y}$$ (47)

From equation (47) it is clear that when $s_x = s_y$, the two regression coefficients are equal to each other and to the correlation coefficient.

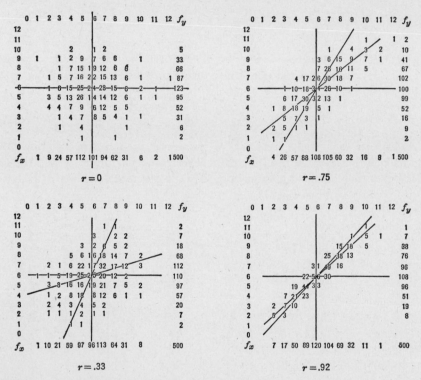

Fig. 42. Scatter diagrams and regression lines for distributions with different sizes of r.

Figure 42 shows the position of the regression lines for four selected values of r.

Consider a correlation plot in which the two standard deviations are equal and in which $r = .60$. The regression lines will occupy the position indicated in sketch A of Figure 43. Now imagine that the grid is elastic and that you pull it horizontally, thus stretching out the x-distribution and increasing the variability of x and decreasing that of y. If you pull until $s_x = 2s_y$, the lines will assume the position B. If you pull the grid vertically until $s_y = 3s_x$, the lines will be drawn up into position C.

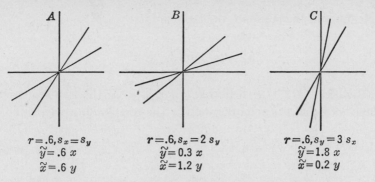

$$r=.6, s_x=s_y$$
$$\tilde{y}=.6\,x$$
$$\tilde{x}=.6\,y$$

$$r=.6, s_x=2\,s_y$$
$$\tilde{y}=0.3\,x$$
$$\tilde{x}=1.2\,y$$

$$r=.6, s_y=3\,s_x$$
$$\tilde{y}=1.8\,x$$
$$\tilde{x}=0.2\,y$$

Fig. 43. Position of regression lines for different relative values of the standard deviations and the same value of the correlation coefficient.

Exercise 25*

Substitute each of the given sets of values of r, s_x, and s_y in equation (47) and make a sketch of the resulting pairs of regression equations. Study the set of sketches thus obtained in order to justify the generalizations stated below.

Sketch	r	s_x	s_y	Sketch	r	s_x	s_y
1	1.00	2	2	11	0	1	4
2	1.00	3	1	12	−.3	2	2
3	1.00	1	2	13	−.3	2	1
4	.8	2	4	14	−.6	2	2
5	.8	5	5	15	−.6	3	1
6	.5	3	3	16	−.9	5	5
7	.5	4	1	17	−.9	1	3
8	.2	5	1	18	−1.00	4	4
9	.2	3	3	19	−1.00	3	1
10	0	2	2	20	−1.00	1	2

1. When $r = 1.00$ and also when $r = -1.00$, the two regression lines coincide.

2. When $r = 0$, the regression lines are identical with the lines of means.

3. When r is positive, both lines lie in quadrants I and III. When r is negative, both lines lie in quadrants II and IV. It is impossible for one line to lie in quadrants I and III while the other lies in quadrants II and IV.

4. When the standard deviations of the two traits are equal, the lines are symmetrically placed with respect to the two axes, and make equal angles with those axes. When the standard deviation of the horizontal trait is larger, the pair of regression lines lies nearer the horizontal than the vertical axis. When the standard deviation of the vertical trait is larger, the pair lies nearer to the vertical axis.

CHAPTER XIII

REGRESSION AND CORRELATION—COMPUTATIONS

Choice of Method. In Figure 37, it is apparent that intelligence quotient and language score tend to vary together in this group of children, and that, as we proceed across the table from the very low to the very high language scores, the average intelligence quotient tends to increase. (The word "average" is used here to suggest that the statement relates to almost any measure of central tendency, not specifically to the mean.) It appears also that as we pass from a column of low to one of high language scores, the shift in average intelligence quotient is less pronounced than the shift in average language score. Furthermore, even when language score is held relatively constant, as in a selected column, intelligence scores exhibit considerable variation.

Clearly there is need for some numerical index of the extent or degree to which any two measures tend to vary together. Many statistics have been designed to measure such relationship, or association, or going-together-ness, but the *coefficient of correlation* which was defined in the preceding chapter as the mean proportional between the slopes of the two regression lines is, of all these statistics, by far the most important. In fact such other measures of relationship as have not fallen into disuse and oblivion are equal to this correlation coefficient under some special set of circumstances. Generalizations of this coefficient have recently been made which open new applications of great usefulness, and there is an extensive theory which could easily occupy an entire text. Here we shall take up only the more elementary aspects of correlation.

Formula for *r* Obtained from Slopes of Regression Lines. When the regression lines are so placed as to make the totality of the squares of the residual errors as small as possible, the equations for their slopes are:

$$b_{yx} = \frac{\Sigma xy}{\Sigma x^2} \text{ and } b_{xy} = \frac{\Sigma xy}{\Sigma y^2} \tag{48}$$

If then we define r as

$$r = \sqrt{b_{yx}\, b_{xy}} \tag{46}$$

we shall have

$$r = \frac{\Sigma xy}{\sqrt{\Sigma x^2}\sqrt{\Sigma y^2}} = \frac{\Sigma xy}{\sqrt{(\Sigma x^2)(\Sigma y^2)}} \tag{49}$$

which is algebraically equal to

$$r = \frac{\Sigma xy}{N s_x s_y} \qquad (50)$$

These are the formulas most frequently used as *definitions*. Obviously neither one would be convenient as a computing pattern, because it is not economical to compute with deviations from the mean.

For the derivation of formulas (48) and (49), see Appendix B.

Mean z-Score Product. A measure of co-variation should indicate the strength of the tendency of high scores in one trait to occur in connection with high scores in the other. What is a high score? It is a score which is far above the mean of its group in terms of the standard deviation of that group. In Chapter IX such a score was called a z-score.

$$z_x = \frac{X - \overline{X}}{s_x} = \frac{x}{s_x} \text{ and } z_y = \frac{Y - \overline{Y}}{s_y} = \frac{y}{s_y} \qquad (23)$$

If for each individual in a group such a standard measure of z_x and of z_y is available, an index of relationship might be developed by multiplying together the pair of z-scores for each individual, summing for all individuals, and dividing by the number of cases. The result is sometimes called a *product moment*, because it is the mean of a set of products, and would be indicated by the expression

$$r = \frac{1}{N}\Sigma \frac{x}{s_x} \cdot \frac{y}{s_y} = \frac{1}{N}\Sigma z_x z_y = \frac{\Sigma z_x z_y}{N} \qquad (51)$$

Interpretation of the Mean z-Score Product. 1. If there is a perfect linear relationship between X and Y, so that the individual who receives a high score on one receives a proportionately high score on the other, we shall have,

for individual 1, $\quad z_{x_1} = z_{y_1} \text{ or } \dfrac{x_1}{s_x} = \dfrac{y_1}{s_y}$

for individual 2, $\quad z_{x_2} = z_{y_2} \text{ or } \dfrac{x_2}{s_x} = \dfrac{y_2}{s_y}$

and in general, $\quad z_{x_i} = z_{y_i} \text{ or } \dfrac{x_i}{s_x} = \dfrac{y_i}{s_y}$

The expression for r then becomes

$$r = \frac{1}{N}\Sigma z_x z_y = \frac{1}{N}\Sigma \frac{x}{s_x} \cdot \frac{x}{s_x} = \frac{1}{N}\Sigma \frac{x^2}{s_x^2} = 1$$

or

$$r = \frac{1}{N}\Sigma z_x z_y = \frac{1}{N}\Sigma \frac{y}{s_y} \cdot \frac{y}{s_y} = \frac{1}{N}\Sigma \frac{y^2}{s_y^2} = 1$$

2. If there is a perfect *inverse* relationship, so that the x score of any individual is proportionately as far below $\overline{X}$ as his y-score is above $\overline{Y}$, we shall have

$$z_{x_i} = -z_{y_i} \text{ or } \frac{x_i}{s_x} = -\frac{y_i}{s_y} \text{ or } \frac{-x_i}{s_x} = \frac{y_i}{s_y}$$

Then the expression for the mean z-score product will be

$$r = \frac{1}{N}\Sigma z_x z_y = \frac{1}{N}\Sigma \frac{x}{s_x} \cdot \frac{-x}{s_x} = -\frac{\Sigma x^2}{N s_x{}^2} = -\frac{\Sigma y^2}{N s_y{}^2} = -1$$

3. If there is some tendency for the individual who is high in one test to be high in the other, but not a perfect correspondence, then the majority of the products $z_x z_y$ will be positive, but their sum will be smaller than in the case mentioned in (1), and though positive, the expression for r will be less than unity.

The z_y scores corresponding to a particular z_x score will have a certain amount of spread, but will tend to be concentrated in a limited range and to have a mean value intermediate between that of z_x and 0. A similar statement holds for the z_x scores corresponding to a particular z_y.

4. If an individual who scores high on one test tends to score low on the other, positive z_x values will tend to be accompanied by negative z_y values and the mean of the $z_x z_y$ products will be negative, but less than unity.

5. If there is no tendency for an individual who scores high on one test to be high on the other, the products $z_x z_y$ will be negative as often as positive. Any given value of z_x is as likely to be accompanied by a high as by a low value of z_y. The sum of products will, therefore, approach zero.

This index which we would obtain by summing up the products of the standard scores and dividing by N is the *coefficient of correlation*. The coefficient of correlation is a number which indicates the extent to which high scores on one measure tend to go with high scores on another measure, and vice versa. It has a possible range from $+1.00$, when each standard score on one test is accompanied by an equally high standard score on another test, through 0.00, when there is no tendency for high scores on one test to be associated with either high or low scores on the other test, to -1.00, when high scores on one test are associated with low scores on the other test, the paired standard scores being of equal size but opposite sign.

From this definition of the correlation coefficient as the mean of a set of product terms, there come the expressions *product moment coefficient,* *product moment r*, and *Pearson product moment*. The idea of correlation was discovered by Sir Francis Galton, but it was his friend, associate, and biographer, Karl Pearson,* who developed a computational routine simple enough to make the idea widely available to scientific workers. Hence the correlation coefficient we are discussing is often called the *Pearson r*.

Computational Formulas for r, b_{yx}, and b_{xy}. Formulas (46), (47), (48), (49), and (50) are to be considered as definitions rather than as guides for computation, just as in Chapter VIII the variance was defined as

$$s_x^2 = \frac{\Sigma x^2}{N} \tag{8}$$

but formulas (9) and (10) were developed to provide a more economical procedure for computation. There are a large number of different routines by which Σxy can be obtained, and consequently a large number of different procedures for computing the correlation and regression coefficients. Only a few of the most important will be given here. The resourceful student can easily manipulate these algebraically to produce equivalent formulas which may provide an easier numerical computation in some particular case. (Multiplying both numerator and denominator by N is one such device.)

A. Definition in terms of deviations from the mean in score units (compare formula (8) on page 115):

$$b_{yx} = \frac{\Sigma xy}{\Sigma x^2} \quad \text{and} \quad b_{xy} = \frac{\Sigma xy}{\Sigma y^2} \tag{48}$$

$$r = \frac{\Sigma xy}{\sqrt{\Sigma x^2}\sqrt{\Sigma y^2}} = \frac{\Sigma xy}{\sqrt{(\Sigma x^2)(\Sigma y^2)}} \tag{49}$$

B. Definition in terms of deviations in interval units from the mean:

$$b_{yx} = \frac{i_y}{i_x} \cdot \frac{\Sigma xy}{\Sigma x^2} \quad \text{and} \quad b_{xy} = \frac{i_x}{i_y} \cdot \frac{\Sigma xy}{\Sigma y^2} \tag{52}$$

$$r = \frac{\Sigma xy}{\sqrt{\Sigma x^2}\sqrt{\Sigma y^2}} \tag{49}$$

* About 1893, Karl Pearson, who had been appointed to the staff of University College, London, began to lecture and to write on what was then a little-known field—statistical theory and method. Gathering about him a small but brilliant group of scientists and mathematicians, writing prodigiously himself and stimulating others to write, publishing the statistical journal, *Biometrika*, he practically created a new science. In recent years other men have made discoveries and developed new theories which are an extension of and an improvement upon Pearson's work. His vast creativeness provided the foundation on which his successors could build, and in building, they have at various points leveled up the foundation stones. For an account of his life and work, see the biography written by Egon S. Pearson, "Karl Pearson; an appreciation of some aspects of his life and work," Part I, 1857–1906, *Biometrika*, XXVIII (1936), 193–257, and Part II, 1906–1936, *Biometrika*, XXIX (1937–38), 111–248.

C. Computing routine in terms of deviation from an arbitrary origin in interval units (compare formula (9) on page 115):

$$b_{yx} = \frac{i_y}{i_x} \cdot \frac{\Sigma x'y' - \dfrac{(\Sigma x')(\Sigma y')}{N}}{\Sigma (x')^2 - \dfrac{(\Sigma x')^2}{N}} \quad \text{and} \quad b_{xy} = \frac{i_x}{i_y} \cdot \frac{\Sigma x'y' - \dfrac{(\Sigma x')(\Sigma y')}{N}}{\Sigma (y')^2 - \dfrac{(\Sigma y')^2}{N}} \tag{53}$$

$$r = \frac{\Sigma x'y' - \dfrac{(\Sigma x')(\Sigma y')}{N}}{\sqrt{\Sigma (x')^2 - \dfrac{(\Sigma x')^2}{N}}\sqrt{\Sigma (y')^2 - \dfrac{(\Sigma y')^2}{N}}} \tag{54}$$

D. Computing routine in terms of gross scores (compare formula (10) on page 115):

$$b_{yx} = \frac{\Sigma XY - \dfrac{(\Sigma X)(\Sigma Y)}{N}}{\Sigma X^2 - \dfrac{(\Sigma X)^2}{N}} \quad \text{and} \quad b_{xy} = \frac{\Sigma XY - \dfrac{(\Sigma X)(\Sigma Y)}{N}}{\Sigma Y^2 - \dfrac{(\Sigma Y)^2}{N}} \tag{55}$$

$$r = \frac{\Sigma XY - \dfrac{(\Sigma X)(\Sigma Y)}{N}}{\sqrt{\Sigma X^2 - \dfrac{(\Sigma X)^2}{N}}\sqrt{\Sigma Y^2 - \dfrac{(\Sigma Y)^2}{N}}} \tag{56}$$

E. Computing routine in terms of deviation from any arbitrary origin in interval units, with indication of the appropriate frequency (see subsequent paragraph entitled "Indication of frequency in formulas"):

$$b_{yx} = \frac{i_y}{i_x} \cdot \frac{\Sigma f_{xy}x'y' - \dfrac{(\Sigma f_x x')(\Sigma f_y y')}{N}}{\Sigma f_x (x')^2 - \dfrac{(\Sigma f_x x')^2}{N}}$$

and

$$b_{xy} = \frac{i_x}{i_y} \cdot \frac{\Sigma f_{xy}x'y' - \dfrac{(\Sigma f_x x')(\Sigma f_y y')}{N}}{\Sigma f_y (y')^2 - \dfrac{(\Sigma f_y y')^2}{N}} \tag{57}$$

$$r = \frac{\Sigma f_{xy}x'y' - \dfrac{(\Sigma f_x x')(\Sigma f_y y')}{N}}{\sqrt{\Sigma f_x (x')^2 - \dfrac{(\Sigma f_x x')^2}{N}}\sqrt{\Sigma f_y (y')^2 - \dfrac{(\Sigma f_y y')^2}{N}}} \tag{58}$$

A brief inspection of the foregoing formulas will make them easy to memorize. Notice the following points:

1. In each group of formulas for the two regression coefficients and r, the numerators are all alike, while the denominator for r is the product of the square roots of the denominators for the two regression coefficients. The pattern may be expressed schematically as follows:

$$b_{yx} = \frac{Num}{D_1} \qquad b_{xy} = \frac{Num}{D_2}$$

$$r = \frac{Num}{\sqrt{D_1 D_2}}$$

2. In the first two groups of formulas, A and B, deviations are taken from the mean, hence no correction term is needed for Σxy, Σx^2, or Σy^2. In groups C, D, and E, deviations are taken from some point other than the mean and a correction term is required in both numerator and denominator. Notice that all of the resulting expressions are of the same general pattern.

Instead of Σxy we have either

$$\Sigma x'y' - \frac{(\Sigma x')(\Sigma y')}{N} \qquad (59)$$

or

$$\Sigma XY - \frac{(\Sigma X)(\Sigma Y)}{N} \qquad (60)$$

Instead of Σx^2 we have either

$$\Sigma (x')^2 - \frac{(\Sigma x')^2}{N} \qquad (61)$$

or

$$\Sigma X^2 - \frac{(\Sigma X)^2}{N} \qquad (62)$$

Instead of Σy^2 we have either

$$\Sigma (y')^2 - \frac{(\Sigma y')^2}{N} \qquad (61)$$

or

$$\Sigma Y^2 - \frac{(\Sigma Y)^2}{N} \qquad (62)$$

When frequency is indicated, instead of $\Sigma f_x x^2$ we have either

$$\Sigma f_x (x')^2 - \frac{(\Sigma f_x x')^2}{N} \qquad (63)$$

or

$$\Sigma f_x X^2 - \frac{(\Sigma f_x X)^2}{N} \qquad (64)$$

and similarly for $\Sigma f_y y^2$.

Instead of $\Sigma f_{xy}xy$ we have either

$$\Sigma f_{xy}x'y' - \frac{(\Sigma f_x x')(\Sigma f_y y')}{N} \tag{65}$$

or

$$\Sigma f_{xy}XY - \frac{(\Sigma f_x X)(\Sigma f_y Y)}{N} \tag{66}$$

3. When computations are carried out in terms of interval rather than score units, the expressions i_x and i_y appear in the formula for regression coefficients. They never appear in the formula for r. When used, i_y is in the numerator for b_{yx} and i_x is in the numerator for b_{xy}. Verify this by looking at formulas (52), (53), and (57). Note that (48) and (55) require no reference to the step interval because computations are made on measures expressed in score units, so that

$$i_x = i_y = 1$$

Indication of Frequency in Formulas. Three kinds of frequency must be clearly distinguished in all the computations which follow: f_x, or the frequency in a given interval of the x-scale; f_y, or the frequency in a given interval of the y-scale; and f_{xy}, or the frequency in a given cell of the joint distribution of x and y. Until the routine of the computation is learned, it is wise to print these frequencies in the formulas, even though the formulas are thereby made to look more formidable. When the routine is understood, it can be taken for granted that Σxy is an abbreviation for $\Sigma f_{xy}xy$. Therefore the f with appropriate subscript will be used whenever there seems to be some danger of misunderstanding the import of a formula, and will usually be omitted otherwise.

The Coefficient of Correlation a Pure Number. Pure numbers, which are unaffected by a change in the unit of measure, are to be contrasted with concrete numbers whose value depends upon the unit. It is meaningless to say that the diameter of a circle is 10 without saying whether it is 10 feet or 10 inches or 10 centimeters or what; but the ratio of the circumference to the diameter is 3.1416 and no additional statement about the units in which diameter and circumference were measured adds any meaning to our understanding of that ratio because $\pi = 3.1416$ is a *pure number*. Being unaffected by the size of the unit in which measurements are made (except in the extreme case noted in Chapter XIV), the coefficient of correlation may be called a *pure number*. In each of the formulas for regression coefficients (52), (53), and (57), it is evident that whenever deviations are not expressed in terms of score units, the width of interval must be taken into account in order to obtain the values for the regression coefficients which would have resulted from computations upon measures expressed in score units. This indicates that the regression coefficients are not pure numbers. In the corresponding formulas for the correlation coefficient (49), (54), and (58), the symbols i_x and i_y do not appear. The correlation coefficient is independent of the choice of unit. A correlation between weight and height would be the same if weight were measured in pounds and height in inches or if weight were measured in kilograms and height in centimeters.

Exercise 26

1. Which of the following are pure and which concrete numbers?

    a. The distance between New York City and Chicago.

    b. The ratio of the distance between New York City and Chicago to the distance between Chicago and San Francisco.

    c. The side of a square.

    d. The ratio of the diagonal of a square to its side.

    e. A mean.

    f. A median.

    g. A standard deviation.

    h. A variance.

    i. A coefficient of variation.

    j. The tenth percentile of a set of scores

    k. The percentile rank of a selected individual in a given group on a given test.

    l. The standard score $\dfrac{x}{s}$ of a selected individual.

    m. The transformed score $Z = 50 + \dfrac{10\,x}{s}$ of a selected individual.

    n. A coefficient of correlation.

Computation of Σxy. In order to throw into relief the principal steps in this procedure, a miniature distribution with only 50 cases and with a very small number of step intervals has been used for two different computational routines. These are presented in the two subdivisions of Table XLV. The class intervals could have been omitted from the first table since the value of r is determined by the joint frequency distribution and not by the scale values of the intervals, when deviations are expressed in interval form.

Method A. On the adjacent grid, x' values are indicated along the lower edge of the chart and y' values along the right-hand margin. The figure written in the corner of each cell is the product of the x' value attaching to the column and y' value attaching to the row in which that cell is located. Thus if $x' = 3$ and $y' = -2$, $x'y' = -6$.

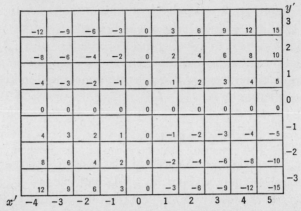

For method A, the joint frequency distribution is plotted in the manner in which Figures 37 and 38 were obtained in the previous chapter. Then an arbitrary origin is taken at some convenient point near the middle of the X-scale, and the x' values are indicated along the horizontal margin. An arbitrary origin is taken at some convenient point near the middle of the Y-scale and the y' values are indicated along the vertical margin. The appropriate $x'y'$ product is then written into each cell of the table, as in the preceding sketch. In Table XLVA, these $x'y'$ products have been written as very small numbers in the lower right-hand corners of the cells. In practice, it is often convenient to use a colored pencil for this purpose. There are on the market prepared charts with these products already printed on the chart. In Table XLVA each f_{xy} frequency is represented by a large number printed near the center of its cell. Multiply each f_{xy} by the corresponding $x'y'$ value. These results appear in the upper left-hand corners of the cells in Table XLVA. Sum for all cells paying attention to signs, and compare with the value shown on the chart, which is $\Sigma f_{xy}x'y' = 57$. In similar fashion, multiply each f_y by its corresponding y', obtaining $\Sigma f_y y' = -19$; and multiply each f_x by its corresponding x', obtaining $\Sigma f_x x' = 35$. To obtain $\Sigma f_{xy}xy$, substitute these values in the formula

$$\Sigma f_{xy}xy = \Sigma f_{xy}x'y' - \frac{(\Sigma f_x x')(\Sigma f_y y')}{N} \qquad (65)$$

or

$$\Sigma xy = \Sigma x'y' - \frac{(\Sigma x')(\Sigma y')}{N} \qquad (59)$$

$$= 57 - \frac{(35)(-19)}{50} = 70.3$$

The result is in terms of interval units. For the computation of r, it is usually left in interval units since i_x and i_y do not appear in the formula for r. In the computation of the regression coefficients, multiplication by one or the other step interval will be needed.

Method A is valuable as an expository device, because computation follows directly from the formula. Students appear to understand what they are doing better if they have seen and understood this routine. However, it has neither swiftness nor accuracy to commend it. Errors are easy to make, and there is no check except by repetition, using a new origin.

Method B. The essential characteristic of this method is the recognition that for any given row, the y' value is constant, so that for that row $\Sigma f_{xy}x'y' = y'\Sigma f_{xy}x'$. For example, from the chart for method A, it is seen that the contribution to $\Sigma f_{xy}x'y'$ made by the row whose class sort is 33–37, is $2(-2)(-2) + 4(-1)(-2) + 1(0)(-2) + 1(2)(-2) = -4(-2) - 4(-2) + 0(-2) + 2(-2) = -6(-2)$. Since -2 is a common factor, this result could have been more easily obtained as

$$-2[2(-2) + 4(-1) + 1(0) + 1(2)] = -2[-4 - 4 + 0 + 2]$$
$$= -2(-6) = 12$$

as has been done on the chart for method B. In the third column at the right of the chart, the sum of the $f_{xy}x'$ is set down for each row separately. The sum of all these entries gives the value previously found for $\Sigma f_x x'$, and provides a check for this value. In the fourth column at the right of the table, each row sum has been multiplied by the y' value for that row. The sum of all such products is $\Sigma f_{xy}x'y'$.

A similar method, applied to the columns, yields a check for $\Sigma f_{xy}x'y'$.

This method is somewhat quicker than A, and has the advantage of giving a check for $\Sigma x'y'$, for $\Sigma x'$ and for $\Sigma y'$.

Completed Computation of r, b_{yx}, and b_{xy}. The computation of $\Sigma(x')^2$ and $\Sigma(y')^2$ is shown in Table XLVB. Note that this method provides a check on $\Sigma x'y'$, $\Sigma x'$, and $\Sigma y'$ each of which is computed twice. It provides no check for $\Sigma(x')^2$ or $\Sigma(y')^2$. For the data in this small table, we have

$$\Sigma x'y' = 57 \qquad \Sigma(x')^2 = 135 \qquad i_x = 3$$
$$\Sigma x' = 35 \qquad \Sigma(y')^2 = 117 \qquad i_y = 5$$
$$\Sigma y' = -19 \qquad N = 50$$

TABLE XLVA

First Method of Obtaining Σxy

(1) Arbitrary origin in middle of distribution
(2) Deviations in interval units
(3) Values of $x'y'$ products written into cells, so that f_{xy} can be readily multiplied by corresponding $x'y'$

In each cell below: the plain number is the $x'y'$ product written into the cell; the **bold** number is the frequency; the number in parentheses is the product $\times$ frequency.

	9-11	12-14	15-17	18-20	21-23	24-26	27-29	f_y	y'	$f_y y'$
53-57	−4	−2	0 **1** (0)	2	4	6 **3** (18)	8 **1** (8)	5	2	10
48-52	−2	−1 **1** (−1)	0 **1** (0)	1 **4** (4)	2 **5** (10)	3	4	11	1	11
43-47	0	0 **1** (0)	0 **2** (0)	0 **6** (0)	0 **3** (0)	0	0	12	0	0
38-42	2	1 **1** (1)	0 **2** (0)	−1 **3** (−3)	−2 **2** (−4)	−3 **1** (−3)	−4	9	−1	−9
33-37	4 **2** (8)	2 **4** (8)	0 **1** (0)	−2	−4 **1** (−4)	−6	−8	8	−2	−16
28-32	6 **2** (12)	3 **2** (6)	0	−3 **1** (−3)	−6	−9	−12	5	−3	−15
f_x	4	9	7	14	11	4	1	50		−19
x'	−2	−1	0	1	2	3	4			
$f_x x'$	−8	−9	0	14	22	12	4	35		

$$\Sigma f_x x' = 35$$
$$\Sigma f_y y' = -19$$
$$\Sigma f_{xy} x'y' = 57$$
$$\Sigma f_{xy} xy = 57 - \frac{(35)(-19)}{50}$$
$$= 70.3$$

232

TABLE XLVB

Second Method of Obtaining Σxy

(1) Reference point in same position as for A
(2) Deviations in interval form as for A
(3) Summation by arrays giving a short cut to Σxy and also a check

	9–11	12–14	15–17	18–20	21–23	24–26	27–29	f_v	y'	$\Sigma f_{xy}x'$	$y'\Sigma f_{xy}x'$	$f_y y'$	$f_v(y')^2$
53–57			1			3	1	5	2	13	26	10	20
48–52		1	1	4	5			11	1	$14-1=13$	13	11	11
43–47		1	2	6	3			12	0	$12-1=11$	0	0	0
38–42		1	2	3	2	1		9	-1	$10-1=9$	-9	-9	9
33–37	2	4	1		1			8	-2	$2-8=-6$	12	-16	32
28–32	2	2		1				5	-3	$1-6=-5$	15	-15	45
										$\Sigma f_{xx'}=35$	$\Sigma f_{xy}x'y'=57$	$\Sigma f_y y'=-19$	$\Sigma f_v(y')^2=117$

	9–11	12–14	15–17	18–20	21–23	24–26	27–29	
f_x	4	9	7	14	11	4	1	
x'	-2	-1	0	1	2	3	4	
$\Sigma f_{xy}y'$	-10	-14	-1	-2	1	5	2	$\Sigma f_y y' = -19$
$x'\Sigma f_{xy}y'$	20	14	0	-2	2	15	8	$\Sigma f_{xy}x'y' = 57$
$x'f_x$	-8	-9	0	14	22	12	4	$\Sigma f_{xx'} = 35$
$f_x(x')^2$	16	9	0	14	44	36	16	$\Sigma f_x(x')^2 = 135$

$$\Sigma f_{xy}x'y' = 57 - \frac{(35)(-19)}{50} = 70.3$$

Therefore

$$r = \frac{57 + (35)(19)/50}{\sqrt{135 - \dfrac{(35)^2}{50}}\sqrt{117 - \dfrac{(19)^2}{50}}} = \frac{70.3}{\sqrt{(110.5)(109.78)}}$$

$$= \frac{70.3}{\sqrt{12130.7}} = 0.638$$

$$b_{yx} = \frac{5}{3} \cdot \frac{57 + (35)(19)/50}{135 - (35)^2/50} = \frac{5}{3} \cdot \frac{70.3}{110.5} = 1.060$$

$$b_{xy} = \frac{3}{5} \cdot \frac{57 + (35)(19)/50}{117 - (19)^2/50} = \frac{3}{5} \cdot \frac{70.3}{109.78} = 0.384$$

Check: $r^2 = (0.638)^2 = 0.40704$

$b_{yx}b_{xy} = (1.060)(0.384) = 0.40704$

Since intermediate computations are carried to 3 places only, the check would usually hold for 3 places only, but here is accurate for 5.

Practice in Computation. Checking. Most persons have to compute a rather large number of correlations before they can depend upon their skill. No attempt will be made to include in this book enough drill to insure competence on the part of each student. Published researches abound in scatter diagrams. An instructor is likely to have fresh data of his own which will be of interest to the class. Data may even be set down arbitrarily and if computations are made first from one origin and then from another, a complete check on the accuracy of the work can be obtained.

The computation of a correlation coefficient should *always be checked*. Even the most seasoned computer makes an occasional slip. Important research findings about to be published have sometimes had to be revised at the last minute because a computer with a reputation for accuracy overlooked a minus sign. There are certain computational methods, one of which is described in Appendix C, which provide a complete check on every step. The novice, not yet ready to use such methods, should check by taking a new origin and carrying the computation out a second time.

A useful set of check formulas is available for comparing values obtained in one computation with values obtained in another for which the origin has been shifted one interval to the left and one interval down:

$$\Sigma(x' + 1)(y' + 1) = \Sigma x'y' + \Sigma x' + \Sigma y' + N \qquad (67)$$
$$\Sigma(x' + 1)^2 = \Sigma(x')^2 + 2\Sigma x' + N \qquad (68)$$
$$\Sigma(y' + 1)^2 = \Sigma(y')^2 + 2\Sigma y' + N \qquad (68)$$
$$\Sigma(x' + 1) = \Sigma x' + N \qquad (69)$$
$$\Sigma(y' + 1) = \Sigma y' + N \qquad (69)$$

For the 50 cases previously considered, this means that if the origin is shifted to the row whose class sort is 38–42 and to the column whose class sort is 12–14, we shall obtain

$$\Sigma(x' + 1)(y' + 1) = 57 + 35 - 19 + 50 = 123$$
$$\Sigma(x' + 1)^2 = 135 + 2(35) + 50 = 255$$
$$\Sigma(y' + 1)^2 = 117 - 2(19) + 50 = 129$$
$$\Sigma(x' + 1) = 35 + 50 = 85$$
$$\Sigma(y' + 1) = -19 + 50 = 31$$

Exercise 27

1. Verify, by direct computation from the table, the check figures given in the preceding paragraph.

2. Using each of these sets of figures, complete the computation of the coefficients of correlation and regression.

3. From the scatter diagram of Figure 37, using the class sort 22–24 as the arbitrary origin for X and the class sort 105–111 as the arbitrary origin for Y, verify the following values (both x' and y' being in interval units):

$$\Sigma x' = -37 \qquad \Sigma(x')^2 = 521 \qquad i_x = 3$$
$$\Sigma y' = 33 \qquad \Sigma(y')^2 = 711 \qquad i_y = 7$$
$$\Sigma x'y' = 337 \qquad N = 109$$

4. From the data of question 3, find the values of the following:

$$\overline{X} = \qquad\qquad r = \qquad\qquad \tilde{y} =$$
$$\overline{Y} = \qquad\qquad b_{yx} = \qquad\qquad \tilde{x} =$$
$$s_x = \qquad\qquad b_{xy} =$$
$$s_y = \qquad\qquad b_{yx}b_{xy} =$$

5. Using the equation for $\tilde{y}$ developed in question 4, find the intelligence quotient most likely to be associated with a language score of 30; of 13; of 25.

Illustration:

$$b_{yx} = 1.60 \qquad\qquad \overline{X} = 22.0 \qquad\qquad \overline{Y} = 110.1$$

if

$$X = 30 \qquad\qquad x = 30 - 22.0 = 8.0$$
$$\tilde{y} = (1.6)(8.0) = 12.8 \text{ and } \tilde{Y} = \tilde{y} + \overline{Y} = 12.8 + 110.1 = 122.9$$

Check the reasonableness of this answer by inspection of Figure 38.

6. Using the equation for $\tilde{x}$ developed in question 4, find the language score associated with an intelligence quotient of 85, of 130, of 118.

7. A given child has an intelligence quotient of 86 and a language score of 14. If someone who did not know his language score tried to estimate it from his intelligence quotient, how large an error would be made? If someone who did not know his intelligence coefficient tried to estimate it from his language score, how large an error would be made?

8. Answer similar questions for these children, whose scores are taken from Appendix A:

Child	Intelligence Quotient	Language Score
3	117	26
21	124	29
43	121	28
55	101	17
80	126	19
93	124	14

9. From the data of Appendix A, compute each of the 21 correlation coefficients, the 7 means, and 7 standard deviations, and enter them in a schedule similar to the following.

	$\overline{X}$	s	\multicolumn{6}{c}{Correlation}
			2	3	4	5	6	7
1. Age	___	___	___	___	___	___	___	___
2. Intelligence Quotient	110.1	___		___	___	___	.58	___
3. Arith. Computation	7.9	___			.295	___	___	___
4. Arith. Reasoning	4.9	___				___	___	___
5. Reading Speed		___					___	___
6. Language	22.0	___						___
7. History—Civics	___	___						

Regression Equation in Gross Score Form. For most practical purposes it is more convenient to have the regression equation set up to predict a gross score rather than a deviation score. Suppose, for example, that classification tests have been given to the entering freshmen in a college, or to a large group of persons applying for jobs in industry. (In such cases the regression equations are likely to be multiple regression equations making use of a number of variables, but the same argument holds.) In such cases time is an important matter. It may take a few seconds to transform the equation in deviation form to the equation in gross score form, but when that has been done, the process of applying the equation to each of hundreds or thousands of individuals will take far less time because it can be applied to the gross scores without the necessity of changing them to deviation scores.

Substituting $\tilde{y} = \tilde{Y} - \overline{Y}$ and $x = X - \overline{X}$ in $\tilde{y} = b_{yx}x$ reduces it to

$$\tilde{Y} - \overline{Y} = b_{yx}(X - \overline{X})$$

or

$$\begin{aligned}
\tilde{Y} &= b_{yx}X - b_{yx}\overline{X} + \overline{Y} \\
\tilde{Y} &= b_{yx}X + (\overline{Y} - b_{yx}\overline{X}) \\
\tilde{Y} &= b_{yx}X + k
\end{aligned}$$

where k is the constant $\overline{Y} - b_{yx}\overline{X}$ whose numerical value can be found.

Suppose, for example, that the equation $\tilde{y} = 1.24x$ has been found, and that $\overline{Y} = 38.4$ while $\overline{X} = 51.2$. Then

$$\tilde{Y} = 1.24X + [38.4 - (1.24)(51.2)]$$

or

$$\tilde{Y} = 1.24X - 25.1$$

In the same way $\tilde{x} = X - \overline{X}$ and $y = Y - \overline{Y}$ may be substituted in $\tilde{x} = b_{xy}y$. The two regression equations in gross score form are:

$$\tilde{Y} = b_{yx}X + (\overline{Y} - b_{yx}\overline{X}) \quad \text{and} \quad \tilde{X} = b_{xy}Y + (\overline{X} - b_{xy}\overline{Y}) \tag{70}$$

It may be of some interest, though not of very great importance, to see that the change from equation (45) to equation (70) expresses a translation of the origin from M to O in Figure 44. Referred to M as origin, the regression equations have no constant term because their graphs pass through M. Referred to zero as origin, the equations must be written with a constant term, because in general the graphs do not pass through the zero point, though in a special case one or the other graph may happen to do so.

$$OB = AM = \overline{Y} \qquad\qquad OA = BM = \overline{X}$$
$$DB = b_{yx}\overline{X} \qquad\qquad CA = b_{xy}\overline{Y}$$
$$OD = OB - DB = \overline{Y} - b_{yx}\overline{X} \qquad OC = OA - CA = \overline{X} - b_{xy}\overline{Y}$$
$$\tilde{Y} = b_{yx}X + OD \qquad\qquad \tilde{X} = b_{xy}Y + OC$$

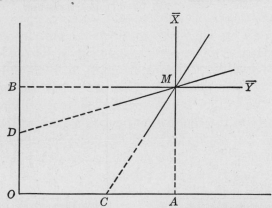

Fig. 44. Lines of regression in relation to the intersection of the means (M) and to the zero point (O).

Computation of a Correlation Coefficient Without Plotting. Although the computation of the correlation coefficient without plotting is relatively easy, it involves some hazard. Plotting the scatter diagram often reveals peculiarities of the data which might not be discovered if the corre-

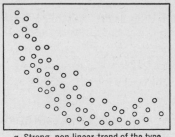

a. Strong, non-linear trend of the type often found when per capita cost is correlated with some measure closely related to size of group.

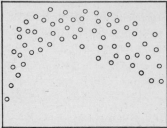

b. Non-linear trend of the type often found when some physical trait is correlated with age over a rather long age range.

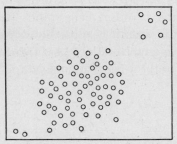

c. Correlation very near zero for most of the group, but spuriously inflated by the presence of a few extreme cases.

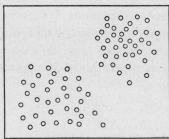

d. Spurious positive correlation produced by combining two groups one of which considerably exceeds the other as to the mean of each trait.

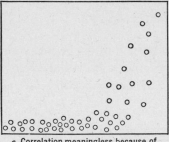

e. Correlation meaningless because of large number of cases with nearly uniform scores in trait Y.

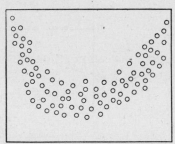

f. Very high non-linear relationship in data for which r would be approximately zero.

Fig. 45. Sketches illustrating peculiarities of distribution such that the computed value of r misrepresents the true relationship between the traits.

lation coefficient were computed without plotting. The diagram may reveal some peculiar trend in the data which is of great importance. The drift may be so strongly curvilinear that the formula for r, based as it is on the assumption of linear regression, may give too low an estimate of the relationship. There may be one or two extreme cases which are exercising a great influence upon the size of r. There may be a large number of undistributed scores, that is, scores that are all alike or nearly alike. This tends to make the value of r meaningless. For example, if a large proportion of the group studied received zero scores on one trait, or received perfect scores, those scores would be undistributed, and there would be no discrimination among the members of the group receiving these uniform scores. Several sketches are presented in Figure 45 illustrating schematically certain type situations in which a study of the scatter diagram would be very important.

Nevertheless, it is sometimes desirable to compute r without plotting, entering the raw data directly in a computing machine. Such computations should be done with gross scores. Obtain the following values:

$$\Sigma X \qquad \Sigma X^2 \qquad \Sigma(X + Y) \qquad \Sigma(X + Y)^2$$
$$\Sigma Y \qquad \Sigma Y^2 \qquad \Sigma(X - Y) \qquad \Sigma(X - Y)^2$$

Check these relationships;

$$\Sigma X + \Sigma Y = \Sigma(X + Y) \qquad (71)$$
$$\Sigma X - \Sigma Y = \Sigma(X - Y) \qquad (72)$$
$$\Sigma(X + Y)^2 + \Sigma(X - Y)^2 = 2\Sigma X^2 + 2\Sigma Y^2 \qquad (73)$$

and compute

$$\Sigma XY = \tfrac{1}{4}\{\Sigma(X + Y)^2 - \Sigma(X - Y)^2\} \qquad (74)$$
$$\Sigma XY = \tfrac{1}{2}\{\Sigma(X + Y)^2 - \Sigma X^2 - \Sigma Y^2\} \qquad (75)$$

Complete the computation of r by formula (56) and of the regression coefficients by formula (55). The pattern of computation is illustrated in Table XLVI. The student should complete the computation and check the results.*

* On a computing machine with wide carriage, it is possible to obtain all at the same time, ΣX, ΣY, ΣX^2, ΣY^2, and ΣXY. A routine for doing this will be found on pages 49–51 of *Computation of Descriptive Statistics*, by Jack W. Dunlap (published by the Ralph C. Coxhead Corp.). While the procedure outlined there has special reference to the Mathematon, its general pattern is applicable to other large capacity machines. Two suggestions should, however, be added to Dunlap's instructions: 1. Divide the cases up into small subgroups of 20 or 25 cases each, record the five sums separately for each subgroup, and clear the machine. This serves two purposes, facilitating the finding of errors if such occur, and avoiding the necessity of watching the dials lest the figures for one sum carry over into another. 2. Check the results for each subgroup separately, either by obtaining $\Sigma(X + Y)$ and $\Sigma(X + Y)^2$ or by obtaining $\Sigma(X - Y)$ and $\Sigma(X - Y)^2$.

TABLE XLVI

Computation of a Correlation Coefficient Without Plotting

$X = $ *Score in Arithmetic Computation*
$Y = $ *Score in Arithmetic Reasoning*

(Data from Appendix A)

Case	X	Y	X^2	Y^2	$X + Y$	$(X + Y)^2$	$X - Y$	$(X - Y)^2$
1	12	11	144	121	23	529	1	1
2	13	4	169	16	17	289	9	81
3	5	8	25	64	13	169	−3	9
4	8	6	64	36	14	196	2	4
5	7	4	49	16	11	121	3	9
—	—	—	—	—	—	—	—	—
—	—	—	—	—	—	—	—	—
—	—	—	—	—	—	—	—	—
40	15	5	225	25	20	400	10	100
41	10	4	100	16	14	196	6	36
42	11	5	121	25	16	256	6	36
43	5	1	25	1	6	36	4	16
44	5	4	25	16	9	81	1	1
—	—	—	—	—	—	—	—	—
—	—	—	—	—	—	—	—	—
—	—	—	—	—	—	—	—	—
108	9	2	81	4	11	121	7	49
109	10	6	100	36	16	256	4	16
Σ	856	538	7912	3322	1394	20210	318	2258

Checks:

$$\begin{aligned} \Sigma X &= 856 \\ + \Sigma Y &= 538 \\ \Sigma(X + Y) &= \overline{1394} \end{aligned} \qquad \begin{aligned} \Sigma X &= 856 \\ - \Sigma Y &= 538 \\ \Sigma(X - Y) &= \overline{318} \end{aligned}$$

$$\begin{aligned} \Sigma(X + Y)^2 &= 20210 \\ - \Sigma(X - Y)^2 &= \underline{2258} \\ \\ 4\Sigma XY &= 17952 \\ 2\Sigma XY &= 8976 \end{aligned} \qquad \begin{aligned} \Sigma X^2 &= 7912 \\ + \Sigma Y^2 &= \underline{3322} \\ &11234 \\ - \Sigma(X - Y)^2 &= \underline{2258} \\ 2\Sigma XY &= \overline{8976} \end{aligned}$$

Solution

$$r = \frac{\Sigma XY - \dfrac{(\Sigma X)(\Sigma Y)}{N}}{\sqrt{\Sigma X^2 - \dfrac{(\Sigma X)^2}{N}}\sqrt{\Sigma Y^2 - \dfrac{(\Sigma Y)^2}{N}}}$$

$$= \frac{4488 - \dfrac{(856)(538)}{109}}{\sqrt{7912 - \dfrac{(856)^2}{109}}\sqrt{3322 - \dfrac{(538)^2}{109}}} = .295$$

Published Correlation Charts. A large number of prepared correlation charts are now commercially available. The use of these charts may effect a very great saving of time when many correlations are to be computed. The first such chart, designed by Ruger, and now out of print, was merely a large grid, printed in red, with $x'y'$ products printed in the corners of the cells, and wide margins on which to make computations.

If a commercial chart is to be used, the following characteristics seem desirable:

1. The routine should be an efficient one.

2. Complete checks should be provided for every value which enters into the final computations. Very few charts meet this essential requirement, most of them providing a check for Σxy only, and some not even for that.

3. The chart should be printed on durable paper, of convenient size for filing. Blanks and instructions should be given enough space to minimize eye strain. Space should be provided in which to write such essential information as the description of the data, names of traits, intervals, name of computer, date, and any peculiarities of the situation which should be recalled if reference is made to the sheet at some much later date.

4. If the same chart can be used for either machine or hand computations, that is often a convenience. It is at least essential to select a chart adapted to whichever manner of computation is to be employed.

Of the many charts now on the market, two seem to the writer to have an advantage over the others because of the completeness of the checks which they provide and the saving of time they make possible.* These

---

* The Kelley chart also provides complete checks, but it checks everything twice, thus requiring an unnecessary expenditure of time. Kelley himself calls it "the long method."

are the Cureton-Dunlap, published by the Macmillan Company, and the Durost-Walker, published by the World Book Company. The Cureton-Dunlap chart is published in two forms, one for hand computation and one for machine computation. The Durost-Walker chart can be used for either hand or machine work. The latter chart is based upon the device for computing a variance by continued summation which is described in Appendix C. Since the main purpose of this text is not to teach efficient computational routines but to lay a basis for interpretation of data, the Durost-Walker chart, the method of which the writer thinks very economical, but which is not obviously related to the usual formula for r, will receive no further discussion in the text proper. Full instructions for its use are presented in Appendix C. It is recommended that students who expect to carry out large-scale correlational studies learn this very expeditious method, because, when mastered, it is extremely fast and the checks are so arranged as to catch errors almost as soon as they occur.

It is much better for the beginner not to use any kind of prepared chart until he has mastered the general plan. A chart is not a crutch to help the novice. It is a means of speeding up operations after they are well understood. When computations are to be filed away, it is important that all the pertinent information which may be needed at some future time shall be recorded on the sheets. This is more likely to be done on a prepared chart which has blanks calling for such information than on an ordinary piece of coordinate paper.

Correlation Among Ranks. At the close of Chapter V there was introduced a measure of relationship between two sets of ranks, computed by the formula

$$R = 1 - \frac{6\Sigma d^2}{N(N^2 - 1)} \tag{76}$$

This is also a measure of correlation; it is, in fact, exactly equivalent to the result of applying the product moment formula to the ranks. For example, suppose that nine members of a Boy Scout patrol have been ranked by their leader and also by their public school teacher on their readiness to cooperate in group undertakings. It would be well-nigh impossible to assign scores on this trait to the boys, but it might not be too difficult to place the nine names in a rank order. The purpose is to see how closely the two adults, with different personalities, seeing the boys under different circumstances, agree in their appraisal of the ranking of the boys on this trait.

Boy	X Rank Given by Scout Leader	Y Rank Given by Teacher	d Difference in Ranks	d^2
Sam	1	3	2	4
George	2	4	2	4
Colin	3	1	-2	4
Tom	4	2	-2	4
Watson	5	9	4	16
Harry	6	5	-1	1
John	7	7	0	0
Ted	8	6	-2	4
Ralph	9	8	-1	1
			0	38

$$R = 1 - \frac{6(38)}{9(80)} = \frac{41}{60} = .68$$

If the product moment method were used, we should find

$$\Sigma X^2 = (1^2 + 2^2 \cdots + 9^2) = 285 \qquad \Sigma X = 45$$
$$\Sigma Y^2 = (1^2 + 2^2 \cdots + 9^2) = 285 \qquad \Sigma Y = 45$$
$$\Sigma XY = 3 + 8 + 3 + 8 + 45 + 30 + 49 + 48 + 72 = 266$$

$$r = \frac{266 - \dfrac{(45)(45)}{9}}{285 - \dfrac{(45)^2}{9}} = \frac{266 - 225}{285 - 225} = \frac{41}{60} = .68$$

The outcome of two computations, both utilizing *ranks*, is identical.

If, then, we make use of ranks, formula (76) is not different in its outcome from the product moment formulas previously used, but is merely a convenient short cut. The two are algebraically identical when scores are distributed evenly along the scale of scores at intervals of 1 unit, there being just one case in every interval, beginning with 1. This is of course not the way scores are usually distributed. They are more likely to pile up toward the middle of the distribution, and the procedure of ranking transforms the natural shape of their distribution to a rectangular shape.

The chief usefulness of the rank formula is for those situations in which it is not possible to obtain actual scores, but in which it is possible to place individuals in order in their possession of some trait. The difficulty of assigning ranks is prohibitive when the group is large, and such data would not usually be obtainable for N larger than 25 or 30.

The rank order formula is also used sometimes for very small groups for which scaled data are available, the scores being first changed into ranks. This results in some loss of information and in general has little to recommend it except speed and convenience. But for very small groups, no estimate of correlation is very reliable, anyway. If there are several scores of the same size there will be ties in rank, and when this occurs, the complete equivalence of rank formula and the product moment formula no longer obtains.

Illustration of Transformation of Scores to Ranks

Case	X Score	Y Score	X Rank	Y Rank
1	40	·22	3	1
2	37	19	$5\frac{1}{2}$	5
3	39	18	4	6
4	28	11	8	7
5	42	20	2	3
6	46	20	1	3
7	37	20	$5\frac{1}{2}$	3
8	35	10	7	8

Note the ties in rank. The two values of X which would have had ranks of 5 and 6 had one score been a little larger than the other are each assigned a rank of $\dfrac{5+6}{2} = 5\frac{1}{2}$, while the three values of Y which would have had ranks 2, 3, and 4 had their scores been distinguishable from each other are each assigned the rank of $\dfrac{2+3+4}{3} = 3$.

By applying the rank order formula to the ranks we obtain

$$1 - \frac{6(\Sigma d^2)}{N(N^2 - 1)} = 1 - \frac{6(21.5)}{8(63)} = \frac{125}{168} = .744$$

By applying the product moment formula to the ranks we obtain

$$\frac{\Sigma XY - \dfrac{(\Sigma X)(\Sigma Y)}{N}}{\sqrt{\Sigma X^2 - \dfrac{(\Sigma X)^2}{N}}\sqrt{\Sigma Y^2 - \dfrac{(\Sigma Y)^2}{N}}}$$

$$= \frac{192 - \dfrac{(36)^2}{8}}{\sqrt{203.5 - \dfrac{(36)^2}{8}}\sqrt{202 - \dfrac{(36)^2}{8}}} = \frac{30}{40.74} = .736$$

By applying the product moment formula to the original scores we obtain

$$\frac{\Sigma XY - \dfrac{(\Sigma X)(\Sigma Y)}{N}}{\sqrt{\Sigma X^2 - \dfrac{(\Sigma X)^2}{N}}\sqrt{\Sigma Y^2 - \dfrac{(\Sigma Y)^2}{N}}}$$

$$= \frac{5443 - \dfrac{(304)(140)}{8}}{\sqrt{11748 - \dfrac{(304)^2}{8}}\sqrt{2590 - \dfrac{(140)^2}{8}}} = \frac{123}{165.7} = .742$$

These figures illustrate the fact that the rank order and the product moment formulas are not identical when there are ties in rank, and that the correlation computed for the original scores is not identical with that obtained from the ranks.

The rank order coefficient is useful in cases where the equality of units cannot be ascertained. The *amount* of the trait is thus not known, but the *order* of individuals can perhaps be determined.

CHAPTER XIV

CORRELATION AND REGRESSION—INTERPRETATION

The Size of a Correlation Coefficient. You have now learned the procedures for computing a coefficient of correlation, and you know that such a coefficient will have a value somewhere between -1.0 and $+1.0$, but you probably have a very uneasy feeling as to your understanding of how large any given correlation is. You do not know, for example, whether $r = .40$ is to be called "large" or "small." Now the terms "large" and "small" are not absolute terms.

Several different bases exist for interpreting the size of a coefficient of correlation, and some confusion has arisen because a coefficient which might be called "large" in one connection would be considered "small" in another. To draw up a numerical scale and to say that coefficients in one particular range are large, in another negligible, only adds to this confusion. We shall have to consider many aspects of correlation in order to build up some feeling about the import of the size of a coefficient under particular circumstances.

Interpretation in Terms of Correlations Commonly Obtained. If a research worker says he found a high correlation between two traits, he sometimes means only to say that the value he has obtained is higher than experience has led him to expect in studies of that type. So many factors affect the size of a correlation coefficient, that if a list of typical values of r for specified traits were made it would very likely be misinterpreted. After several attempts to make a list indicating the size of r most commonly found in certain situations, the undertaking has been abandoned because the author could find no way to keep the descriptions simple and at the same time not misleading.

If a research worker obtained a correlation of, say, .60 between pupil achievement and some teacher trait he would rightly consider it very high in relation to the low correlations usually found. If he obtained a correlation of .60 between two forms of the same test he would consider it very low—too low, in fact for the test to be appropriate for the measurement of individuals.

Interpretation in Terms of Sampling Reliability. A fuller treatment will be presented in Volume II, *Statistical Inference*, but the problem must be mentioned here, if only to distinguish it from other aspects of correlation. Suppose that the value of the correlation coefficient in some

246

universe or population, is, let us say .70, and suppose that a large number of random * samples all of the same size are drawn from that universe, let us say one thousand samples of 100 cases each. If the correlation coefficient is computed for each sample, some coefficients will be larger than .70 and some smaller. If the frequency distribution of these thousand values of r is plotted, it will be seen to be negatively skewed, reaching further below .70 than above. This frequency distribution of the values of r obtained from successive random samples of uniform size out of the same population is called the sampling distribution of r. When there is no linear relationship in the population, i.e., when the population value (ρ) is zero, this distribution of sample values is symmetrical. As the population value approaches $+1.00$, the distribution of sample values becomes more and more negatively skewed. As the population value approaches -1.00, the distribution of sample values becomes more and more positively skewed.

When the population value, or ρ, is zero † and N is not small, the sampling distribution of r is normal and has a standard deviation of $\dfrac{1}{\sqrt{N-1}}$.

Suppose, for example, that two traits such as height and spelling ability for children of the same age are uncorrelated (i.e., $\rho = 0$) in a large population, and that many samples of 65 cases each are drawn at random from that population. For each sample the correlation between these traits is computed. All of these sample correlation coefficients will be near zero, but some of them will be positive and some negative. The standard deviation of them all will be around $\dfrac{1}{\sqrt{65-1}} = .125$. By reference to tables of the normal distribution you can see that

99% of the area under that curve lies between $\pm 2.58\sigma$
98% of the area under that curve lies between $\pm 2.33\sigma$
97% of the area under that curve lies between $\pm 2.17\sigma$
96% of the area under that curve lies between $\pm 2.05\sigma$
95% of the area under that curve lies between $\pm 1.96\sigma$

* For an explanation of "random" see Chapter XV.

† The formula for the standard deviation of r given in most elementary texts is $\dfrac{1-r^2}{\sqrt{N-1}}$. The r in this formula is the unknown population ρ. If you are trying to decide whether one might believe there was no correlation in the population, you are considering a population in which $\rho = 0$ and therefore $\dfrac{1-\rho^2}{\sqrt{N-1}} = \dfrac{1}{\sqrt{N-1}}$. Only when the true population value is zero or nearly zero is it safe to assume that sample values of r would be distributed normally

Therefore we should expect that

99% of these samples would have a value of r between $\pm 2.58(.125) = \pm .32$
98% of these samples would have a value of r between $\pm 2.33(.125) = \pm .29$
97% of these samples would have a value of r between $\pm 2.17(.125) = \pm .27$
96% of these samples would have a value of r between $\pm 2.06(.125) = \pm .26$
95% of these samples would have a value of r between $\pm 1.96(.125) = \pm .245$

If, therefore, for a sample of 65 cases you should obtain a correlation of, say, $r = .21$ between two traits, you would feel that this might easily have occurred through the accidents of sampling from an uncorrelated population. You would not be sure that the two traits were correlated at all *in the universe*, though they are certainly correlated in your sample. You would therefore say that this correlation is *not significantly different from zero*. On the other hand, if for a sample of 65 cases you should obtain, say, $r = .48$, you should find it exceedingly hard to believe that this came from a random sample of an uncorrelated population. To picture to yourself how very rare such an occurrence would be, go back to Figure 27, and copy off one of the normal curves there on tracing paper. Mark the mean value 0, and lay off the standard deviation scale on the base line, marking the point which is 1σ from the mean (.125), the point which is 2σ from the mean (.25), etc. (These are the points now marked 1, 2, etc.) Where is the point .48? How often do you think one would obtain a sample with a correlation as large as this or larger in a sample of 65 cases when the correlation in the universe was zero? If you obtained a correlation of .48 in such a sample, would you want to maintain that the correlation in the population was zero? In such a case one says the *correlation is significantly different from zero*.

For samples of 65 cases we may say that any r whose numerical value is larger than

.32　is significantly larger than zero at the .01 level
.29　"　　　　"　　　　　"　　　"　　"　"　"　.02　"
.27　"　　　　"　　　　　"　　　"　　"　"　"　.03　"
.26　"　　　　"　　　　　"　　　"　　"　"　"　.04　"
.245 "　　　　"　　　　　"　　　"　　"　"　"　.05　"

We have here touched only the fringes of a rather complicated subject, but at least you see that to say r is significant is not to say that it is large enough to be useful for all purposes but merely that it is numerically too large to be interpreted as due to accidents of sampling from an uncorrelated population. You have reason to believe that there is some correlation (positive or negative) in the population.

The procedure for deciding whether r is or is not "too large" to be consistent with the hypothesis that there is no correlation in the population requires too much discussion to be treated adequately in a first-semester course. The usual formula for the probable error of r is consistently misused, and should be avoided. Satisfactory methods cannot be presented until the student has studied sampling and analysis of variance.

Exercise 28

1. If a series of random samples of 145 cases each are drawn from a population in which the correlation is zero, what would be the standard deviation of the distribution of the correlation coefficients in these samples? What would be the range on either side of zero in which you would expect to find the middle 90% of such r's?

2. Supply the numbers to fill in the following table:

N	Standard deviation of set of r's from random samples when $\rho = 0$ in universe	Value which r must exceed numerically to be significant at the		
		.05 level	.03 level	.01 level
50				
129				
227				
421				
626				

3. Which of these correlation coefficients are significantly different from zero at the .01 level?

a. $r = .28$, $N = 40$ d. $r = -.09$ $N = 1154$
b. $r = .21$ $N = 355$ e. $r = .51$ $N = 26$
c. $r = .12$ $N = 568$ f. $r = .53$ $N = 17$

Interpretation in Terms of Accuracy of Prediction. Figure 42 of Chapter XII indicates the way in which scores crowd more closely about the regression lines as r increases, so that the residual errors are smaller. Read the discussion on residual in Chapter XII. In Figure 41 are shown the points representing the paired x- and y-scores of 16 individuals. In Part A, the y-residuals of these 16 individuals are shown; in Part B, the x-residuals.

A measure of the amount of scattering of scores about the line of regression of y on x would be some sort of group measure of the y-residuals. Obviously the sum of the residuals is zero, because the residuals balance each other around any line through the intersection of the means. As in the past this difficulty can be met by squaring residuals, and finding their mean square. Such a measure would be similar to the variance, and its square root to the standard deviation.

The accompanying scheme has been set up in such a way as to emphasize the similarities and the differences between the two entries in each horizontal row. Study this scheme, pair by pair, until you understand the meaning of the new terms and symbols.

Item	Scores	Residuals
Symbol for variance	$s_y{}^2$ $s_x{}^2$	$s^2{}_{y \cdot x}$ $s^2{}_{x \cdot y}$
Value around which fluctuation is measured	Mean	Regression line
Verbal definition of variance	Variance $= \dfrac{1}{N}$ times the sum of the squares of the deviations of the scores from their mean	Residual variance $= \dfrac{1}{N}$ times the sum of the squares of the deviations of the scores from their regressed values
Formula for variance	$s_y{}^2 = \dfrac{\Sigma(Y - \overline{Y})^2}{N} = \dfrac{\Sigma y^2}{N}$	$s^2{}_{y \cdot x} = \dfrac{\Sigma(Y - \tilde{Y})^2}{N}$ $= \dfrac{\Sigma(y - \tilde{y})^2}{N} = \dfrac{\Sigma(y - b_{yx}x)^2}{N}$ $= s_y{}^2(1 - r^2)$
Standard deviation	$s_y =$ standard deviation of scores	$s_{y \cdot x} = s_y\sqrt{1 - r^2} =$ standard deviation of residuals $=$ standard error of estimate

Symbolism. The symbol $s_{y \cdot x}$, read "s sub y dot x," is used to represent the standard deviation of the y residuals, called the *standard error of estimate of* y, or the *standard error made in predicting* y *from* x. The symbol $\sigma_{y \cdot x}$, found in some texts, has the same meaning. The subscript to the left of the point, called a *primary subscript*, names the variable whose dispersion is under consideration. The subscript to the right of the point, called a secondary subscript, names the variable used in the regression equation for estimating the variable named by the primary subscript. The symbol $s^2{}_{y \cdot x}$ represents the *residual variance in* y *after variation related to* x *has been allowed for by a regression equation.*

Formula for Standard Error of Estimate. The following formulas are derived by simple algebra from the equation of the regression line. They depend on no assumptions other than the assumption that regression is linear and that r has such a value as will make the sum of the squares of the errors of estimate as small as possible.

$$s^2_{y \cdot x} = s_y{}^2(1 - r_{xy}{}^2) \text{ and } s^2_{x \cdot y} = s_x{}^2(1 - r_{xy}{}^2) \tag{77}$$
$$s_{y \cdot x} = s_y\sqrt{1 - r_{xy}{}^2} \text{ and } s_{x \cdot y} = s_x\sqrt{1 - r_{xy}{}^2} \tag{77a}$$

From these formulas it follows that $s^2_{y \cdot x}$ cannot be larger than $s_y{}^2$, and that $s^2_{x \cdot y}$ cannot be larger than $s_x{}^2$, that r^2 cannot be larger than 1.00 and that r cannot be numerically larger than 1. A derivation of these formulas is presented in Appendix B.

Partition of the Variance. The total variance of one trait can now be separated into two additive portions: (1) the variance which is accounted for by variation in the related trait and (2) the residual variance which is independent of variation in the related trait. The partition of a variance into two or more such portions has very great importance for statistical inference and is the basis for the technique of *analysis of variance*. Out of it also comes a test for the significance of r. At present, however, we cannot treat analysis of variance but only prepare the student to understand it when it is developed more fully in a second course.

To illustrate the general problem we may use data gathered by Ethel M. Elderton in a study of over ten thousand Glasgow children. She found the standard deviation of the weight in pounds and of the height in inches of these children to be $s_w = 12.97$ and $s_h = 5.36$. The correlation between height and weight she found to be $r = .91$. Of the total variation in weight, part is associated with differences in height, and would disappear if measurements were made only on children of uniform height. Part of the variation is independent of height and would remain even if all the heights were uniform, or even if height were allowed for by a regression equation in which weight was predicted by height. This residual variation of the weights over and above the variations to be expected because of differences in height, is the variation of the residuals.

The variation in weight which is associated with variation in height is the variation of the regressed values of weight predicted from height by the equation

$$\tilde{w} = r_{wh}\frac{s_w}{s_h}h.$$

In Chapter IX, it was seen that multiplying all values of a variate by a constant has the effect of multiplying the standard deviation of the variate by the constant and the variance by the square of the constant. That is, if $\tilde{y} = bx$, $s_{\tilde{y}} = bs_x$.

Therefore

$$s_{\tilde{y}}^2 = \left(r\frac{s_y}{s_x}\right)^2 s_x^2 = r^2 s_y^2 \qquad (78)$$

and

$$s_{\tilde{y}} = rs_y \qquad (78a)$$

Hence

$$s_{\tilde{w}}^2 = r_{wh}^2 s_w^2$$

$$s_{\tilde{w}}^2 = (.91)^2 s_w^2 = .83 s_w^2$$

The variation in weight which is independent of variation in height is the variation of the residuals $w - \tilde{w}$.

$$s_{w \cdot h}^2 = s_w^2(1 - r_{hw}^2) = .17 s_w^2$$

The deviation of the weight of a child from the group mean is made up of two additive portions, the regressed value $\tilde{w} = r\dfrac{s_w}{s_h}h$ and the residual $w - \tilde{w}$, so that $w = \tilde{w} + (w - \tilde{w})$. The variance of the weights of the group of children is also made up of two additive portions, the variance of regressed values, which is $r_{wh}^2 s_w^2$, and the variance of residuals, which is $s_w^2(1 - r_{wh}^2)$, so that

$$s_w^2 = s_w^2 r_{wh}^2 + s_w^2(1 - r_{hw}^2)$$
$$s_w^2 = s_{\tilde{w}}^2 + s_{w-\tilde{w}}^2$$

This relationship usually comes as a surprise. It is algebraically inevitable.

Predictive Value of Correlation Coefficient. An interpretation can now be made of the effect of a given size of r in reducing errors of estimate. The more successful the prediction, the larger is the variance of regressed scores and the smaller is the variance of residuals. Since

$$s_y^2 = s_{\tilde{y}}^2 + s_{y-\tilde{y}}^2 = r^2 s_y^2 + (1 - r^2)s_y^2$$

we have

$$1 = \frac{s_{\tilde{y}}^2}{s_y^2} + \frac{s_{y-\tilde{y}}^2}{s_y^2} = r^2 + (1 - r^2)$$

From this it appears that r^2 is the ratio of the variance of predicted scores to the total variance, or is the proportion of the variance in one trait which is associated with variation in the other correlated trait. It also appears that $1 - r^2$ is the ratio of residual variance to total variance, or the proportion of variance in one trait which remains even when all effect of variation in the other trait is removed. The predictive value of

r is obviously the same whether r is positive or negative. The term "predictive value" must be recognized as an abstraction for which no measure can be obtained until it is defined in more objective terms. Its general meaning would seem to be related to the fact that the larger r is, the less residual error occurs in estimates obtained from a regression equation. The concept is quite clear so long as we do not insist upon trying to set up a numerical scale of "predictive value" or "improvement over chance prediction." The latter term produces only confusion of thought and should be deleted from our statistical vocabulary.

Has a correlation of .70 sufficient predictive value to be used as the basis of judgments about individuals? The standard error of estimate would be $s_{1 \cdot 2} = s_1 \sqrt{1 - .49} = .71 s_1$. The residual variance would be $s_{1 \cdot 2}^2 = s_1^2 (1 - .49) = .51 s_1^2$. The reduction in error afforded by knowledge of the standing of an individual in the related trait would be very valuable for a study of a group, but not sufficiently great to warrant predictions about individuals in any important matter.

Is a correlation of .80 twice as valuable as one of .40 for purposes of prediction? The proportions of the variance of one trait not accounted for by variation in the other are respectively .36 and .84, which suggests that $r = .80$ is much more than twice as good as $r = .40$ for prediction. It would, however, be specious to say it is $\dfrac{.80}{.40}$ times as valuable or to say it is $\dfrac{.84}{.36}$ times as valuable, or to try to state any numerical ratio whatever. "Predictive value of r" is a trait for which units have not been made equal by any satisfactory definition. To define it in terms of reduction in variance and to define it in terms of reduction in standard deviation produce widely disparate results, yet it would be difficult to argue that one definition is good and the other bad.

If the correlation between two forms of a test (the "reliability of the test") is .85, is the test reliable enough to use for individual predictions? The standard error of estimate is $\sqrt{1 - (.85)^2} = .52$ times as large as the standard deviation of either form, if the two tests have been equated to have the same standard deviation. This means a larger discrepancy between the two forms than any test expert would be likely to tolerate if he is using his test to make pronouncements about individuals. If, however, he is using the test only to study group behavior, it would generally be considered satisfactory to use a test with lower reliability even than this.

The expression $\sqrt{1 - r^2}$ has been called the *coefficient of alienation* and designated by the letter k.

Exercise 29

1. For each of the following sets of data, find the regression equation to predict X from Y. Find the variance of X values around their regression line, and find the variance of the regressed scores.

	N	$\overline{X}$	$\overline{Y}$	s_x^2	s_y^2	r_{xy}	Equation	$s_{x \cdot y}^2$	$s^2_{\tilde{z}}$
a.	43	59.3	13.7	6.1	3.4	.87	_____	_____	_____
b.	216	28.5	38.2	12.5	17.2	.54	_____	_____	_____
c.	307	21.5	76.2	8.4	15.0	.25	_____	_____	_____
d.	135	46.2	51.5	5.5	7.2	−.18	_____	_____	_____
e.	183	27.1	23.5	4.6	8.5	−.94	_____	_____	_____
f.	572	17.6	17.8	6.3	6.5	.01	_____	_____	_____

2. The correlation between height and age for a very large number of children ranging in age from 5 to 15 has been found to be .83. What proportion of the variance of height is due to difference in age? What proportion independent of age? If a group could be selected completely uniform as to age, how would you expect the height variance of this group to be related to the height variance of the original group?

3. The correlation between two forms of a vocabulary test is .92. For the group on which the test was standardized, $\overline{X}_A = 51.2$, and $\overline{X}_B = 52.5$, while $s_A = 5.2$, and $s_B = 5.4$. Somewhat later, an investigator is making a study in which he uses form A only, but when he looks for the records of these individuals on form A they have been mislaid. The form B records are available, and he decides to substitute them.

    a. If he uses the form B scores exactly as they stand, what error will he commit?

    b. If he sets up a regression equation and estimates each individual's A score from his B score, what will be the standard deviation of these substi-tute values? What will be the standard deviation of the errors he would make in estimating A from B?

4. For each of the values of r given below compute r^2, $1 - r^2$, and $\sqrt{1 - r^2}$.

r	r^2	$1 - r^2$	$\sqrt{1 - r^2}$
0	_____	_____	_____
.20	_____	_____	_____
.30	_____	_____	_____
.40	_____	_____	_____
.50	_____	_____	_____
.60	_____	_____	_____
.70	_____	_____	_____
.80	_____	_____	_____
1.00	_____	_____	_____

Factors Which Affect the Size of *r*.   The interpretation of correlation studies is somewhat difficult because the size of a coefficient of correlation depends not only upon the strength of the intrinsic relationship between the traits in question but upon a number of other factors such as the accuracy with which measurement has been made, the selection of cases, and the shape of the distributions of the traits. We shall now ask what effect each of various factors is likely to have upon a computed correlation coefficient.

Changes in Origin and Change in Scale.   These have no effect whatever upon the size of *r*. If every measure in one distribution is multiplied by the same number, increased by the same number, divided by the same number, or decreased by the same number, or if it is affected by two of these operations at once, the value of *r* remains invariant.

Grouping Error.   This has a negligible effect on *r*. However, if the step interval is made very large, so that the number of intervals in one or both traits is small, say less than 10, Sheppard's corrections for *broad categories* may have to be applied (see the references listed at the end of Chapter IX). The use of broad grouping has a negligible effect on the numerator of *r*, but tends slightly to increase the denominator and thus to decrease *r*.

Variable Errors of Measurement.   By now you are aware that nothing can be measured with complete precision. Every good research worker eliminates from his measures all possible bias and reduces accidental errors of observation and measurement to a minimum, but he can never completely free his observations from accidental error. If these variable errors which remain are purely chance errors, they are as likely to be positive as to be negative, and to have a negligible effect on measures of central tendency. They tend to increase measures of variability, and they tend to decrease measures of relationship. This is an important matter. It means that an observed correlation is almost always lower than the correlation between true measures of the same traits would be. It means that if measurement is made with unreliable instruments, the observed correlation coefficient may be very low even when the traits concerned are closely related.

This phenomenon is known as *attenuation*. To illustrate it, take the scores with random errors attached, given in Table XXX, and draw up a scatter diagram. Compare this with Figure 37. A cursory inspection of the two should convince you that the random errors have increased the variability and reduced the correlation coefficient. Computation will show the following (obtained from the ungrouped scores in Appendix A):

	Computations based upon	
	Original scores	Scores with errors attached
Mean language score	21.98	22.08
Mean intelligence quotient	110.04	110.02
Standard deviation of language scores	6.5	10.3
Standard deviation of intelligence quotients	17.5	19.6
Correlation coefficient	.59	.20

A formula designed to estimate the correlation between true scores from observed correlation between fallible scores is known as the *correction for attenuation*. It is part of the general subject of the reliability of test scores. This subject is not difficult, but is too extended to insert in a one-semester course. Believing that formulas should not be presented unless there is time to develop their conceptual background, the author is not presenting, in this introductory course, this or other formulas dealing with test reliability.

Reliability of a Test. If unchanging subjects are measured twice with a perfectly reliable instrument by a perfectly reliable agent, the correlation between the two sets of scores is 1.00. Most measurements, however, are affected by unreliability in the subject, the instrument, the user. Under some situations one kind of unreliability can be minimized, under other situations another. If two persons, whom we will call *A* and *B*, each measure 100 line segments, using the same ruler throughout, they are measuring unchanging subjects (the line segments) with a reliable instrument, and the only source of difference between their results is unreliability in the performance of the agents (*A* and *B*). If a group of children take the same objective test, that is, the same form of the test, on two different days, the chief source of error is changes in the children including their learnings based on the first application. The instrument is the same, and the agent administering the test has relatively little effect on a standardized test. If two forms of the same test are given on the same day to the same children, alternating the forms so that practice effect is minimized, the chief source of unreliability is the test itself. Each form contains a sample of all possible questions which might have been asked, and a particular child makes a higher score on one form than on the other more or less by accident, because the items in one form happen to be more familiar to him than those in the other. The correlation between scores on two forms of a test given to the same subjects at approximately the same time is called a *reliability coefficient*, the *reliability of the test*, or sometimes a self-*r*. The correlation between scores on the same test given to the same subjects at two different times is called a *retesting coefficient*.

The best standardized tests have reliability coefficients of .90 or more. The reliability of a test is related to its length and is increased if the test is lengthened by the addition of equally good items.

Selection of Cases. Only a little thought is needed to see how the size of r depends upon the selection of cases. The correlation between height and weight, for example, is about .70 for children of the same age, but is about .90 for children ranging from five to fifteen years of age. The correlation between age and intelligence quotient should be approximately zero for any unselected group. However, if it is computed for the children in a single school grade, a very sizable negative correlation will be found, because within the grade group, the older children are the duller. Removing extreme cases from a group, or removing the mediocre cases so that only the extremes are left, is likely to change the size of all correlation coefficients obtained. The coefficients are still valid *for the group studied*, but care must be taken not to refer to them as applicable to the traits in general.

Sometimes two groups with widely separated means are thrown together to form one bivariate distribution. The correlations obtained from a composite group of this sort are spurious and meaningless.

This phenomenon is well illustrated by data gathered by Simpson,[*] who studied two groups: A, consisting of professors and advanced students in Columbia University; and B, consisting of unemployed men in New York missions, none of whom had ever held a position demanding a high grade of intelligence. Among the tests he administered were these:

x_1—Auditory memory for words
x_2—Auditory memory for a connected passage
x_3—Visual recognition of forms

The following correlations were obtained:

	Group A	Group B	Combined groups
r_{12}	.23	.73	.82
r_{13}	.37	.15	.71
r_{23}	.14	.06	.66

Often the presence of a single extreme case presents the research worker with a dilemma. Thus Rowell found a fourteen-year-old child with IQ of 45 in a third-grade class. Either to include him or to exclude him from her computations would obviously be to misrepresent the situa-

* *Correlations of Mental Abilities*, New York, Teachers College Bureau of Publications, 1912.

tion. Under such circumstances the best procedure is probably to state the situation so the reader can understand it and show how the extreme case affects results. Rowell (unpublished study) found correlations as follows:

Traits	With extreme case	Without extreme case
CA and IQ	−.500	−.430
CA and MA	−.171	−.078
MA and IQ	−.917	−.919

Effect of Variation in a Third Trait. The apparent interrelatedness of two traits is almost always affected by their relations to still other traits. The correlation between height and weight is one thing when the group is of uniform age and is something else when it is of varying age. In educational studies, variation in the age of subjects usually increases the correlation between any other traits, though occasionally the opposite effect is observed. The technique for removing from a correlation coefficient the spurious effect of variation in a third trait, or in several other traits, is to compute what is known as a *partial correlation coefficient*, sometimes called *net correlation*.

To present the formulas involved in partial correlation and closely related topics and to make them meaningful would require many pages. That treatment will be reserved for a more advanced course.

Effect of Range upon Test Reliability. The correlation between two forms of the same test is always increased by an increase in the variability of the scores. So striking is this phenomenon, that now whenever the reliability of a test is published, it is considered essential to state for what group it was computed, and what was the standard deviation of that group.

Linearity. When the regression is non-linear, the product moment correlation coefficient underestimates the strength of the relationship, and another method of measuring relationship is needed. The *correlation ratio*, developed for situations of this sort, is identical with *r* when the means of the arrays lie exactly on a straight line and is always larger than *r* when they do not. Under no circumstances can it be less than *r*. The formula for this measure and further discussion of its properties will not be included in this introductory course.

Figure 46 presents the regression curves of several physical characteristics on age for 7000 males.* In most of these there is an early period

* Ruger, H. A., and Stoessiger, Brenda, "On the growth curves of certain characters in man (males)," *Annals of Eugenics*, 2 (April, 1927), 76–110. The data upon which the paper is based were recorded by Sir Francis Galton in his first Anthropometric Laboratory at the Health Exhibition at South Kensington in 1884.

in which the curve rises steeply and almost as a straight line. If data were gathered for these years only, regression would be nearly linear and correlation positive. In the period of young adulthood, for most of these curves correlation is nearly zero, and the regression line nearly horizontal. If data were gathered for the years from 20 to 80, most of these data would show negative correlation. It is clear that a straight regression line would not fit these data well, and that consequently the correlation coefficient, r, is not a satisfactory measure of strength of relationship.

Non-Normality of Distribution. For distributions of a single variate, rather extensive studies have been made of the properties of various non-normal distributions. For the bivariate distribution, almost all that is known about correlation is predicated on the assumption of normality. The derivation of the formula for r itself does not make any assumption beyond the assumption that regression is linear, but most of the ways in which r is used are based on the assumption of normality in the traits. If one or both traits have distributions which are greatly skewed, the interpretation of r is not clear.

Concomitance and Causation. Observing that an increase, or decrease, in one phenomenon is usually accompanied by an increase or decrease in another, most persons are ready to hail one of them as the "cause" of the other. This tendency to a fallacious imputation of causal influence was the subject of a cartoon in the New York *World-Telegram* some years ago, in its series of "Metropolitan Movies." Two women, imperfectly sheltered by large umbrellas, are exchanging confidences in the midst of a torrential downpour. "They say it's the radios that cause this rain. Certainly we never had so much rain, and we never had so many radios before."

The critically minded person rejects the idea that any persistent concomitance is purely fortuitous, without some fundamental explanation other than chance. He also rejects the idea that concomitance between A and B is logical ground for asserting either that A has caused B or B has caused A. He is vividly aware of the multitude of situations in which the link between A and B is produced by the relation of each to some third factor C. A child notices that each fall, during the first week of school, vast congregations of blackbirds hold raucous treetop conferences. Adults would smile if they heard him say that school had opened at the call of the blackbirds, or that the blackbirds were gathering because school had opened. Yet those same adults, finding a high correlation in some statistical research, might not hesitate to interpret it in terms of causation.

A somewhat fanciful description of a fictitious research problem may be helpful. A research worker has made a study of the relationship be-

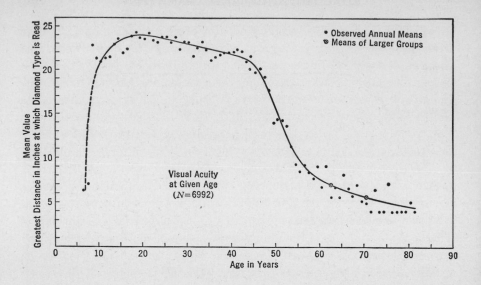

Visual Acuity
at Given Age
(*N*=6992)

• Observed Annual Means
⊗ Means of Larger Groups

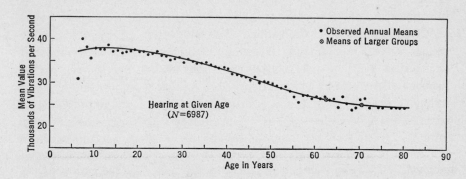

Hearing at Given Age
(*N*=6987)

• Observed Annual Means
⊗ Means of Larger Groups

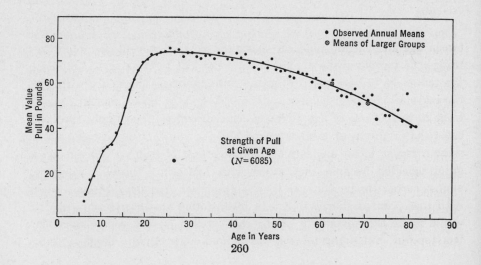

Strength of Pull
at Given Age
(*N*=6085)

• Observed Annual Means
⊗ Means of Larger Groups

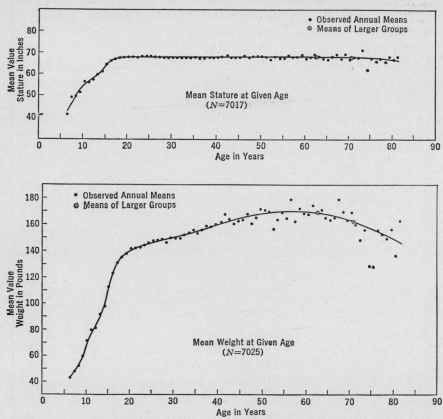

Fig. 46. Curvilinear regression curves of various physical characters on age for males. (From Ruger, H. A., and Stoessiger, B., "On the growth curves of certain characters in man (males)," *Annals of Eugenics*, II, April, 1927, 76–110.)

tween age and certain physical characteristics in women. Among other things, he measures the angle between the feet in walking or standing, the tendency to "toe out." This he finds increases markedly with age, the correlation being, let us say, $r = .50$ for a group of women ranging from 20 to 70 years of age. The association is genuine enough, and indicates that a group of women aged 50 to 70 would be almost certain to show a larger mean angle than a group aged 20 to 40. Conversely, a group selected because they stood with feet nearly parallel would be almost certain to be younger than a group selected because they stood with toes pointed sharply out. In interpreting this correlation, no one would make the mistake of saying that women grow older *because* their feet toe out, but many persons would make the equally illogical statement that as women grow older their feet tend to turn out more and more, that change in the angle between the feet increases with age for the individual woman. Only a little reflection, however, reveals that through the years there has been a change in the type of posture generally approved, so that toeing out, once definitely taught, is now discouraged.

The direction of causation is schematically illustrated in Figure 47, wherein three "causal" relationships are represented as lying back of a

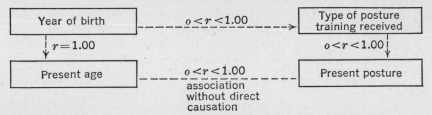

Fig. 47. Schematic pattern of relationships underlying an observed relationship between age and posture.

given observed association or concomitance. The direction of these relationships is not revealed by statistical data but inferred from an extra-statistical argument. A correlation coefficient reveals only the presence of a mutual association, a tendency to co-variation, and gives no clue as to the chain of causes which have produced it.

The hazardous nature of inference about cause is readily seen with respect to variates which fluctuate with time. Draw up a list of variates which have shown an increase over a period of years, such as the proportion of city dwellers in the United States, the number of inmates in institutions for the insane, the average length of human life, the number of automobile accidents, the average salary paid to elementary school teachers, the consumption of tobacco, the number of high school graduates, etc. Call this List A. Draw up a List B to contain the names of variates which have shown a general decrease with the passage of years, such as the percentage of illiteracy in the United States, the proportionate number of blacksmiths, the time required to go from New York to San Francisco, the number of deaths from smallpox, etc. Now observe that over a period of years any two items from List A will show a positive correlation, any two items from List B will likewise show a positive correlation, and any item from List A will show a negative correlation with any item from List B. Such correlations are obviously spurious, and result from the fact that each variate has a strong secular trend rather than from any direct relation between the variates themselves.*

* For a discussion of the elimination of secular trend in such problems, see a text in economic or business statistics.

CHAPTER XV

SAMPLE AND UNIVERSE *

It will be seen that the test of significance does no more, and attempts no more, than to answer the straightforward question, "Could these samples have been drawn from the same population?" It calculates a probability. If the probability is very small the answer is "No." If it is not so small as to reach the level of significance required, the answer is "Yes, they could." The answer is never "Yes, they must have been."

R. A. Fisher

In investigations which deal with matters of any general interest, the findings are usually applied to a much larger area than the cases actually studied. In a group of 1006, a man finds 51 children left-handed and he considers that to be evidence that about 5 per cent of all children are left-handed. A psychologist compares 100 hard-of-hearing children with 200 normal children in respect to certain traits, and even if he states his findings as applicable only to the children studied, his readers assume them to be characteristic of differences between hard-of-hearing and normal children in general.

The idea that information obtained from a relatively small number of cases actually examined can be used to throw light on the characteristics of a vast universe which has not been examined is an exciting idea, which ceases to amaze us only when familiarity renders it commonplace. That the sample not only furnishes an estimate of some characteristic of the unknown population, but also furnishes a measure of the amount of confidence which can be placed in that estimate, is still more remarkable.

Situations in Which Samples Are Employed. At first it may seem to some readers that it is a negligent investigator who works with a sample rather than with the total population about which he desires information. Why should samples ever be employed?

1. Some populations are infinite, and could never be exhausted. A good illustration of this situation is provided by the experiments in penny-tossing described on page 272 of this chapter. The total possible number of trials would include all that could be made by every human being if he did nothing else all his life, and would extend into the future as long as human beings continue to inhabit this globe. Any particular

* This chapter could appropriately be used as the introduction for a second-term course in Statistical Inference.

set of trials, no matter how large, constitutes a sample out of this truly inexhaustible population of trials.

2. Some populations are vast and inaccessible even though finite. Suppose an investigator wants to know the distribution of left-handedness, for children under ten years of age, among the various peoples of the world, and he conceives of his population as including all children now living, but not including children of former or future eras. The number of children under ten now living in the world is certainly finite, denumerable, but too vast for any investigator to compass. In mathematical language this population is not infinite, but so far as any statistical study is concerned, it might nearly as well be. Again, suppose a student wishes to make a vocational study of the 10,000 graduates of a given university during the last 15 years. While 10,000 is a very reasonable number of cases to cover in many kinds of research, in this particular one the time and correspondence required to get adequate data on each case may be such that a greater amount of total information can be secured by reducing the number of cases and increasing the amount of information concerning each. Here the sample is from a finite universe.

3. In certain kinds of research, measurement means the destruction of the individual. This is the typical situation in studies of the strength of materials. To measure the tensile strength of cloth, cloth must be destroyed, to measure the breaking load of steel, steel must be broken. Hence, in much industrial research the idea of studying an entire population is fantastic and even the use of large samples is prohibitive.

4. Some data may be so difficult or so expensive to obtain that it is unreasonable to study more than a sample.

Population, Universe. An aggregate of individuals having a common character, or characteristic, is called a *population*, *universe*, or *supply*. An *individual* or *element* of that population is not necessarily a person, but might be, e.g., a city, a group of persons, the day's output of a manufacturing plant, a matched pair of children, a throw of dice, a period of time. Unless the aggregate of individuals have some trait in common, they do not constitute a universe. Thus 100 textbooks, 80 children, 5 school buildings, and 200 white mice might conceivably be related in some fashion, but they do not constitute a population because there is no trait common to them all which is meaningful in the aggregate.

Individual Character, Group Character. Suppose that a study is to be made of all the school buildings put up during a given period with the aid of federal funds; each building is an individual and all the buildings erected during that given period with federal aid constitute the universe. Any measure obtained for a single building, such as the total cost of materials, is an *individual character*, and a summary for the entire group of individual characters such as the range of cost of materials, the mean cost, some measure of the variation in cost, is a *group character*.

Suppose, for example, that we are concerned to know whether method A or method B in the teaching of science results in higher gains in certain learnings measured by a particular test, and that we wish to eliminate the influence of age, IQ, and sex upon the outcome. Suppose further that we match up 150 pairs of children in such a way that the members of each pair are of the same sex, IQ, and age, and then we place one member of each pair in a class taught by method A and the other member in a class taught by method B. An individual is now a pair of children matched for age, sex, and IQ and taught by different methods. The individual character or trait measured is the difference in gains made by the two children in that pair, as indicated by scores on the chosen test. The mean of all such differences for all pairs is a group character or group trait.

In this case, it is appropriate to postulate a hypothetical universe consisting of all the matched pairs which are conceivable, and to generalize the findings of this sample of 150 pairs to the hypothetical universe of matched pairs, rather than to children in general.

Randomness. The criterion for randomness is that every individual in the population shall have the same probability of being chosen in the sample. This criterion implies that all choices be independent, for if the probability of choice of individual *A* is related to the prior choice of individual *B*, then not all individuals have the same probability of being selected. The best way of insuring randomness in a sample is to utilize some mechanical device for selecting the cases. Any form of lottery would serve, but it is quite unnecessary to incur the expense of such equipment. If each individual in the population can be identified by a name or a number or a symbol, these names or numbers or symbols can be written on tickets or on pieces of paper placed inside capsules, put in a hopper, stirred well, and then drawn forth one at a time by some mechanical device or by a person who is in some way prohibited from exercising any conscious choice. The person drawing the names may be blindfolded or the capsules may have identical exteriors so that it is impossible to make conscious selection. A still easier, less expensive, and equally valid method of random selection is provided by the use of random numbers. It is necessary first to assign a unique number to each individual in the universe, so that the individual is selected as soon as his number is selected.

One list of random sampling numbers was published by **L. H. C.**

Tippett in 1927,* another by R. A. Fisher and F. Yates in 1938.† The use of such a table has such great advantages over the older methods of drawing names by lot that it will be described here in some detail.

03	47	43	73	86
97	74	24	67	62
16	76	62	27	66
12	56	85	99	26
55	59	56	35	64

The first block of numbers in Fisher's table is reproduced above. The table includes 300 similar blocks, arranged on 6 pages of 10 rows and 5 columns each. To read it, one may begin at any point on any page and read in any direction, up or down, right or left. The reader should decide where he will begin reading and in which direction before he opens the book, lest after he sees the page he be influenced by the desire to include or exclude a particular individual. Suppose it is desired to select 20 individuals at random out of a group of 80, and suppose it has been agreed to start reading in the 4th two-digit column and to read downwards. Because 80 has only 2 digits, we shall need only a two-digit column.

Examination of the block of numbers reproduced here indicates that the individuals numbered 73, 67, 27, and 35 are to be included. The number 99, being larger than 80, does not represent any individual in the universe from which selection is to be made, and so is disregarded. This column of figures is read down to the bottom of the page and then a new column, chosen in advance, is read until 20 numbers less than 80 have been selected. When a number which has already been included in the sample occurs a second time, the second occurrence is disregarded.

If the name of every individual in a universe has been placed on a list, and if that list is available to the person drawing the sample, each name can be assigned a number and the numbers can be selected in some mechanical fashion. If events or individuals are arranged in chronological order, like tools coming from a production line, or like births occurring in a maternity hospital, or like applicants registering in an employment agency, a number can be assigned to each and a random sample of the individuals can be secured by taking a random sample of the numbers. If individuals are arranged in some definite spatial pattern, so that to each individual there corresponds one and only one point on some chart

---

* *Random Sampling Numbers*, with foreword by Karl Pearson, Cambridge University Tracts for Computers.

† Table XXXIII in *Statistical Tables for Biological, Agricultural and Medical Research*, Oliver & Boyd, London.

or diagram or map, it is usually possible to select individuals at random by selecting points at random. A rather unusual illustration of this situation is reported by Hotelling as coming out of a series of conferences on agricultural problems during a trip he made to India in 1941. A survey was needed of the amount of jute raised in a given area. The area could not be photographed from the air partly because of expense and partly because at certain stages it is difficult to distinguish jute from other crops. On a map of the region, two coordinate axes were drawn. Then two numbers were drawn at random with the help of a table of random numbers. The first was considered the abscissa and the second the ordinate of a point, and a pin was placed in the map at the point thus determined. Other points were obtained in the same way, and at each point a small unit square was drawn on the map. The totality of the unit squares so chosen then constituted a random sample of the area, and a worker was sent out to investigate the amount of jute raised in these specified squares.

If it is not possible to identify an individual by the position of his name on a list or by some correspondence to a point in time or space, or in some other ordered structure, there is no way to take a random sample of the whole universe. In other situations, it may be possible, but far too difficult or expensive to choose a random sample directly.

It has been demonstrated again and again that whenever conscious selection enters the sampling procedure, randomness is forfeited. Try sometime, in a situation in which you have no emotional commitment, to make a random selection. You might try to pick leaves "at random" from a tree, or to pick marbles "at random" from a pile, or the like. Either you will have a bias toward the big ones, or toward the small, or you will begin to balance the large off against the small, or you will try to choose only the middle-sized. The one thing which is certain in advance is that you cannot, in the long run, choose samples which will behave the way random samples behave.

In many cases, taking from a list names spaced at regular intervals may be expected to produce a random sample. It is conceivable, however, that bias might be unwittingly introduced by this method. See the paper by Stephan on "Practical problems of sampling procedure" in the list of references at the end of this chapter. It would in most cases be wiser and very little additional trouble to take names chosen by the aid of random numbers rather than names at equally spaced intervals.

When sampling is truly random, formulas are available for each of the common statistics for estimating the expected variation of that statistic from sample to sample.

Sampling by Subdivision or by Stratification. Both terms are in current use, but the former appears to describe more accurately the essential process. Sometimes the research worker either knows or surmises that the universe he wishes to sample can be divided into a number of groups each of which is relatively homogeneous with respect to the character sampled, and that either the frequency or the size of that character varies considerably from subgroup to subgroup. This situation permits the research worker to take advantage of a plan of sampling which is more efficient than that of drawing a sample at random from the entire population. If available time and resources will permit him to examine a sample of N cases, he should divide N into as many subsamples as there are subdivisions in the population, and should make the number of cases in the subsamples proportional to the number of cases in the subdivisions, or strata, of the population. Then each subsample should be drawn *at random* from the corresponding subdivision of the population. Such a procedure may be considered a modified form of random sampling, and special formulas are available for estimating the variation of the statistics among such samples. To say that this is a "more efficient" method of sampling than that of drawing samples at random from the whole population means that this method will in the long run produce samples with statistics which are more like the corresponding population values and which fluctuate less from sample to sample.

Thus in the surveys by Gallup and by the magazine *Fortune* the country is divided into geographic regions and within each region the number of ballots is held proportional to the census figures on certain other "controls," such as age, sex, and economic status. A breakdown is nearly always taken on economic status, and may be taken on any other control which there is reason to believe will be related to opinion on the particular issue under consideration.

This method of sampling has not yet been widely utilized by educators. A recent study by Rope * illustrates how it can be advantageously employed in a community survey.

Sampling by subdivision requires that the following conditions be met:

1. There must be a fairly high relationship between the character to be sampled and the basis on which the universe is subdivided. Knowledge of this relationship may come from previous research or from the accumulated experience of the research worker. Shrewdness in selecting the basis of subdivision is a major contributing factor in the success of such studies.

* *Opinion Conflict and School Support*, Teachers College, Columbia University, Contributions to Education, No. 838. New York, 1941.

2. Prior information must be available as to the proportion of the universe in each of the subdivisions.

3. It must be possible to obtain a random sample of the individuals within each subdivision.

Purposive Sampling. Sometimes the sampler segregates a certain portion of the population and draws his sample only from this portion. Ordinarily the portion segregated has certain criteria with the same average as the population, and he trusts this similarity to give him a sample representative of the universe. Thus one might select a county believed to be typical of a state, and draw a sample at random from the county, or one might select 5 or 6 cities in different parts of a state, and draw samples within the cities. This method is often cheaper and more readily accomplished than drawing a sample at random from the entire universe. It is not feasible at all, however, unless there is considerable advance information about the universe. Moreover, it has been shown (see articles by Neyman and by Snedecor, in reference list) that the controls are seldom effective and the resulting sample is likely not to be representative of the population, at least as regards measures of variability and correlation. The political aphorism, "As Maine goes, so goes the nation," is an instance of belief that Maine may be considered a purposive sample of the nation in regard to political convictions. The use of a single intact school or class as a sample in a study whose conclusions are to be applied widely to other schools or classes has similar limitations. If a research worker can study a specified number of individuals, he will obtain more information about the population by taking a large number of small groups than by taking a small number of larger, intact groups. *No doubt many of the contradictions found in the outcomes of research studies in education can be traced to placing too much reliance upon the use of a whole class or a small number of whole classes as a sample from which to generalize.*

Accidental Sampling. Far too much published research is based upon cases chosen because they come conveniently to hand rather than upon cases chosen carefully as a random sample of the universe to which generalization is made. Most readers will need to read only one or two issues of a professional periodical before coming on a study in which the author makes generalizations which are so phrased as to refer to a universe from which his cases could not possibly be considered to be a random sample. Perhaps he intended to study universe A, but was able to secure only a biased sample thereof, and so his findings really relate to some other universe which we may call B. However, he does not want to generalize to B because he is not interested in B!

Biased Sample. Even when a random sample by accident has statistics which do not agree with the population values, it is not considered biased. A sample is biased if one class or several classes of individuals in the population are given a consistently better opportunity to be included than are the other classes.

Thompson (see reference in list at end of chapter) asked a certain number of students to state the number of their brothers and sisters. Can the proportion of students reporting families of a given size be taken as evidence of the proportion of families of that size in the total population? In the first place, this would give a bias in favor of large families, since the probability of selecting a child from a large family is greater than from a small family. A second kind of bias operating in the opposite direction would arise if some of the families represented were not yet complete. Still another source of bias inheres in the well-known fact that families of higher social status are more likely to send their children to college and at the same time have a lower fertility rate.

The expert in a field may recognize sources of bias in a sample which are not apparent to one less familiar with the area. *One of the first responsibilities of a person intending to conduct a study by sample is to be so conversant with his material and so discerning in planning his sampling techniques that he can eliminate all the important sources of bias.*

Adequacy of Sample. The size of a sample is not an indication of its representativeness or its randomness, but size is related to the amount of chance variability to be expected from one sample to another. A sample of one individual might be drawn wholly at random, and therefore be unbiased, but it is not adequate to provide the sampler with much confidence in the accuracy of the estimates it provides as to the group characters of the population. Later discussion will attempt to clarify this relationship between size of sample and reliability of estimates it furnishes. For the present it is mentioned only to make it clear that a large sample may be a biased sample and worthless while a small sample may be random and unbiased, though possibly erratic.

Hypothetical Universe. The procedures used to obtain samples in educational research are often such that the individuals observed cannot be interpreted as forming a random sample of any existent universe. In that situation, one must either refrain from generalizing, or must construct a *hypothetical universe* of which the observed group may be considered to be a random sample, and must generalize to this artificially created universe.* There is no other alternative.

Suppose, for example, that a group of white and Negro boys of a given

---

* See Fisher, R. A., *Statistical Methods for Research Workers*, 6th edition, 1936, p. 7.

age are matched child for child with respect to parents' income, parents' education, living conditions, and the child's educational opportunities, the two groups being then compared with respect to certain tests of achievement, capacity, and personality. The Negro children thus selected will almost certainly be chosen from the more privileged of their race and the white from the less privileged of theirs, so that the sample is not a random sample of any population now existing. The study cannot be used to form an estimate of differences between white and Negro children in general. It is defensible, however, to define a hypothetical universe in which an individual is a pair of children matched on all the different background traits, and to assume that the cases studied are a set of matched pairs chosen at random from this hypothetical universe of matched pairs. Sometimes groups are equated by matching mean and standard deviation, instead of matching case for case. In such a situation the constructed universe is a universe of infinitely many matched groups, the pair of groups observed being considered as a single individual drawn at random from a universe of matched groups. To generalize to this kind of artificial universe will seem highly unsatisfactory to most research workers, but the data afford no rational grounds for anything else.

Meaning of Term "Sampling Distribution." Suppose that from all the children in New York City between the ages of 8 and 14 a thousand random samples of 50 children each could be drawn. Suppose the intelligence quotient of each child is obtained, that being an individual character, and for each sample the mean intelligence quotient is found, that being a group character. No one would expect these thousand sample means to be uniform. If they are tabulated, they will yield a frequency distribution, which may be called a sampling distribution of the mean,* because it is the frequency distribution of the means obtained from successive random samples of the same size from a given population. It can be proved mathematically that the sampling distribution of the mean is characteristically normal, and the frequency distribution of any observed set of means obtained from random samples of uniform size will tend toward the normal if enough samples are taken. Note that it is the *number of samples* which must be increased in order to produce this result, not the *number of cases in a single sample*. The mean of this distribution of means will approximate the population mean. The standard deviation of the sampling distribution of means is called the *standard error of the*

---

* More precisely, the term "sampling distribution of the mean" (or sampling distribution of any other statistic) is applied to the mathematical equation describing the curve which the distribution of sample *means* would approach if infinitely many random samples of uniform size were drawn. Any particular set of observed means, even for a large number of samples, will show some slight accidental irregularities.

mean, which may be thought of as an abbreviation of the phrase, "the standard deviation of a set of means which differ from each other only because each involves *a sampling error.*"

Suppose now that for each of the samples described in the preceding paragraph the percentage of boys is obtained. That percentage is a group character or statistic. A thousand percentages result, which when tabulated yield what might be called the *sampling distribution* of the percentage. If among all the New York City children approximately 50% are boys, as is probably the case,* then the mean of this sampling distribution of percentages will also be approximately 50%. The standard deviation of the distribution of percentages may be called the *standard error of the percentage,* because, except for sampling errors, these percentages would each have been 50%. The sampling distribution will be approximately normal in form.

Suppose that for each sample the percentage of left-handed children is found. For the original population this is probably somewhere near 5%, and some of the samples will show values above and some below 5%, but in this case the distribution of percentages will not be symmetrical, but will show positive skewness.

Every statistic which you have learned to compute has a sampling distribution. The mathematical equation for most of the important statistics has been derived, though not yet for all. Not all such sampling distributions are normal.

Sampling Distribution from Empirical Data. A true understanding of what is meant by such terms as "significant difference," "standard error," "statistically reliable," etc., is possible only to those who have grasped the idea of a sampling distribution, who are able in their imaginations to visualize such a distribution even when none is present to the senses. To aid in developing the fundamental concepts, we shall now examine certain distributions of means, of variances, and of standard deviations from empirical data.

Each student in a class in elementary statistics threw 10 pennies and recorded the number of heads which appeared. He made 16 such throws, which were considered a sample of 16 cases, each individual in the sample being one throw of 10 pennies. For the sample, the student computed three different statistics, namely the mean, the variance, and the standard deviation. The means of 260 such samples of 16 cases have already been presented in Table XXXIX and the variances in Table XL.

If 10 perfectly balanced coins are thrown and the number of heads recorded, the mean number of heads will approach 5.00, the variance will

* In general about 51 out of every 101 births are male.

approach 2.5, and the standard deviation will approach $\sqrt{2.5} = 1.58$ as more and more throws are made. These values are *population characters* or parameters, and will be designated by the symbols μ, σ^2, and σ in contrast to the corresponding values found in a particular sample, which will be indicated by the symbols $\overline{X}$, s^2, and s as in our previous work. (μ is the small Greek letter, *mu*, corresponding to our *m*. It is used here to suggest the word "mean.") Any group character obtained from a sample will be called a *statistic*, while the corresponding group character of the population is a *parameter*. For these data we have $\mu = 5$ and $\overline{X}$ is a variable, sometimes larger and sometimes smaller than 5; $\sigma^2 = 2.5$ and s^2 is a variable sometimes larger and sometimes smaller than 2.5; $\sigma = 1.58$ and s is a variable sometimes larger and sometimes smaller than 1.58.

Sampling Distribution of the Mean. Table XXXIX and Figures 26 and 36 (upper curve) illustrate the statement that *the means of a set of random samples of the same size fluctuate around the mean of the population in a normal distribution* for which the *standard deviation is $\dfrac{\sigma}{\sqrt{N}}$.*

First, note from Figures 26 and 36 (upper curve) that this distribution of means is very close to the ideal normal form. Second, note that its mean is very close to 5 (actually 5.036). Third, note that its standard deviation of 0.43 is very close to $\dfrac{\sigma}{\sqrt{N}}$ or $\dfrac{1.58}{\sqrt{16}} = 0.395$.

The amount by which the mean of any one of these samples departs from the population parameter is called a *sampling error*. A sampling error is not a mistake, is not caused by a wrong procedure, but arises from the accidents of sampling among individuals who vary one from another. *The standard deviation of the sampling distribution of the means of all the random samples of a given size which might be drawn from a given population is called the standard error of the mean.*

Size of Sample as Related to Frequency Distribution of the Mean. In order to illustrate the change in the frequency distribution of the mean as the sample size increases, each of the students who contributed to Table XXXIX obtained 4 samples of 16 cases each and combined them into one sample of 64 cases, computing the mean, variance, and standard deviation for it also. The means of these samples of 64 are shown in column (4) of Table XLVII, column (2) being a repetition of Table XXXIX. In another class each student obtained 3 samples of 25 cases each which were combined in 1 sample of 75 cases. The means from these are shown in columns (3) and (5) of Table XLVII. Thus the sets of 16 and 64 are from identical throws. The sets of 25 and 75 are

TABLE XLVII

Mean Number of Heads Appearing in Successive Random Samples of Throws of Ten Pennies for Samples of 16, 25, 64, and 75 Cases Respectively

Mean	Frequency in Samples of Given Size			
	16	25	64	75
(1)	(2)	(3)	(4)	(5)
6.4	2			
6.3				
6.2				
6.1	2			
6.0				
5.9	4	1		
5.8	5	1		
5.7	6		1	
5.6	11	1	2	
5.5	7	3	1	
5.4	23	8	2	
5.3	21	8	6	3
5.2	18	12	8	3
5.1	25	21	5	9
5.0	24	10	13	8
4.9	28	18	12	10
4.8	21	31	9	11
4.7	19	11	6	4
4.6	13	9		
4.5	9	7		
4.4	9	3		
4.3	2			
4.2	6			
4.1	2			
4.0	1			
3.9	2			
Number of Samples	260	144	65	48
Mean of Means	5.035	4.96	5.035	4.96
Variance of Means	0.185	0.0809	0.0558	0.0270
Standard Deviation of Means	0.43	0.29	0.24	0.16

also from identical throws, but the sets of 16 and 64 are not from the same throws as the sets of 25 and 75.

The generalizations which follow are based on mathematical theory and illustrated by the data from penny tossing.

The mean of a sample is an unbiased estimate of the mean of the population. This is illustrated by the fact that when 260 samples of 16 cases are combined into 65 samples of 64 cases (a "case" being a throw), the mean of the distribution remains unchanged at 5.035. Also when 144 samples of 25 cases are combined into 48 samples of 75 cases, the mean remains unchanged at 4.96. This generalization may be expressed symbolically as

$$\tilde{\mu} = \overline{X} \tag{79}$$

If μ is used to indicate the population mean, $\tilde{\mu}$ may be understood to represent the best estimate of that mean which can be obtained from the observation of a single sample. The tilde was used in similar fashion in Chapters XII, XIII, and XIV to designate an estimate of one variable based upon information about a second variable.

The variability of the distribution of means decreases steadily as the size of the sample is increased. In Table XLVII the range of the means is seen to shrink as the size of the sample increases. The variance of the means also decreases, the variance of samples of 64 being about one-fourth as great as the variance of samples of 16, and the variance of samples of 75 being about one-third as great as the variance of samples of 25. The standard deviation of the means likewise shifts from 0.43 to 0.29 to 0.24 to 0.16 as N increases from 16 to 25 to 64 to 75. Apparently there is a close inverse relationship between sample size and sampling variability of the mean. This is the phenomenon referred to when one says that "the reliability of the mean increases as the size of the sample increases." Obviously, the mean of any given sample can be trusted less if the means of a series of random samples would be expected to show great diversity than if they would be expected to be relatively uniform.

The sampling distribution of the mean is normal, when the population from which samples are drawn is itself normally distributed. When samples are drawn from a non-normal universe, the distribution of means of successive random samples tends to be more nearly normal than the distribution of scores in the parent population.

Formula for the Standard Error of the Mean. If the standard deviation of the population is called σ the formula for the standard error of the mean in samples of N cases is

$$\sigma_{\overline{x}} = \frac{\sigma}{\sqrt{N}} \tag{80}$$

For reasons which can be mathematically demonstrated, if 10 perfectly balanced pennies were thrown a very large number of times, the standard deviation of the number of heads appearing should be approximately $\sqrt{2.5} = 1.58$. Formula 80 would then suggest that the expected values of the standard deviations of these several distributions of means would be as follows:

When $N = 16$, $\sigma_{\bar{x}} = \dfrac{1.58}{\sqrt{16}} = 0.40$ whereas the empirical value is 0.43.

When $N = 25$, $\sigma_{\bar{x}} = \dfrac{1.58}{\sqrt{25}} = 0.32$ whereas the empirical value is 0.29.

When $N = 64$, $\sigma_{\bar{x}} = \dfrac{1.58}{\sqrt{64}} = 0.20$, whereas the empirical value is 0.24.

When $N = 75$, $\sigma_{\bar{x}} = \dfrac{1.58}{\sqrt{75}} = 0.18$ whereas the empirical value is 0.16.

This is rather striking agreement between theory and observation in view of the very small number of samples drawn. If more means of samples were computed, it is quite likely that the agreement between theory and observation would be even closer.

The Probable Error. Deeply imbedded in our scientific vocabulary, this term is one of the oldest of current statistical terms. A knowledge of its origin clarifies its meaning and its frequent misuse in present-day writings. Early in the nineteenth century, Gauss, Encke, Bessel, and other German astronomers were studying the accuracy of observations and the variation among errors of observation. The term "probable error" was given to a deviation from the true position of a point of such a magnitude that, if the number of observations be indefinitely increased, one-half of the errors may be expected to be numerically greater and one-half numerically less than this value. Bessel appears to have been the first to use the term, speaking of *der wahrscheinliche Fehler* in a treatise on the position of the pole star, published in 1815. Almost immediately the term was adopted by other astronomers and by writers on geodesy and artillery fire appearing in French as *l'erreur probable* and sometimes as *l'erreur moyenne*, in English as *the probable error* and in Latin (then commonly used for scientific writing) as *error probabilis*.

In a normal distribution, which was the only form known to the astronomers of that day, one-half of the area under the curve is enclosed between the ordinates at $\pm 0.6745\sigma$. Hence it is customary to define the probable error of any statistic as 0.6745 times its standard error. However, it must be noted that *this relationship holds only for normally distributed measures*. The probable error of a mean therefore is a meaningful term, but the probable error of a correlation coefficient, which is not normally distributed except in samples from a population in which the true value is zero, is meaningless and misleading.

As long ago as 1889, Galton inveighed against the use of the term. "It is astonishing that mathematicians, who are the most precise and perspicacious of men, have not long since revolted against this cumbrous, slip-shod, and misleading phrase. They really mean what I should call the Mid-Error, but their phrase is too firmly established for me to uproot it. I shall, however, always write the Probable when used in this sense, in the form of 'Prob.,' thus 'Prob. Error' as a continual protest against its illegitimate use, and as some safeguard against its misrepresentation."

The customary symbol for probable error is either p.e. or P.E. To write these with a subscript designating the statistic is awkward. The term is not needed, inasmuch as the standard error provides all the information which the probable error can furnish.

Sampling Distribution of the Variance. *The sampling distribution of the variance is not normal, but displays a slight positive skewness.* This skewness is noticeable in Figures 29 and 36 (lower curve). It is easily recognized in the first two columns of Table XLVIII, where the difference between the highest score and the mean is about twice as great as the difference between the mean and the lowest score. In every one of the four distributions, the mean is larger than either the mode or the median, another evidence of positive skewness. However, as sample size increases, the distribution of the variance becomes more nearly symmetrical and more nearly normal, until for samples of, say, 50 or more it may be treated as a normal distribution.

The variance of small samples tends to be smaller than the variance of larger samples from the same universe. In Table XLVIII, the mean variance of samples of 64 cases is slightly larger than that of samples of 16 cases; the mean variance of samples of 75 cases is slightly larger than that of samples of 25 cases. These differences are not accidental. In our computation we used the formula $s^2 = \dfrac{\Sigma X^2}{N} - \left(\dfrac{\Sigma X}{N}\right)^2$. We note that in so doing there is a tendency for the resulting variance of a small sample to be too small. To overcome this tendency of the variance of a small sample to be too small, the population variance may be estimated by the formula

$$\bar{\sigma}^2 = \frac{N}{N-1}s^2 \qquad\qquad \textit{not ok} \qquad\qquad (81)$$

$$= \frac{\Sigma(X-\overline{X})^2}{N-1} = \frac{\Sigma X^2}{N-1} - \frac{(\Sigma X)^2}{N(N-1)} \quad \textit{ok} \qquad (82)$$

TABLE XLVIII

Variance of the Number of Heads Appearing in Successive Random Samples of Throws of Ten Pennies for Samples of 16, 25, 64, and 75 Cases Respectively

Variance	Frequency in Samples of Given Size			
	16	25	64	75
5.3–5.4	1			
5.1–5.2	1			
4.9–5.0	1	1		
4.7–4.8				
4.5–4.6	2	1		
4.3–4.4	2	2		
4.1–4.2	3	1		
3.9–4.0	5	2		
3.7–3.8	3	2		
3.5–3.6	8	1		
3.3–3.4	7	5	1	1
3.1–3.2	15	6	5	2
2.9–3.0	16	10	3	4
2.7–2.8	21	12	12	6
2.5–2.6	23	12	11	7
2.3–2.4	25	15	12	10
2.1–2.2	33	22	11	9
1.9–2.0	22	19	7	7
1.7–1.8	19	12	1	1
1.5–1.6	19	13	1	1
1.3–1.4	18	6		
1.1–1.2	7	2		
.9–1.0	3			
.7–.8	2			
Number of Samples	256	144	64	48
Mean of Variances	2.39	2.37	2.47	2.41
Variance of Variances	0.67	0.51	0.15	0.15
Standard Deviation of Variances	0.82	0.71	0.38	0.39

and the population standard deviation by the formula

$$\tilde{\sigma} = s\sqrt{\frac{N}{N-1}} \qquad \text{not ok} \qquad (81a)$$

$$= \sqrt{\frac{\Sigma(X-\overline{X})^2}{N-1}} = \sqrt{\frac{\Sigma X^2}{N-1} - \frac{(\Sigma X)^2}{N(N-1)}} \qquad \text{ok} \qquad (82a)$$

Note that $\frac{N}{N-1}$ is greater than 1 so that s^2 is being corrected in the right direction.

A number of modern writers on statistics prefer to use formulas (82) and (82a) as definitions of the sample variance and standard deviation instead of the formulas used in this text. Each practice has certain advantages. When (82) is used as the definition for sample variance, then the variance of a small sample tends to be the same as that of a large sample from the same population.

There is no ultimate disagreement between the two methods, because in the formula for estimating the standard error of a statistic from data obtained from a sample [see formulas (83) and (84)], if (82a) is used as definition of s, then $\tilde{\sigma}_{\overline{X}}$ is written $\tilde{\sigma}_{\overline{X}} = \frac{s}{\sqrt{N}}$ and this has the same value as formula (83) when each is reduced to a computing routine with raw scores. Were the term standard deviation now being defined for the first time, it would be preferable to use formula (82a) as such definition. However, the term is now half a century old, and deeply rooted. The definition used in this text is still used in all but a few of the other texts which the student is likely to consult. Moreover, the use of N in the denominator seems to the beginning student of statistics far more reasonable than the use of $N-1$. Therefore, after some admitted hesitation, this text has followed the current practice of defining the standard deviation of a sample as

$$s = \sqrt{\frac{\Sigma(X-\overline{X})^2}{N}} \qquad \text{not ok} \qquad (8a)$$

and using the formula

$$\tilde{\sigma} = \sqrt{\frac{\Sigma(X-\overline{X})^2}{N-1}} \qquad \text{ok} \qquad (82a)$$

to indicate the sample estimate of the standard deviation of the population.

It is not immediately obvious why the mean variance and the mean standard deviation should be smaller in small samples than in large. The following illustrations are offered in an attempt to make this relationship seem reasonable. 1. Suppose you are drawing random samples from a population of adult males. It is more likely that all the heights in a sample would fall within a range of, say, one inch if the sample contained five cases than if it contained 500. What is true of the range here is true of any other measure of variability. 2. If a sample is made so small that it contains only 1 case, its variance and its standard deviation are zero. 3. The check formula

$$N_c s_c^2 = N_1(s_1^2 + d_1^2) + N_2(s_2^2 + d_2^2) + \cdots + N_k(s_k^2 + d_k^2) \quad (30)$$

indicates that s_c^2 is larger than the mean of the variances in the component groups because it receives the contributions of the d's as well as of the several s's.

Returning now to the four variance distributions in Table XLVIII, it will be of interest to apply formula (81) to the mean variance in each distribution to obtain an estimate of the population variance. We obtain

$$\left(\frac{16}{15}\right)(2.39) = 2.55$$

$$\left(\frac{25}{24}\right)(2.37) = 2.47$$

$$\left(\frac{64}{63}\right)(2.46) = 2.51$$

$$\left(\frac{75}{74}\right)(2.45) = 2.44$$

These may be compared with the value $\sigma^2 = 2.50$ which was previously stated—without explanation—as the variance of the number of heads appearing in repeated throws of 10 perfectly balanced coins.

It is easy to see in Table XLVIII that the distribution of variances becomes less variable as the number of cases in the sample increases. Thus the variance of the variances in samples of 16 cases is about 4 times as large as in samples of 64 cases, while the variance of the variances in samples of 25 cases is about 3 times as large as in samples of 75 cases. Like the mean, the variance appears to be less variable and therefore more reliable as the sample becomes larger.

Because of the asymmetry of the sampling distribution of the variance, its standard error is not often used in tests of significance, and its formula will not be presented here. It may be stated, however, that the theoretical values of $\sigma_s{}^2$ for the four sizes of sample under consideration are in fairly close agreement with the empirical values shown in the last line of Table XLVIII.

Sampling Distribution of the Standard Deviation. The same samples which produced the distributions of the mean and the variance have also yielded distributions of the standard deviation, presented in Table XLIX. The sampling distribution of the standard deviation is slightly skewed for small samples but is approximately normal for large ones, and is always less skewed than the distribution of the variance.

TABLE XLIX

Standard Deviation of Number of Heads Appearing in Successive Random Samples of Throws of Ten Pennies for Samples of 16, 25, 64, and 75 Cases Respectively

Standard Deviation	Frequency in Samples of Given Size			
	16	25	64	75
2.3	1			
2.2	2	1		
2.1	4	4		
2.0	8	3		
1.9	11	2		
1.8	21	11	4	2
1.7	30	18	12	7
1.6	33	22	17	15
1.5	43	26	23	13
1.4	36	27	5	9
1.3	26	12	2	2
1.2	25	14	1	
1.1	10	4		
1.0	3			
.9	2			
.8	1			
Number of Samples	256	144	64	48
Mean of Standard Deviations	1.52	1.52	1.56	1.55
Variance of Standard Deviations	0.068	0.052	0.015	0.014
Standard Deviation of Standard Deviations	0.26	0.23	0.12	0.12

The standard error of the standard deviation is

$$\sigma_s = \frac{\sigma}{\sqrt{2N}} \qquad (83)$$

Therefore

When $N = 16$, $\sigma_s = \dfrac{1.58}{\sqrt{32}} = 0.28$ whereas the empirical value is 0.26

When $N = 25$, $\sigma_s = \dfrac{1.58}{\sqrt{50}} = 0.22$ whereas the empirical value is 0.23

When $N = 64$, $\sigma_s = \dfrac{1.58}{\sqrt{128}} = 0.14$ whereas the empirical value is 0.12

When $N = 75$, $\sigma_s = \dfrac{1.58}{\sqrt{150}} = 0.13$ whereas the empirical value is 0.12

Standard Error Formulas Based on Information from Sample. In problems of penny-tossing, it is possible to obtain an estimate of the standard deviation of the population based on the hypothesis of perfectly balanced coins, and to use this value in the formulas for the standard error. More commonly, however, the standard deviation of the population is quite unknown, the only information being that which is provided by a single sample. If the standard deviation of the sample has been computed with N in its denominator, then the formulas for the standard errors we have been discussing would be:

$$\tilde{\sigma}_{\bar{X}} = \frac{s}{\sqrt{N-1}} \qquad (84)$$

$$\tilde{\sigma}_s = \frac{s}{\sqrt{2(N-1)}} \qquad (83a)$$

Exercise 30

1. Which of the following can be described by the phrase "sampling distribution"?

a. The observed distribution of the weights of 25 month-old babies.

b. The unknown distribution of the weights of all month-old babies.

c. The distribution from sample to sample of the mean weight of month-old babies, all the samples having 25 cases and all being of the same race, taken in sequence from the birth records of some imaginary country which requires that babies be brought to a central registry for examination at monthly intervals.

d. The distribution from city to city of the mean weight of all month-old babies, the number of cases not being uniform from sample to sample, and some samples containing more children of the underprivileged groups than others.

e. The distribution of scores on a test given to a sample of 30 men selected at random from an army corps.

f. The distribution of means obtained from 50 samples of men drawn at random from the employees of a large manufacturing concern, each sample containing 8 men.

g. The distribution of the percentage of undernourished children in a series of samples from the New York City elementary schools, one sample being taken from each school.

h. The distribution of the number of days' work lost through strikes in a given industry for each year since 1900.

i. The distribution of the number of manufactured articles which fail to meet specified standards in 25 samples of 10 articles each, chosen by taking every 100th completed article.

j. The distribution of scores in the universe from which a series of samples is chosen.

2. The mean of a very large population is known to be 45.6 and the standard deviation to be 7.2. One thousand samples of 144 cases each are drawn at random, and the mean $\overline{X}$, and standard deviation s, computed for each sample.

What is the best estimate you can make from these facts of:
The mean of the set of means?
The standard deviation of the set of means?
The standard deviation of the set of standard deviations?

3. If the number of cases in each sample is increased, (a) the distribution of the means of successive random samples will probably be more variable _____, less variable _____, unchanged _____, changed slightly but in a random fashion _____; (b) the central tendency of the distribution of the means will probably be a little higher _____, a little lower _____, unchanged _____, changed slightly but in a random fashion _____.

4. A study has yielded the following data:

$$\overline{X} = 62.5, \qquad s^2 = 17.6, \qquad s = 4.2, \qquad N = 317$$

What is the best estimate that can be made for the population mean? The population variance? The population standard deviation? The standard error of the mean? The standard error of the standard deviation? Are these estimates necessarily correct? Why?

Sampling Distribution of the Ratio of a Mean to Its Standard Error.

It has already been said that the sampling distribution of the mean is normal. If each one of the sample means is divided by the constant $\sigma_{\overline{X}}$ $\left(\text{equal to } \dfrac{\sigma}{\sqrt{N}}\right)$, that division will not change the shape of the distribution of means, but only its scale. However, when $\tilde{\sigma}_{\bar{x}}\left(\text{equal to } \dfrac{s}{\sqrt{N-1}}\right)$ has to be used in place of $\sigma_{\bar{x}}$, the ratio

$$t = \frac{\overline{X}}{\tilde{\sigma}_{\bar{x}}} = \frac{\overline{X}}{\dfrac{s}{\sqrt{N-1}}} = \frac{\overline{X}\sqrt{N-1}}{s} \tag{85}$$

has a variable in its denominator as well as in its numerator, and has a sampling distribution differing somewhat in shape from that of $\overline{X}$. The sampling distribution of t becomes more and more nearly normal as N increases, and may be treated as normal for N larger than about 30. However, for small samples the distribution of t is not normal and a probability table different from those based on the normal distribution is required. At the close of this chapter are several references to such tables.

An alert student will probably note that this new measure, t, seems to be very similar to the value $z = \dfrac{x}{s}$ used in earlier sections of the book and will wonder why a change in terminology has been made. The reasons are purely historical. The distribution of $t = \dfrac{\overline{X}\sqrt{N-1}}{s}$ was first explored by W. S. Gosset (1876–1937), who wrote under the pseudonym "Student." The ratio of any normally distributed statistic to an estimate of the standard error of that statistic is today widely referred to as "'Student's' t" or simply as "t."

Estimate of Population Mean, Variance and Standard Deviation when the Estimate Can be Based on Two or More Samples. Suppose that two random samples of the same population have the statistics N_1, $\overline{X}_1$, s_1, and N_2, $\overline{X}_2$, s_2. Each sample taken alone provides an estimate of each population parameter, but the two estimates will, in general, not be in perfect agreement. We wish to know how to combine them to obtain the best estimate of each parameter based upon the pooled information provided by both samples.

For the mean

$$\tilde{\mu} = \frac{N_1\overline{X}_1 + N_2\overline{X}_2}{N_1 + N_2} \tag{86}$$

$$= \frac{\displaystyle\sum_{i=1}^{N_1} X_{i1} + \sum_{i=1}^{N_2} X_{i2}}{N_1 + N_2} \tag{87}$$

For the variance

$$\tilde{\sigma}^2 = \frac{N_1 s_1{}^2 + N_2 s_2{}^2}{N_1 + N_2 - 2} \tag{88}$$

$$= \frac{\sum\limits_{i=1}^{N_1} (X_{i1} - \overline{X_1})^2 + \sum\limits_{i=1}^{N_2} (X_{i2} - \overline{X_2})^2}{N_1 + N_2 - 2} \tag{89}$$

$$= \frac{\sum\limits_{i=1}^{N_1} X^2{}_{i1} + \sum\limits_{i=1}^{N_2} X^2{}_{i2} - \dfrac{\left(\sum\limits_{i=1}^{N_1} X_{i1}\right)^2}{N_1} - \dfrac{\left(\sum\limits_{i=1}^{N_2} X_{i2}\right)^2}{N_2}}{N_1 + N_2 - 2} \tag{90}$$

If the estimates are to be based not on two but on k samples, these formulas may be generalized as follows

$$\tilde{\mu} = \frac{N_1 \overline{X}_1 + N_2 \overline{X}_2 + \cdots + N_k \overline{X}_k}{N_1 + N_2 + \cdots + N_k} \tag{91}$$

$$= \frac{\sum\limits_{j=1}^{k} N_j \overline{X}_j}{\sum\limits_{j=1}^{k} N_j} \tag{92}$$

$$= \frac{\sum\limits_{j=1}^{k} \sum\limits_{i=1}^{N_j} X_{ij}}{\sum\limits_{j=1}^{k} N_j} \tag{93}$$

$$\tilde{\sigma}^2 = \frac{N_1 s_1{}^2 + N_2 s_2{}^2 + \cdots + N_k s_k{}^2}{N_1 + N_2 + \cdots + N_k - k} \tag{94}$$

$$= \frac{\sum\limits_{j=1}^{k} N_j s_j{}^2}{\sum\limits_{j=1}^{k} N_j - k} \tag{95}$$

$$= \frac{\sum\limits_{j=1}^{k} \sum\limits_{i=1}^{N_j} X^2{}_{ij} - \sum\limits_{j=1}^{k} \dfrac{\left(\sum\limits_{i=1}^{N_j} X_{ij}\right)^2}{N_j}}{\sum\limits_{j=1}^{k} N_j - k} \tag{96}$$

Formulas for $\bar{\sigma}$ can be written at once from the corresponding formulas for $\bar{\sigma}^2$. Examining these formulas more carefully, we see that certain ones are very easy to remember. If (91) and (94) are committed to memory, the entire group is memorized. Formula (86) is a special case of (91), and (88) is a special case (of 94). All formulas for the standard deviation follow so obviously from the corresponding formulas for the variance that no special effort of memorizing is demanded. The remaining formulas in the group show by what operations on the gross scores the values in the preceding formulas can be most economically obtained. It is not recommended that (86), (88), (91), or (94) be used for computational models when raw scores are available, though they are useful when only derived statistics rather than original scores are available.

Reliability of a Difference Between Two Means. A very large number of research studies in the social fields have as their chief objective the comparison of the performance of the same group under different situations or the comparison of the performance of different groups under similar situations. We wish to compare the outcomes of different environmental influences, different methods of teaching, different motivations, rewards and punishments, and so on. We wish to compare, on a variety of measures, boys and girls, deaf and hearing children, delinquent and normal, bilingual and unilingual, good readers and poor readers, and so on. We wish to compare initial and final scores made by the same group after a particular experience, and frequently we wish to compare the gain made by one group with the gain made during the same period by a comparable group subjected to a different experience. Research publications are full of studies in which the chief interest relates to the reliability of such differences, studies whose full import cannot be fully grasped by the person who does not understand the logic employed.

Suppose, for example, two groups of individuals have been taught by methods A and B respectively, and suppose that, in general, method A and method B are equally effective in raising the mean level of performance. In one experiment, because of individual differences and sampling accidents, the persons taught by method A may show slightly greater increase than those taught by method B, while in another experiment, the persons taught by method B may show the greater increase. Obviously in this situation a small difference favoring either method should not be interpreted as evidence of the general superiority of that method. On the other hand, suppose that, in general, method A tends to produce a greater increase in score than does method B. Now in a particular study, errors of sampling may entirely wipe out this real difference, perhaps even to the extent of having the group taught by method A make the lower mean score. In this case it would be a mistake to say that no difference exists in the population because none exists in the samples studied. Even if, in the long run, when applied to all the children who might conceivably be taught by them, two methods of teaching produce identical results, nevertheless in any particular sample one method or the other might have an appearance of superiority. Therefore, when we find one method showing a larger mean, we cannot be sure whether this reflects a similar situation in the population or is solely due to sampling errors.

We have previously seen that the mean, the standard deviation, and the variance are statistics which fluctuate from sample to sample. We must now recognize that a difference between two means is also a sample statistic, and that therefore it, too, has a sampling distribution and a standard error, that it, too, provides an estimate of the unknown population difference, and that it, too, furnishes a basis for testing hypotheses about that population.

The general problem of the significance of a difference between two means includes three subsidiary problems: How is the standard error to be computed? What is the shape of the sampling distribution? What is the logical process by which sample values can be used to provide information about the unknown population? These will now be taken up separately.

The Standard Error of the Difference Between the Means of Two Random Samples. The best estimate is given by the formula:

$$\tilde{\sigma}_{\bar{X}_1 - \bar{X}_2} = \sqrt{\frac{\tilde{\sigma}^2}{N_1} + \frac{\tilde{\sigma}^2}{N_2}} \qquad (97)$$

$$= \tilde{\sigma}\sqrt{\frac{1}{N_1} + \frac{1}{N_2}} = \tilde{\sigma}\sqrt{\frac{N_1 + N_2}{N_1 N_2}} \qquad (98)$$

if it is appropriate to make the assumption that the two samples are random samples from the same population. In this case, $\tilde{\sigma}$, the estimate of the standard deviation of that population, is the square root of the estimate of the population variance, given by formulas (94), (95), or (96).

If it does not seem appropriate to make the assumption that the samples are from the same population or from populations having the same variance, as would be the case, for example, if the observed variances s_1^2 and s_2^2 were very different from each other, then the best estimate of the standard error of the difference between the means is

$$\tilde{\sigma}_{\bar{X}_1 - \bar{X}_2} = \sqrt{\frac{s_1^2}{N_1 - 1} + \frac{s_2^2}{N_2 - 1}} \qquad (99)$$

Shape of the Sampling Distribution of the Difference Between Two Means. If the combined number of cases in the two samples is not too small, say, not less than 30, the distribution of

$$t = \frac{\overline{X}_1 - \overline{X}_2}{\tilde{\sigma}_{\overline{X}_1 - \overline{X}_2}} \tag{100}$$

is a normal distribution. If the samples are very small, the distribution of t is not normal, and special probability tables of the t-distribution must be used.

Testing a Statistical Hypothesis. The hypotheses which can be tested statistically are always hypotheses about unknown population values, or parameters. The test always consists of an examination of the hypothesis to see whether it can reasonably account for the statistics observed in a particular sample on the assumption that the latter is a random sample from a population in which the hypothesis is true. If the statistics in the sample under observation differ so greatly from the population parameters specified by the hypothesis that it is not reasonable to maintain that these statistics might have been produced by the fluctuations of random sampling from a population in which the hypothesis holds, then the hypothesis must be rejected as untenable. If the sample statistics are not inconsistent with the hypothesis about the population parameters, the hypothesis is accepted. This does not mean it is "proved," but merely that it is shown to be a tenable hypothesis, perhaps one of many tenable hypotheses.

Two Risks of Error. The research worker may reach a wrong conclusion in either of two different ways: he may reject the hypothesis when it really is true; or he may accept the hypothesis when it is false, that is, when some other hypothesis is true. Sometimes one danger has more serious consequences and sometimes the other, as will now be illustrated in some non-statistical situations.

Suppose a valuable treasure is known to be deposited in a certain spot accessible only by means of a rotten-looking board across a deep ravine. The treasure will become the property of John Smith if he can cross the board and reach it. John Smith now sets up a hypothesis about the board, namely, that it will support his weight. To test the hypothesis— though not statistically—he chips off fragments of the board and examines them to see whether or not they exhibit a degree of decay inconsistent with his hypothesis. On the basis of this examination of a sample of the board he either rejects the hypothesis or accepts it. Now even if he reaches the decision which most wise and experienced persons would approve in the light of the sample examined, he still runs a certain risk of making a wrong decision. On the one hand, he may reject his hypothesis when it is true. This means that actually the board would support his weight, but he concludes it would not and so loses the treasure. On the other hand, he may accept the hypothesis when it is false. This means that the board actually will not bear his weight, but he concludes it would, and so he gets a fall. He must decide which risk of error is more serious in the light of the whole situation, and must make his decision as to rejection or acceptance not only on the basis of the objective examination of his sample, but also on the subjective values inherent in his need of the treasure and the aspect of the ravine. If he is bankrupt and the possession of the treasure may save him from ruin, he will probably consider the second danger relatively unimportant, and so will not reject the hypothesis unless there is exceedingly strong evidence against it. If he is well-to-do, and the ravine is deep and treacherous in appearance, he may consider the first risk less grievous than the second, and so may reject the hypothesis even if there is but slight evidence against it.

The first type of error can be minimized by arbitrarily regulating the level of significance demanded, that is, by rejecting a hypothesis only when there is a very small probability that if true it would produce the observed data. The regulation of the second kind of error is a problem for higher mathematics. It is mentioned here to correct a general misapprehension that extreme rigor in controlling the first kind is always desirable and is sufficient protection from error, and to correct the idea that there is a level of significance which is equally satisfactory for all problems. The wind stresses likely to be encountered by the Empire State Building were not known—could not be known—at the time it was built. The engineers might err by strengthening the building far beyond what would eventually prove necessary and thus unduly adding to its cost, or they might err by underestimating the wind stresses which would play upon a very tall building, and so inviting its collapse. Obviously, the latter danger was so serious that it must be avoided at all cost, and the former danger was accepted as relatively unimportant. On the other hand, a firm manufacturing office equipment might make desk chairs so strong that they would support several times the weight of the heaviest known man, thus adding to their cost, but since the collapse of an office chair is not so serious a catastrophe as the collapse of a building, most buyers would prefer to accept a lower margin of safety in order to secure a lower price.

The first step in testing a hypothesis is its precise formulation. It must be formulated with such definiteness as to furnish numerical values of the parameters. For example, suppose a group of boys and a group of girls have been given a test of music appreciation and the investigator wishes to make certain comparisons. Such hypotheses as the following cannot be tested statistically because they are too vague and do not yield any single value of the parameters about which the statistics may be assumed to vary: "Boys in general score higher than girls," i.e., $\mu_b - \mu_g > 0$, or conversely; "Boys in general are more variable than girls," i.e., $\sigma_b - \sigma_g > 0$, or conversely. In order to make these hypotheses so precise that it will be possible to calculate the probability of obtaining a deviation of given size or larger from the stated parameter, that parameter must be specified exactly. We cannot test the hypothesis that $\mu_b - \mu_g$ is some indefinite number greater than zero, but we can test the hypothesis that it is a particular number, any particular number which seems of interest in the situation. Again and again the most pertinent and interesting hypothesis to be tested is the hypothesis that some particular population value is zero. This is called the *null hypothesis*.

A sample of boys has a mean 39.2 and a sample of girls has a mean 37.6. Would the mean of all boys be higher than the mean of all girls if the entire population were tested? The question cannot be answered directly, but we can explore the hypothesis that $\mu_b - \mu_g = 0$. *Should the hypothesis that $\mu_b - \mu_g = 0$ not prove untenable, we do not know that $\mu_b = \mu_g$ but merely that we have insufficient cause for asserting that μ_b is unequal to μ_g. The hypothesis is set up not because we believe it true, but in order that we may criticize its reasonableness.* Then it is necessary to determine, on the assumption that the given hypothesis is true, the sampling distribution of whatever statistic is under consideration, and from that sampling distribution to determine the probability that random sampling from a population in which the hypothesis holds would produce statistics deviating as much from the hypothetical parameters as those of the observed sample. The original derivation of the mathematical equation for this sampling distribution is a task for a mathematician, but after his work is done, tables can be constructed from which the required probability can be almost mechanically read. In practice this step is usually completely routinized and accomplished merely by reference to the appropriate table. Here we are considering only those problems for which reference is made to the normal probability table.

A final step is the decision as to whether the hypothesis shall be rejected or retained. The investigator decides in advance upon some arbitrarily selected level of significance which he considers appropriate to the problem in hand. He may, for example, agree that whenever an observed statistic differs from the corresponding parameter specified in his hypothesis by an amount which would occur by chance in only 1%

of all random samples from a population in which the hypothesis was true, he will reject the hypothesis. This is called the .01 _level of signifi-cance._ If the investigator should continue, day in and day out, for many years, rejecting hypotheses whenever the probability is $p = .01$ of obtaining a discrepancy between theoretical statistic and obtained parameter at least as large as in the data observed, he would reject 1% of all the true hypotheses he examined.

The region occupied by these extreme samples, for which the hypothesis is rejected, is called a _critical region._

Suppose, for example, we have set up the hypothesis that the unknown population from which a given sample of 225 cases is drawn at random has a normal distribution with a mean of 40 and a standard deviation of 13.5. Then the standard error of the mean is estimated as $\tilde{\sigma}_{\overline{x}} = \dfrac{13.5}{15} = 0.9$. If now we are rejecting hypotheses at the .01 level, we shall reject whenever we draw a sample in which the mean is removed from 40 by as much as $(2.58)(0.9)$ in either direction. (A table of the normal probability curve will show that the most extreme 1% of the area under such a curve, which is the most extreme 0.5% at each end, lies beyond the ordinates at $\pm 2.58\sigma$.) The scale is therefore divided at the point $40 - (2.58)(0.9) = 37.7$ and again at $40 + (2.58)(0.9) = 42.3$. The region between these two points is a _region of acceptance_. If the mean observed for a sample falls in the region of acceptance, that sample throws no suspicion upon the hypothesis. This is, of course, not a proof that the hypothesis is true, but only an assurance that these data do not contradict it. If a sample mean falls in the region of rejection, the hypothesis must be considered untenable. It has, of course, not been proved false, for at the .01 level, 1% of true hypotheses will be thus rejected.

The choice as to the level of significance at which hypotheses shall be rejected is a purely subjective one. As has been indicated, not all of the risks of life can be appropriately placed on the same level. It may be that not all the results of statistical analysis demand the same level of significance. Perhaps a very startling discovery, on which the investigator's whole professional reputation will depend, requires more caution about rejecting a hypothesis which is actually true than about accepting a hypothesis when some other is the correct one or vice versa. Usually, however, a rule-of-thumb procedure should be decided upon. The one most commonly in use at present is: to reject a hypothesis when, if it were true, 1 per cent or less of the random samples would be more extreme than the sample under observation; to retain a hypothesis when, if it were true, 5 per cent or more of the random samples would be more extreme than the sample under observation; to express doubt, for percentages between .01 and .05, until results are confirmed by later studies.

Each experimenter may properly set up his own definition of significance, so long as he informs his readers as to what it is. However, the fact that some of the available tables are made up for the .05 and .01 levels of significance only, encourages the use of the rule stated above.

Testing the Null Hypothesis. Let us test the hypothesis that the two distributions shown in Table XV on page 75 are in reality drawn at random from the same population; in other words, that there is no difference between sophomore men and women of the type attending this particular college in regard to their mean score on the Science Section of the Cooperative Contemporary Affairs test. From Table XV, the following computations are made:

	Men	Women	Both	Check
Number of cases, N	120	130	250	$120 + 130 = 250$
Sum of scores, ΣX	908	832	1740	$908 + 832 = 1740$
Mean	7.57	6.40		
Sum of squares of scores,				
ΣX^2	9636	8118	17754	$9636 + 8118 = 17754$
$(\Sigma X)^2/N$	6870.5	5324.8		
Ns^2	2765.5	2793.2		
s^2	23.05	21.49		

Inasmuch as the two variances seem to be about the same size, we shall use formula (90) for estimating the variance of the population and (98) for estimating the standard error of the difference between the means.

$$\tilde{\sigma}^2 = \frac{9636 + 8118 - \dfrac{(908)^2}{120} - \dfrac{(832)^2}{130}}{120 + 130 - 2}$$

$$= \frac{5558.7}{248} = 22.41$$

$$\tilde{\sigma}_{\overline{X}_1 - \overline{X}_2} = \sqrt{22.41\left(\frac{1}{120} + \frac{1}{130}\right)} = \sqrt{0.3591} = 0.599 \text{ or } 0.6$$

$$\overline{X}_1 - \overline{X}_2 = 7.57 - 6.40 = 1.17$$

$$t = \frac{\overline{X}_1 - \overline{X}_2}{\tilde{\sigma}_{\overline{X}_1 - \overline{X}_2}} = \frac{1.17}{0.6} = 1.95$$

The difference of 1.17 in favor of the men is 1.95 times as large as its own standard error. Think of a normal distribution of differences fluctuating about $\mu = 0$ with standard deviation equal to $\tilde{\sigma}_{\overline{X}_1 - \overline{X}_2} = 0.6$. On such a distribution the observed difference of 1.17 is located at the point 1.95 above the mean, which is at $\mu = 0$. Reference to a table of areas of the normal curve reveals the information that 0.026 of the area under the curve lies above the ordinate at the point $+1.95$ while another 0.026 of the area lies below the ordinate at the point -1.95. All together 0.052 of the area lies in these two end portions of the curve. If we reject the null hypothesis that $\mu_1 - \mu_2 = 0$, we shall be rejecting at the .052 level, i.e., we shall be rejecting on the basis of evidence such as would lead us to reject 5.2% of true hypotheses. The usual research worker would feel that the evidence was not strong enough to cause him to reject the null hypothesis, but would hold it in the back of his mind that further research might reveal a significant difference.

Reliability of the Mean Difference Between Two Measures of the Same Individuals. A very common type of investigation is that in which groups are matched person for person on some background trait or traits, one member of each pair being placed in group A and the other in group B. Groups A and B may be differentiated as to the possession of some qualitative trait, such as sex, race, etc.; or they may be differentiated as to the amount of some quantitative trait they possess, such as mental age, reading ability, etc., or they may be undifferentiated at the time of pairing and may be subsequently exposed to different treatments. The two groups are then compared with respect to some criterion trait which we will call X. If the means of the two groups are equal, or so nearly equal that the null hypothesis is tenable for the population, there is no evidence that the criterion trait is related to the trait which differentiates the groups.

Each pair constitutes one individual. The difference in the scores of the two members of the pair constitutes the measure of that individual. The mean and standard deviation of those individual measures is computed, and then the standard error of the mean. The mean is then compared with its own standard error to see whether it could reasonably be considered to have arisen through the accidents of sampling from a population in which the true value of the mean difference is zero.

In Table L are data obtained by Long on certain motor measurements of 37 matched pairs of deaf and hearing girls. In Table LI are the computations for testing whether the mean difference for strength of grip is reliably different from zero. The mean difference observed for this group is -2.32, which is to be interpreted as meaning that these 37 hearing girls scored 2.32 points higher on the average than these deaf girls. The variance of the 37 differences was 50.60, and the estimated standard error of the mean, 1.19. If we set up the hypothesis that in the popula-

TABLE L

Motor Abilities of 37 Pairs of Deaf and Hearing Girls

(*From John A. Long*, Motor Abilities of Deaf Children,
*Teachers College, Columbia University, Bureau of Publications,
New York, N. Y., 1932*)

Pair Number	Tapping with Right Hand		Grip		Balance		Tapping with Best Hand	
	D	H	D	H	D	H	D	H
1	1.3	25.7	10	16	2.0	2.3	18.3	25.7
2	17.0	27.7	14	12	2.0	1.0	17.0	27.7
3	26.3	26.0	12	17	2.7	3.7	26.3	26.0
4	29.7	26.3	21	18	2.7	3.3	29.7	28.7
5	23.0	26.3	19	15	3.0	10.0	23.0	26.3
6	22.7	24.0	12	21	2.7	2.7	22.7	24.0
7	22.0	35.0	19	16	3.7	8.3	22.3	35.0
8	20.7	28.7	17	22	1.3	6.0	30.7	28.7
9	29.0	30.3	19	18	2.0	4.3	29.0	30.3
10	30.0	26.3	25	16	4.3	7.7	30.0	26.3
11	26.7	37.3	23	28	1.0	1.3	26.7	37.3
12	36.0	30.7	25	22	1.7	4.0	36.0	30.7
13	30.7	31.3	24	21	5.0	5.3	30.7	31.3
14	22.3	25.0	15	21	1.0	2.0	22.3	25.0
15	38.3	38.7	25	30	1.7	2.7	38.3	38.7
16	28.7	24.0	13	25	3.3	4.7	28.7	24.0
17	34.3	32.3	25	31	3.0	4.7	34.3	32.3
18	35.7	26.3	23	23	3.3	2.3	35.7	26.3
19	32.3	30.7	23	35	8.0	10.0	32.3	33.0
20	33.0	31.0	15	28	2.3	8.0	33.0	31.0
21	27.3	36.7	18	33	1.7	4.3	29.3	36.7
22	27.7	31.7	19	23	2.0	4.7	27.7	31.7
23	29.0	28.7	34	20	2.0	7.0	34.0	34.0
24	35.3	30.7	32	45	2.7	3.3	35.3	30.7
25	30.3	27.7	29	39	1.0	1.7	32.3	27.7
26	39.0	32.0	26	29	2.0	5.0	39.7	32.0
27	35.7	28.0	35	32	1.3	4.0	35.7	28.0
28	31.7	31.3	31	25	2.3	6.7	31.7	31.3
29	37.7	36.7	29	26	4.3	6.7	37.7	36.7
30	39.3	35.3	31	33	5.3	10.0	39.3	35.3
31	30.7	31.3	31	38	2.3	3.7	30.7	32.0
32	26.7	27.3	22	28	2.0	8.7	26.7	30.7
33	35.7	33.0	34	19	1.7	3.7	35.7	33.0
34	34.0	32.0	22	32	3.0	3.0	34.0	32.0
35	25.3	30.3	27	29	4.0	7.0	25.3	30.3
36	29.7	33.3	31	31	4.7	6.3	29.7	33.3
37	35.3	29.3	29	28	1.3	7.3	35.3	29.3

TABLE LI

Computations for Testing Reliability of the Difference in Strength of Grip Between the Means of 37 Pairs of Deaf and Hearing Children

Pair	Score			
	D	H	$D - H$	$(D - H)^2$
1	10	16	-6	36
2	14	12	$+2$	4
3	12	17	-5	25
4	21	18	$+3$	9
5	19	15	$+4$	16
6	12	21	-9	81
7	19	16	$+3$	9
8	17	22	-5	25
9	19	18	$+1$	1
10	25	16	$+9$	81
11	23	28	-5	25
12	25	22	$+3$	9
13	24	21	$+3$	9
14	15	21	-6	36
15	25	30	-5	25
16	13	25	-12	144
17	25	31	-6	36
18	23	23	$0 \quad 0$	0
19	23	35	-12	144
20	15	28	-13	169
21	18	33	-15	225
22	19	23	-4	16
23	34	20	$+14$	196
24	32	45	-13	169
25	29	39	-10	100
26	26	29	-3	9
27	35	32	$+3$	9
28	31	25	$+6$	36
29	29	26	$+3$	9
30	31	33	-2	4
31	31	38	-7	49
32	22	28	-6	36
33	34	19	$+15$	225
34	22	32	-10	100
35	27	29	-2	4
36	31	31	$0 \quad 0$	0
37	29	28	$+1$	1
Total	859	945	-86	2072

tion deaf and hearing children of the type Long studied have the same mean grip, then we must consider this sample to provide an observation departing from that population mean by $\dfrac{2.32 - 0}{1.19} = 1.95$ times its standard error. Tables of the normal probability curve show that about 5% of the area lies outside the ordinates at ± 1.95. If we reject the null hypothesis, we do so at the .05 level of confidence. There is, therefore, a reasonable doubt as to whether deaf and hearing children come from the same population in respect to strength of grip, but the data at hand are insufficient to cause us to maintain that they do not.

Test the reliability of the difference for each of the other traits in Table L. The very reliable difference for balance is not surprising in view of the known relationship between balance and the semi-circular canals of the ears.

Further Development of Statistical Inference in Book II. Statistical inference is always inference about a population from data provided by a sample. The very important and fascinating problems which have been introduced in this chapter will be developed more fully in the forthcoming Book II of this series, where many other techniques for testing hypotheses about populations will be considered.

BIBLIOGRAPHY ON SAMPLING

Cochran, W. G., "The use of the analysis of variance in enumeration by sampling," *Jour. Amer. Stat. Assoc.*, 34 (Sept., 1939), 492–510.

Cornfield, Jerome, "On certain biases in samples of human populations," *Jour. Amer. Stat. Assoc.*, 37 (March, 1942), 63–68.

Craig, A. T., "On mathematics of the representative method of sampling," *Annals Math. Stat.* 10 (1939), 26–34.

Croxton, F. E., and Cowden, D. J., *Applied General Statistics*. New York, Prentice-Hall, 1940. Chapters XII and XIII.

Fisher, R. A., *Statistical Methods for Research Workers*. London, Oliver & Boyd. Numerous editions.

Frankel, Lester R., and Stock, J. Stevens, "On the sample of unemployment," *Jour. Amer. Stat. Assoc.*, 37 (March, 1942), 77–80.

Gouldon, C. H., *Methods of Statistical Analysis*. New York, John Wiley & Sons, 1939.

Hanson, Morris H., and Hurwitz, William N., "Relative efficiencies of various sampling units in population inquiries," *Jour. Amer. Stat. Assoc.*, 37 (March, 1942), 89–94.

Hauser, Philip M., "Proposed annual sample census of population," *Jour. Amer. Stat. Assoc.*, 37 (March, 1942), 81–88.

Kenney, J. F., *Mathematics of Statistics*. New York, D. Van Nostrand Co., Inc., 1939. Part II. For persons with some mathematical training only.

Lindquist, E. F., *Statistical Analysis in Educational Research.* New York, Houghton Mifflin Co., 1940.

——, *A First Course in Statistics.* Houghton Mifflin, 1942, Chapter VIII.

McNemar, Quinn, "Sampling in psychological research," *Psychological Bulletin,* 37 (1940), 331–365. Includes a bibliography of 56 titles.

Mills, F. C., *Statistical Methods.* New York, Henry Holt & Co., 2nd ed., 1938. Chapters XIV, XV, XVIII.

Neyman, Jerzy, "Contribution to the theory of sampling human populations," *Jour. Amer. Stat. Assoc.,* 33 (March, 1938), 101–116. Mathematical basis for "double sampling" is presented, showing that method to be, under favorable conditions, a very powerful tool of research.

——, "On the two different aspects of representative method: the method of stratified sampling and the method of purposive selection," *Jour. Royal Stat. Soc.,* 97 (1934), 5.

——, "On statistical methods in social and economic research, census by sampling and other problems," *Lectures and Conferences on Mathematical Statistics,* The Graduate School of the United States Department of Agriculture, Washington, D. C., 1937, pp. 89–108.

Peters, C. C., and Van Voorhis, W. R., *Statistical Procedures and Their Mathematical Bases.* New York, McGraw-Hill Book Co., 1940. Chapter VI.

Schoenberg, Erika H., & Parton, Mildred, "Methods and problems of sampling presented by the urban study of consumer purchases," *Jour. Amer. Stat. Assoc.,* 32 (June, 1937), 311–322.

Shewhart, W. A., "Random sampling," *Amer. Math. Monthly,* 38 (May, 1931), 245–270. Reprinted in the Bell Telephone System Technical Publications. A statement of the conditions under which a sample has practical significance.

——, *Statistical Method from the Viewpoint of Quality Control.* The Graduate School of the U. S. Department of Agriculture, Washington, 1939, 155 pp. See especially pp. 10–22.

Snedecor, G. W., *Statistical Methods.* Ames, Iowa, Collegiate Press, Inc., 1937.

——, George W., "Design of sampling experiments in the social sciences," *Jour. Farm. Econ.,* 21 (Nov., 1939), 846–855.

—— and King, Arnold J., "Recent developments in sampling for agricultural statistics," *Jour. Amer. Stat. Assoc.,* 37 (March, 1942), 95–102.

Stephan, F. F., "Representative sampling in large scale surveys," *Jour. Amer. Stat. Assoc.,* 34 (June, 1939), 343–352.

——, "Practical problems of sampling procedure," *Amer. Sociological Review,* (Aug., 1936), 569–580.

——, "Stratification in representative sampling," *Jour. of Marketing* (July, 1941), 38–46.

Sukhatme, P. V., "Contribution to the theory of the representative method," *Supplement to Jour. Royal Stat. Soc.,* 2 (1935), 253–268.

Thompson, Warren S., "Size of families from which college students come," *Jour. Amer. Stat. Assoc.* (1925), 481. See criticism of article in the following: G. Pietra, "A particular case of non-representative sampling," *Jour. Amer. Stat. Assoc.*, 21 (Sept., 1926), 330–332; Elbridge Sibley, "The size of families," *ibid.*, 333–334.

Walker, Helen M., "The sampling problem in educational research," *Teachers College Record*, 30 (May, 1929), 760–774.

Wilks, S. S., "On the distribution of statistics in samples from a normal population of two variables with matched sampling of one variable," *Metron*, 9 (1932), 87–126.

W.P.A., Division of Research, Labor Market Research Section, "Sampling procedures and method of operation of the W.P.A. monthly report of unemployment," A 3467, October, 1941. (Prepared by Lester R. Frankel and J. Stevens Stock.)

Yule, G. U., and Kendall, M. G., *An Introduction to the Theory of Statistics*. C. Griffin & Co., Ltd., 1937, pp. 332–335.

APPENDIX A

Scores for 109 Fourth-Grade Pupils on the Modern School Achievement Test

Case Number	Age to Nearest Month	I.Q.	Arithmetic Computation	Arithmetic Reasoning	Reading Speed	Language	History-Civics
			Score on Test of				
1*	121	99	12	11	27	17	24
2	124	83	13	4	12	15	13
3*	103	117	5	8	30	26	10
4*	127	83	8	6	30	12	21
5	115	109	7	4	26	27	13
6	108	111	6	3	17	21	20
7*	106	92	9	9	25	30	12
8*	115	95	5	3	28	12	16
9	140	79	8	3	28	23	11
10	111	115	10	8	20	26	4
11	109	120	5	5	26	19	10
12	119	101	6	4	24	14	20
13	119	87	10	5	8	14	17
14	108	106	7	7	10	16	5
15	131	100	6	5	21	20	8
16*	112	120	13	7	21	19	8
17	118	99	4	4	26	16	10
18	96	119	7	7	20	17	12
19	148	66	10	2	16	11	9
20	132	77	5	3	27	19	21
21*	108	124	8	6	29	29	9
22*	96	125	10	5	30	18	16
23	118	104	9	4	18	23	21
24	123	89	6	5	13	19	13
25*	109	97	8	5	28	26	2
26	106	126	11	11	29	30	18
27*	142	68	5	2	7	17	10
28	109	83	6	3	16	23	15
29	150	64	6	1	11	7	7
30	113	96	4	4	25	26	19
31	117	91	6	4	30	19	2
32*	156	75	12	5	30	18	15
33*	119	103	8	5	14	22	18
34*	129	86	9	4	8	14	6
35	114	118	9	3	24	19	10
36	106	140	13	9	40	31	10
37	114	120	12	9	17	21	18
38	134	93	9	3	17	24	12
39*	109	112	7	2	31	24	18
40	115	116	15	5	41	33	22

* All case numbers starred refer to boys, unstarred numbers to girls.

Case Number	Age to Nearest Month	I.Q.	Score on Test of				
			Arithmetic Computation	Arithmetic Reasoning	Reading Speed	Language	History-Civics
41	109	123	10	4	34	24	23
42	109	105	11	5	22	25	13
43*	101	121	5	1	35	28	22
44*	108	114	5	4	24	16	10
45*	116	113	13	6	18	20	12
46	111	111	8	4	25	19	12
47*	120	114	9	8	36	23	23
48*	118	99	6	2	33	15	18
49*	109	101	12	2	23	16	18
50*	111	112	12	6	25	15	16
51*	116	125	10	3	33	16	23
52	114	105	13	3	44	20	24
53	129	100	8	6	22	18	20
54	106	144	16	5	40	28	20
55	110	101	10	7	14	17	13
56	125	108	8	4	30	22	18
57*	105	112	6	3	30	14	16
58	124	98	9	7	28	21	12
59	111	105	12	1	24	22	13
60*	118	123	7	3	35	24	22
61*	103	148	9	8	43	32	18
62*	129	93	10	2	24	17	12
63	104	129	8	3	39	25	17
64*	116	106	6	5	45	26	20
65	112	111	8	4	35	17	13
66*	111	121	7	2	45	25	17
67*	109	115	12	7	44	20	20
68*	104	130	8	9	39	29	23
69	107	114	15	7	42	30	21
70	117	118	16	12	49	39	18
71*	114	103	6	7	26	30	19
72	108	108	3	2	21	12	3
73	114	123	1	1	26	31	9
74	112	142	2	8	45	30	5
75*	107	120	2	2	26	25	7
76*	109	136	10	5	34	29	10
77*	113	131	5	7	24	28	8
78	108	141	4	9	23	24	10
79*	116	106	8	5	26	22	3
80*	109	126	4	9	24	19	2

* All case numbers starred refer to boys, unstarred numbers to girls.

Case Number	Age to Nearest Month	I.Q.	Score on Test of				
			Arithmetic Computation	Arithmetic Reasoning	Reading Speed	Language	History-Civics
81	110	125	7	7	24	23	2
82	107	131	6	5	40	36	17
83*	113	104	7	3	28	29	19
84*	109	128	10	9	42	30	18
85	109	133	8	7	31	26	9
86	114	127	9	9	28	24	7
87	107	138	3	6	46	36	4
88*	112	132	4	1	44	31	12
89*	107	136	9	2	29	32	5
90*	113	119	3	7	30	22	9
91	115	106	9	4	24	17	3
92*	108	124	1	5	50	29	23
93	108	124	9	4	48	14	7
94*	122	102	6	2	26	20	5
95*	124	83	8	3	10	15	6
96*	126	93	7	6	16	26	14
97	104	113	8	8	30	23	8
98	115	90	0	2	24	18	5
99*	117	103	8	5	27	17	5
100*	111	88	12	5	10	11	6
101*	115	111	9	7	16	17	10
102	103	130	2	2	41	25	2
103	122	91	4	8	32	9	5
104*	113	106	7	3	15	10	6
105	111	115	6	2	43	28	7
106	114	120	1	3	27	26	8
107*	118	116	11	4	40	19	5
108	109	120	9	2	50	35	4
109	118	123	10	6	41	18	4

* All case numbers starred refer to boys, unstarred numbers to girls.

APPENDIX B

MATHEMATICAL NOTES AND PROOFS

I. *Proof of the formulas for computing variance and standard deviation when deviations are taken from an origin other than the mean of the distribution.*

For each of the N individuals in the distribution, assuming that x' is a deviation in score units, we have

$$x_i' = X_i - A$$

Adding together the N equations of this type,

$$\sum_{i=1}^{N} x_i' = \sum_{i=1}^{N} X_i - NA$$

As A is a constant, $\sum_{i=1}^{N} A = NA$. Dividing by N

$$\frac{\sum_{i=1}^{N} x_i'}{N} = \frac{\sum_{i=1}^{N} X_i}{N} - A$$

But $\overline{X} = \frac{\Sigma X}{N}$ and therefore, ceasing to write the limits of summation because they are clear,

$$\frac{\Sigma x_i'}{N} = \overline{X} - A$$

Now let $a = \overline{X} - A$ for convenience.

Since $\qquad\qquad x_i' = X_i - A$

and $\qquad\qquad X_i = x_i + \overline{X}$

then $\qquad\qquad x_i' = x_i + \overline{X} - A$

or $\qquad\qquad x_i' = x_i + a$

and $\qquad\qquad (x_i')^2 = x_i^2 + 2ax_i + a^2$

The N such equations are:

$$(x_1')^2 = x_1^2 \quad + \quad 2ax_1 + a^2$$
$$(x_2')^2 = x_2^2 \quad + \quad 2ax_2 + a^2$$
$$\cdot \quad \cdot \quad \cdot \quad \cdot \quad \cdot \quad \cdot$$
$$(x_N')^2 = x_N^2 \quad + \quad 2ax_N + a^2$$

and their sum is $\displaystyle\sum_{i=1}^{N}(x_i')^2 = \sum_{i=1}^{N} x_i^2 + \sum_{i=1}^{N} 2ax_i + Na^2$

or
$$\Sigma(x')^2 = \Sigma x^2 + 0 + Na^2$$

The middle term reduces to zero because

$$\Sigma 2ax_i = 2ax_1 + 2ax_2 + \cdots + 2ax_N$$
$$= 2a(x_1 + x_2 + \cdots + x_N) = 2a\Sigma x_i = 2a(0) = 0$$

Therefore
$$\Sigma x^2 = \Sigma(x')^2 - Na^2,$$

and
$$\frac{\Sigma x^2}{N} = \frac{\Sigma(x')^2}{N} - a^2$$

But $\quad a = \dfrac{\Sigma x'}{N},\quad$ and so $\quad \dfrac{\Sigma x^2}{N} = \dfrac{\Sigma(x')^2}{N} - \left(\dfrac{\Sigma x'}{N}\right)^2$

By definition
$$s^2 = \frac{\Sigma x^2}{N}$$

and therefore
$$s^2 = \frac{\Sigma(x')^2}{N} - \left(\frac{\Sigma x'}{N}\right)^2$$

and
$$s = \sqrt{\frac{\Sigma(x')^2}{N} - \left(\frac{\Sigma x'}{N}\right)^2}$$

It was assumed at the outset that x' is measured in *score* units.

Now consider the case where x'' is measured not in score units but in class interval units. Let $x' = ix''$, where i is the width of the class interval, not to be confused with the subscript i previously used to designate the variable in the summation.

Then $\quad\qquad\qquad \Sigma x' = i\Sigma x''$
and $\quad\qquad\qquad \Sigma(x')^2 = i^2\Sigma(x'')^2$

and $\quad s^2 = \dfrac{\Sigma(x')^2}{N} - \left(\dfrac{\Sigma x'}{N}\right)^2 = \dfrac{i^2\Sigma(x'')^2}{N} - \left(\dfrac{i\Sigma x''}{N}\right)^2$

$$s^2 = i^2\left[\frac{\Sigma(x'')^2}{N} - \left(\frac{\Sigma x''}{N}\right)^2\right]$$

and $\quad s = i\sqrt{\dfrac{\Sigma(x'')^2}{N} - \left(\dfrac{\Sigma x''}{N}\right)^2}$

These are formulas (9) and (9a) on pages 115 and 116.

Proof of formulas (10), (10a), (11), and (11a) follows the same pattern, and will be given in less detail.

$$x_i = X_i - \overline{X}$$
$$x_i^2 = X_i^2 - 2X_i\overline{X} + \overline{X}^2$$

Adding the N such equations,

$$\sum_{i=1}^{N} x_i{}^2 = \sum_{i=1}^{N} X_i{}^2 - 2\overline{X}\sum_{i=1}^{N} X_i + N\overline{X}^2$$

But $\displaystyle\sum_{i=1}^{N} X_i = N\overline{X}$

Therefore $\qquad\displaystyle\sum_{i=1}^{N} x_i{}^2 = \sum_{i=1}^{N} X_i{}^2 - 2\overline{X}(N\overline{X}) + N\overline{X}^2$

Dropping the limits of summation because they are clear,

$$\Sigma x^2 = \Sigma X^2 - 2N\overline{X}^2 + N\overline{X}^2$$
$$= \Sigma X^2 - N\overline{X}^2$$

Dividing by N

$$s^2 = \frac{\Sigma x^2}{N} = \frac{\Sigma X^2}{N} - \overline{X}^2 \text{ which is formula (11)}$$

But $\overline{X} = \dfrac{\Sigma X}{N}$

and therefore $\quad s^2 = \dfrac{\Sigma X^2}{N} - \left(\dfrac{\Sigma X}{N}\right)^2$ which is formula (10)

II. *Proof of the formulas for obtaining Σxy when deviations are taken from origins other than $\overline{X}$ and $\overline{Y}$.*

For each of the N individuals in the distribution, assuming that x' and y' are deviations in score units, we have

$$x_i' = x_i + a_x$$
$$y_i' = y_i + a_y$$

and $\qquad\qquad x_i'y_i' = x_iy_i + x_ia_y + y_ia_x + a_xa_y$

Adding together the N equations of this type,

$$\sum_{i=1}^{N} x_i'y_i' = \sum_{i=1}^{N} x_iy_i + a_y\sum_{i=1}^{N} x_i + a_x\sum_{i=1}^{N} y_i + \sum_{i=1}^{N} a_xa_y$$

or $\qquad\quad \Sigma x'y' = \Sigma xy \quad\; + 0 \qquad\; + 0 \qquad\; + N a_x a_y$

But $a_x = \dfrac{\Sigma x'}{N}$ and $a_y = \dfrac{\Sigma y'}{N}$

Therefore $\qquad \Sigma x'y' = \Sigma xy + N\left(\dfrac{\Sigma x'}{N}\right)\left(\dfrac{\Sigma y'}{N}\right)$

$$= \Sigma xy + \frac{(\Sigma x')(\Sigma y')}{N}$$

and $\qquad\qquad \Sigma xy = \Sigma x'y' - \dfrac{(\Sigma x')(\Sigma y')}{N}$

This is the numerator in formulas (53) and (54).

Now consider the case where a deviation is measured not in score units but in interval units.

Let $\quad x' = i_x x''$ $\quad$ and $\quad y' = i_y y''$

Then $\Sigma x' = i_x \Sigma x''$ and $\Sigma y' = i_y \Sigma y''$
$\quad x'y' = i_x i_y x''y''$

and $\Sigma x'y' = i_x i_y \Sigma x''y''$

Therefore $\qquad \Sigma xy = \Sigma x'y' - \dfrac{(\Sigma x'')(\Sigma y'')}{N}$

$$= i_x i_y \Sigma x''y'' - \frac{(i_x \Sigma x'')(i_y \Sigma y'')}{N}$$

$$= i_x i_y \left\{ \Sigma x''y'' - \frac{(\Sigma x'')(\Sigma y'')}{N} \right\}$$

This identity is used in deriving formula (53).

When the arbitrary origin is placed at zero, the derivation is similar to the foregoing. Each raw score is itself a deviation from zero.

$$x_i = X_i - \overline{X}$$
$$y_i = Y_i - \overline{Y}$$
$$x_i y_i = X_i Y_i - X_i \overline{Y} - Y_i \overline{X} + \overline{X}\,\overline{Y}$$

Adding the N equations of this type,

$$\Sigma xy = \Sigma XY - \Sigma X\overline{Y} - \Sigma Y\overline{X} + \Sigma \overline{X}\,\overline{Y}$$
$$= \Sigma XY - \overline{Y}\Sigma X - \overline{X}\Sigma Y + N\overline{X}\,\overline{Y}$$
$$= \Sigma XY - \overline{Y}(N\overline{X}) - \overline{X}(N\overline{Y}) + N\overline{X}\,\overline{Y}$$
$$= \Sigma XY - N\overline{X}\,\overline{Y}$$

$$= \Sigma XY - N\left(\frac{\Sigma X}{N}\right)\left(\frac{\Sigma Y}{N}\right) = \Sigma XY - \frac{(\Sigma X)(\Sigma Y)}{N}$$

This provides the numerator in formulas (55) and (56).

III. *Proof of formula (29) and (30) for the mean and variance of a combined group.*

Let $N_1, N_2, \cdots N_k$ be the number of cases in the component sub groups and $N_c = N_1 + N_2 + \cdots + N_k$.

Let $\overline{X}_1, \overline{X}_2 \cdots \overline{X}_k$ be the means of the component subgroups and $\overline{X}_c$ be the mean of the combined group.

Then $\qquad \overline{X}_1 = \dfrac{1}{N_1} \displaystyle\sum_{i=1}^{N_1} X_{i1}$ $\qquad$ and $\qquad N_1\overline{X}_1 = \displaystyle\sum_{i=1}^{N_1} X_{i1}$

and in general

$$\overline{X}_j = \frac{1}{N_j}\sum_{i=1}^{N_j}X_{ij} \quad\text{and}\quad N_j\overline{X}_j = \sum_{i=1}^{N_j}X_{ij}$$

Also
$$\overline{X}_c = \frac{1}{N_c}\sum_{j=1}^{k}\sum_{i=1}^{N_j}X_{ij} \quad\text{and}\quad N_c\overline{X}_c = \sum_{j=1}^{k}\sum_{i=1}^{N_j}X_{ij}$$

Therefore $\quad N_c\overline{X}_c = \sum_{j=1}^{k}N_j\overline{X}_j = N_1\overline{X}_1 + N_2\overline{X}_2 + \cdots + N_k\overline{X}_k,$ which is formula (29).

The deviation of any member of group 1 from $\overline{X}_c$ is

$$X_{i1} - \overline{X}_c = X_{i1} - \overline{X}_1 + \overline{X}_1 - \overline{X}_c$$

Therefore

$$(X_{i1} - \overline{X}_c)^2 = (X_{i1} - \overline{X}_1)^2 + 2(X_{i1} - \overline{X}_1)(\overline{X}_1 - \overline{X}_c) + (\overline{X}_1 - \overline{X}_c)^2$$

Now let $\quad d_1 = \overline{X}_1 - \overline{X}_c \quad$ or in general $\quad d_j = \overline{X}_j - \overline{X}_c$

Then $\quad (X_{i1} - \overline{X}_c)^2 = (X_{i1} - \overline{X}_1)^2 + 2d_1(X_{i1} - \overline{X}_1) + d_1{}^2$

There is one such equation for each of the N_1 members of group 1. Adding these N_1 equations

$$\sum_{i=1}^{N_1}(X_{i1} - \overline{X}_c)^2 = \sum_{i=1}^{N_1}(X_{i1} - \overline{X}_1)^2 + 2\sum_{i=1}^{N_1}d_1(X_{i1} - \overline{X}_1) + \sum_{i=1}^{N_1}d_1{}^2$$

Because d is a constant,

$$\sum_{i=1}^{N_1}d_1{}^2 = N_1d_1{}^2$$

and
$$\sum_{i=1}^{N_1}d_1(X_{i1} - \overline{X}_1) = d_1\sum_{i=1}^{N_1}(X_{i1} - \overline{X}_1)$$

Because the sum of the deviations of the scores in a distribution from the mean of that distribution is zero,

$$d_1\sum_{i=1}^{N_1}(X_{i1} - \overline{X}_1) = 0$$

By formula (12), $\quad N_1s_1{}^2 = \sum_{i=1}^{N_1}(X_{i1} - \overline{X}_1)^2$

Therefore $\quad \sum_{i=1}^{N_1}(X_{i1} - \overline{X}_c)^2 = N_1s_1{}^2 + 0 + N_1d_1{}^2$

There is one such equation for each of the k groups. Adding these k equations,

$$\sum_{j=1}^{k}\sum_{i=1}^{N_j}(X_{ij} - \overline{X}_c)^2 = \sum_{j=1}^{k}N_j s_j^2 + \sum_{i=1}^{k}N_j d_j^2$$

But by formula (12), generalized, $N_c s_c^2 = \sum_{j=1}^{k}\sum_{i=1}^{N_j}(X_{ij} - \overline{X}_c)^2$

Therefore

$$N_c s_c^2 = \sum_{j=1}^{k}N_j s_j^2 + \sum_{j=1}^{k}N_j d_j^2$$

$$= (N_1 s_1^2 + N_2 s_2^2 + \cdots + N_k s_k^2) + (N_1 d_1^2 + N_2 d_2^2 + \cdots + N_k d_k^2)$$

$$= (N_1 s_1^2 + N_1 d_1^2) + (N_2 s_2^2 + N_2 d_2^2) + \cdots + (N_k s_k^2 + N_k d_k^2)$$

$$= N_1(s_1^2 + d_1^2) + N_2(s_2^2 + d_2^2) + \cdots + N_k(s_k^2 + d_k^2)$$

IV. *Derivation of formula* $\mu_4 = \mu_4' - 4\mu_3'\mu_1' + 6\mu_2'(\mu_1')^2 - 3(\mu_1')^4$

Let

$$x_i = X_i - \overline{X} = X_i - A + A - \overline{X} = (X_i - A) - (\overline{X} - A)$$

or

$$x_i = x_i' - a$$
$$x_i^4 = (x_i' - a)^4 = (x_i')^4 - 4(x_i')^3 a + 6(x_i')^2 a^2 - 4(x_i')a^3 + a^4$$

There is one such equation for each of the N members of the group. Adding these N equations and dividing by N, and dropping the subscript i and the limits of summation,

$$\frac{\Sigma x^4}{N} = \frac{\Sigma(x')^4}{N} - 4\frac{\Sigma(x')^3 a}{N} + 6\frac{\Sigma(x')^2 a^2}{N} - 4\frac{\Sigma x' a^3}{N} + \frac{\Sigma a^4}{N}$$

$$= \frac{\Sigma(x')^4}{N} - 4a\frac{\Sigma(x')^3}{N} + 6a^2\frac{\Sigma(x')^2}{N} - 4a^3\frac{\Sigma x'}{N} + \frac{Na^4}{N}$$

But $\mu_4 = \dfrac{\Sigma x^4}{N}$ $\mu_2' = \dfrac{\Sigma(x')^2}{N}$

$\mu_4' = \dfrac{\Sigma(x')^4}{N}$ $\mu_1' = \dfrac{\Sigma x'}{N} = a$

$\mu_3' = \dfrac{\Sigma(x')^3}{N}$

Therefore, substituting these values in the expression for $\dfrac{\Sigma x^4}{N}$,

$$\mu_4 = \mu_4' - 4\mu_1'\mu_3' + 6(\mu_1')^2\mu_2' - 4(\mu_1')^3\mu_1' + (\mu_1')^4$$
$$= \mu_4' - 4\mu_3'\mu_1' + 6\mu_2'(\mu_1')^2 - 3(\mu_1')^4$$

V. *Derivation of the formulas for the two regression coefficients and the correlation coefficient.*

We shall first seek the equation of a straight line expressing the dependence of y on x. This may be written as

$$\tilde{y} = bx + c$$

where b and c are unknown constants which determine the position of the line and where x and $\tilde{y}$ represent the coordinates of any point on the line and vary from point to point. In the adjacent sketch P represents any single selected point on the correlation chart, with coordinates $x = OT$ and $y = TP$. S is a corresponding point on the regression line, with coordinates $x = OT$ and $\tilde{y} = TS$. $SP = y - \tilde{y}$ is a residual error, or error made in estimating y from x.

Obviously the constants b and c should be chosen in such a way as to make the residual errors as small as possible. However, it will be useless

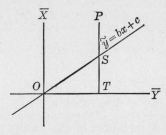

to use the criterion that $\Sigma(y - \tilde{y}) = 0$ because positive and negative deviations will balance each other whenever the line passes through the intersection of the means $\overline{X}$ and $\overline{Y}$. In order to keep the positive and negative residuals from thus annihilating each other, we may square them before summing. This is equivalent to adopting the criterion of *Least Squares*, that the line will be considered to be in the "best" position when the sum of the squares of the residual errors is a minimum.

Let

$$Q = \Sigma(y - \tilde{y})^2$$

As the line moves from position to position, b and c vary. The task is to find those values of b and c which make Q a minimum. This can be done by taking the first derivative of Q with respect to c, and later with respect to b, and setting it equal to zero. This derivative may be found by applying the principle that the derivative of a sum of quantities is equal to the sum of the derivatives of those quantities.

$$Q = \Sigma(y - \tilde{y})^2$$
$$= \Sigma(y - bx - c)^2$$
$$= \Sigma(y^2 + b^2x^2 + c^2 - 2bxy - 2cy + 2bcx)$$

Let
$$0 = \frac{dQ}{dc} = 2\Sigma c - 2\Sigma y + 2\Sigma bx$$
$$0 = 2Nc - 2\Sigma y + 2b\Sigma x$$

But $\Sigma y = 0$ and $\Sigma x = 0$, so

$$0 = 2Nc - 0 + 0$$

Inasmuch as N cannot be zero if there are any observations at all, c must be zero, and the regression line must pass through the intersection of the means $\overline{X}$ and $\overline{Y}$, as shown in the preceding sketch.

Therefore

$$\tilde{y} = bx.$$

The same general procedure will now be used to obtain a "best" value for b.

$$Q = \Sigma(y - \tilde{y})^2 = \Sigma(y - bx)^2$$
$$= \Sigma y^2 - 2\Sigma bxy + \Sigma b^2 x^2$$
$$0 = \frac{dQ}{db} = -2\Sigma xy + 2b\Sigma x^2$$

Therefore

$$b = \frac{\Sigma xy}{\Sigma x^2}$$

and

$$\tilde{y} = \frac{\Sigma xy}{\Sigma x^2} \cdot x$$

is the regression equation to predict y from x.

By parallel reasoning,

$$\tilde{x} = \frac{\Sigma xy}{\Sigma y^2} \cdot y$$

is the regression equation to predict x from y.

There are two regression coefficients, and the letter b is customarily used for each, the two being distinguished by subscripts, as follows:

$$b_{yx} = \frac{\Sigma xy}{\Sigma x^2} \quad \text{and} \quad b_{xy} = \frac{\Sigma xy}{\Sigma y^2}$$

Each of these is a measure of relation between x and y, but one applies when x is used for predicting y and the other when y is used for predicting x. To obtain a measure of *mutual* relation, of co-relation, we may proceed as follows:

Substituting Ns_x^2 for Σx^2 and Ns_y^2 for Σy^2,

$$\tilde{y} = \frac{\Sigma xy}{\Sigma x^2} \cdot x \quad \text{and} \quad \tilde{x} = \frac{\Sigma xy}{\Sigma y^2} \cdot y$$

$$\tilde{y} = \frac{\Sigma xy}{Ns_x^2} \cdot x \quad \text{and} \quad \tilde{x} = \frac{\Sigma xy}{Ns_y^2} \cdot y$$

$$\tilde{y} = \frac{\Sigma xy}{Ns_x} \cdot \frac{x}{s_x} \quad \text{and} \quad \tilde{x} = \frac{\Sigma xy}{Ns_y} \cdot \frac{y}{s_y}$$

Dividing each member of the first equation by s_y and each member of the second by s_x,

$$\frac{\bar{y}}{s_y} = \frac{\Sigma xy}{N s_x s_y} \cdot \frac{x}{s_x} \quad \text{and} \quad \frac{\bar{x}}{s_x} = \frac{\Sigma xy}{N s_x s_y} \cdot \frac{y}{s_y}$$

The expression $\dfrac{\Sigma xy}{N s_x s_y}$ is seen to be a measure of mutual relation, for it occupies the same position in the two equations. We shall substitute for it the single letter r.

$$r = \frac{\Sigma xy}{N s_x s_y}$$

Therefore

$$\frac{\bar{y}}{s_y} = r\frac{x}{s_x} \quad \text{and} \quad \frac{\bar{x}}{s_x} = r\frac{y}{s_y}$$

or

$$\bar{y} = r\frac{s_y}{s_x}x \quad \text{and} \quad \bar{x} = r\frac{s_x}{s_y}y$$

From this it appears that

$$b_{yx} = r\frac{s_y}{s_x} \quad \text{and} \quad b_{xy} = r\frac{s_x}{s_y}$$

It is also clear that $b_{yx} \cdot b_{xy} = \left(r\dfrac{s_y}{s_x}\right)\left(r\dfrac{s_x}{s_y}\right) = r^2$

and therefore

$$r = \sqrt{b_{yx} \cdot b_{xy}}$$

$$= \sqrt{\frac{\Sigma xy}{\Sigma x^2} \cdot \frac{\Sigma xy}{\Sigma y^2}}$$

$$= \frac{\Sigma xy}{\sqrt{(\Sigma x^2)(\Sigma y^2)}}$$

VI. *Derivation of the formula for the residual variance and standard error of estimate, when values are predicted by a regression equation.*

Let

$$s_{y \cdot x}^2 = \frac{1}{N}\Sigma(y - \bar{y})^2 = \frac{1}{N}\Sigma\left(y - r\frac{s_y}{s_x}x\right)^2$$

$$= \frac{1}{N}\Sigma\left(y^2 - 2r\frac{s_y}{s_x}xy + r^2\frac{s_y^2}{s_x^2}x^2\right)$$

$$= \frac{\Sigma y^2}{N} - 2r\frac{s_y}{s_x} \cdot \frac{\Sigma xy}{N} + r^2\frac{s_y^2}{s_x^2} \cdot \frac{\Sigma x^2}{N}$$

Now $\dfrac{\Sigma y^2}{N} = s_y^2$, and $\dfrac{\Sigma x^2}{N} = s_x^2$ and $\dfrac{\Sigma xy}{N} = \dfrac{s_x s_y \Sigma xy}{N s_x s_y} = s_x s_y r$

Substituting these in the expression for $s_{y \cdot x}{}^2$ we have

$$s_{y \cdot x}{}^2 = s_y{}^2 - 2r\frac{s_y}{s_x}(s_x s_y r) + r^2\frac{s_y{}^2}{s_x{}^2} \cdot s_x{}^2$$

$$= s_y{}^2 - 2r^2 s_y{}^2 + r^2 s_y{}^2$$

$$= s_y{}^2 - r^2 s_y{}^2$$

$$= s_y{}^2(1 - r^2)$$

and $\qquad\qquad s_{y \cdot x} = s_y\sqrt{1 - r^2}$

By similar reasoning,

$$s_{x \cdot y}{}^2 = s_x{}^2(1 - r^2)$$

and $\qquad\qquad s_{x \cdot y} = s_x\sqrt{1 - r^2}$

VII. *The Binomial Expansion.*

The terms of the binomial expansion can be found directly by continued multiplication, raising the binomial to the required power. Writing down several of these in tabular form will suggest the general law, which can be proved by mathematical induction.

$$a + b = a + b$$
$$(a + b)^2 = a^2 + 2ab + b^2$$
$$(a + b)^3 = a^3 + 3a^2b + 3ab^2 + b^3$$
$$(a + b)^4 = a^4 + 4a^3b + 6a^2b^2 + 4ab^3 + b^4$$
$$(a + b)^5 = a^5 + 5a^4b + 10a^3b^2 + 10a^2b^3 + 5ab^4 + b^5$$
$$(a + b)^6 = a^6 + 6a^5b + 15a^4b^2 + 20a^3b^3 + 15a^2b^4 + 6ab^5 + b^6$$
$$(a + b)^7 = a^7 + 7a^6b + 21a^5b^2 + 35a^4b^3 + 35a^3b^4 + 21a^2b^5 + 7ab^6 + b^7$$

or in general

$$(a + b)^n = a^n + \frac{na^{n-1}b}{1} + \frac{n(n - 1)}{1 \cdot 2}a^{n-2}b^2 + \cdots$$

$$+ \frac{n(n - 1)(n - 2) \cdots (n - r + 1)}{1 \cdot 2 \cdot 3 \cdots r}a^{n-r}b^r + \cdots + \frac{nab^{n-1}}{1} + b^n$$

VIII. *Proof that the abscissa of the point of inflection of the normal curve is $\pm\sigma$.*

The equation of the normal curve is

$$y = \frac{N}{\sigma\sqrt{2\pi}}e^{-\frac{x^2}{2\sigma^2}}$$

Its first derivative in respect to x is

$$\frac{dy}{dx} = \frac{-Nx}{\sigma^3\sqrt{2\pi}}e^{-\frac{x^2}{2\sigma^2}}$$

Its second derivative in respect to x is

$$\frac{d^2y}{dx^2} = \frac{-N}{\sigma^5\sqrt{2\pi}}e^{-\frac{x^2}{2\sigma^2}}(\sigma^2 - x^2)$$

The value of x which makes the second derivative equal to zero is the abscissa of the point of inflection. The second derivative will be zero if $e^{-\frac{x^2}{2\sigma^2}} = 0$, but $e^{-\frac{x^2}{2\sigma^2}}$ will approach zero only as x approaches infinity. It will also be zero if $\sigma^2 - x^2 = 0$, that is, if $x = \pm\sigma$. There is, therefore, a point of inflection at $x = \sigma$ and at $x = -\sigma$.

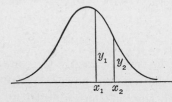

IX. *Mean of a segment of the unit normal curve.*

Let $p =$ proportion of area between the ordinates y_1 and y_2 erected at x_1 and x_2. It is desired to find the mean value of x in this segment.

This mean will be

$$\frac{1}{p}\int_{x=x_1}^{x=x_2} xy\, dx$$

$$= \frac{1}{p}\int_{x=x_1}^{x=x_2} \frac{x}{\sqrt{2\pi}}e^{-\frac{x^2}{2}}\, dx$$

$$= \frac{-1}{p\sqrt{2\pi}}\int_{x=x_1}^{x=x_2} e^{-\frac{x^2}{2}}(-x)\, dx$$

$$= \frac{-1}{p}\left[\frac{1}{\sqrt{2\pi}}e^{-\frac{x^2}{2}}\right]_{x_1}^{x_2}$$

$$= \frac{-1}{p}\left[\frac{1}{\sqrt{2\pi}}e^{-\frac{x_2^2}{2}} - \frac{1}{\sqrt{2\pi}}e^{-\frac{x_1^2}{2}}\right]$$

$$= \frac{-1}{p}[y_2 - y_1]$$

$$= \frac{y_1 - y_2}{p}$$

X. *Moments of the normal curve.*

In the derivations which follow, it has been assumed without proof that $\int_0^\infty e^{-\frac{x^2}{2}}\, dx = \sqrt{\frac{\pi}{2}}$. This can be proved in a number of ways, all of which require more knowledge of mathematics than the other sections of this text presuppose. A proof can be found in any advanced calculus text which has a treatment of the gamma function. A proof will also be found in the following:

Burington and Torrance, *Higher Mathematics* (McGraw-Hill), p. 304.
Elderton, *Frequency Curves and Correlation* (C. and E. Layton), 1st ed.,
    p. 152; 3rd ed., p. 237.
Fry, *Probability and Its Engineering Uses* (D. Van Nostrand Co.), p. 22.
Kenney, *Mathematics of Statistics*, Part II (D. Van Nostrand Co.), p. 35.
Uspensky, *Introduction to Mathematical Probability* (McGraw-Hill), p. 353.

The equation for the normal curve is $y = \dfrac{N}{\sigma\sqrt{2\pi}} e^{-\frac{x^2}{2\sigma^2}}$. The total area under this curve is

$$\int_{-\infty}^{\infty} y\, dx = \int_{-\infty}^{0} y\, dx + \int_{0}^{\infty} y\, dx = 2\int_{0}^{\infty} y\, dx$$

$$= 2\int_{0}^{\infty} \frac{N}{\sigma\sqrt{2\pi}} e^{-\frac{x^2}{2\sigma^2}}\, dx$$

$$= 2\int_{0}^{\infty} \frac{N}{\sqrt{2\pi}} e^{-\frac{1}{2}\left(\frac{x}{\sigma}\right)^2} d\left(\frac{x}{\sigma}\right)$$

$$= 2\frac{N}{\sqrt{2\pi}}\sqrt{\frac{\pi}{2}}$$

$$= N$$

The first moment of the curve is

$$\mu_1 = \frac{1}{N}\int_{-\infty}^{\infty} xy\, dx = \frac{1}{N}\int_{-\infty}^{0} xy\, dx + \frac{1}{N}\int_{0}^{\infty} xy\, dx$$

$$= \frac{1}{N}\int_{-\infty}^{0} \frac{Nx}{\sigma\sqrt{2\pi}} e^{-\frac{x^2}{2\sigma^2}}\, dx + \frac{1}{N}\int_{0}^{\infty} \frac{Nx}{\sigma\sqrt{2\pi}} e^{-\frac{x^2}{2\sigma^2}}\, dx$$

$$= \int_{-\infty}^{0} \frac{-\sigma}{\sqrt{2\pi}} d\left(e^{-\frac{x^2}{2\sigma^2}}\right) + \int_{0}^{\infty} \frac{-\sigma}{\sqrt{2\pi}} d\left(e^{-\frac{x^2}{2\sigma^2}}\right)$$

$$= \frac{-\sigma}{\sqrt{2\pi}}\left[e^{-\frac{x^2}{2\sigma^2}}\right]_{-\infty}^{0} + \frac{-\sigma}{\sqrt{2\pi}}\left[e^{-\frac{x^2}{2\sigma^2}}\right]_{0}^{\infty}$$

$$= \frac{-\sigma}{\sqrt{2\pi}} + \frac{\sigma}{\sqrt{2\pi}}$$

$$= 0$$

The second moment of the curve is

$$\mu_2 = \frac{1}{N}\int_{-\infty}^{\infty} x^2 y\, dx = \frac{2}{N}\int_{0}^{\infty} x^2 y\, dx = 2\int_{0}^{\infty} \frac{x^2}{\sigma\sqrt{2\pi}} e^{-\frac{x^2}{2\sigma^2}}\, dx$$

This can be integrated by parts, letting

$$u = \frac{-x\sigma}{\sqrt{2\pi}} \quad\text{and}\quad dv = \frac{-x}{\sigma^2} e^{-\frac{x^2}{2\sigma^2}} dx$$

whence $\quad du = \dfrac{-\sigma}{\sqrt{2\pi}} dx \quad\text{and}\quad v = e^{-\frac{x^2}{2\sigma^2}}$

Then $\quad \mu_2 = 2\left\{ \left[\dfrac{-x\sigma}{\sqrt{2\pi}} e^{-\frac{x^2}{2\sigma^2}} \right]_0^\infty - \displaystyle\int_0^\infty \dfrac{-\sigma}{\sqrt{2\pi}} e^{-\frac{x^2}{2\sigma^2}} dx \right\}$

$$= 2\left\{ 0 + 0 \quad\quad + \frac{\sigma^2}{\sqrt{2\pi}}\sqrt{\frac{\pi}{2}} \right\}$$

or $\quad \mu_2 = \sigma^2$

If ∞ is substituted for x in the expression $\dfrac{-x\sigma}{\sqrt{2\pi}} e^{-\frac{x^2}{2\sigma^2}}$, the result is of the form $(\infty)(0)$, which is indeterminate. The expression may be written as a fraction $\dfrac{-x\sigma}{\sqrt{2\pi}\, e^{\frac{x^2}{2\sigma^2}}}$ and its limit found by taking derivatives of numerator and denominator. The limit is then seen to be zero as x approaches infinity.

The third moment of the curve is

$$\mu_3 = \frac{1}{N}\int_{-\infty}^{\infty} x^3 y\, dx = \frac{1}{N}\int_{-\infty}^{0} x^3 y\, dx + \frac{1}{N}\int_{0}^{\infty} x^3 y\, dx$$

$$= \int_{-\infty}^{0} \frac{x^3}{\sigma\sqrt{2\pi}} e^{-\frac{x^2}{2\sigma^2}} dx + \int_{0}^{\infty} \frac{x^3}{\sigma\sqrt{2\pi}} e^{-\frac{x^2}{2\sigma^2}} dx$$

The integration may be performed by parts, letting

$$u = \frac{-x^2\sigma}{\sqrt{2\pi}} \quad\text{and}\quad dv = \frac{-x}{\sigma^2} e^{-\frac{x^2}{2\sigma^2}} dx$$

whence $\quad du = \dfrac{-2x\sigma}{\sqrt{2\pi}} dx \quad\text{and}\quad v = e^{-\frac{x^2}{2\sigma^2}}$

Then

$$\int_{a}^{b} \frac{x^3}{\sigma\sqrt{2\pi}} e^{-\frac{x^2}{2\sigma^2}} dx = \left[\frac{-x^2\sigma}{\sqrt{2\pi}} e^{-\frac{x^2}{2\sigma^2}} \right]_a^b - \int_a^b \frac{2\sigma^3}{\sqrt{2\pi}}\, d\!\left(e^{-\frac{x^2}{2\sigma^2}} \right)$$

The expression in square brackets is identically zero when $x = 0$, and its limit is zero as x approaches either $+\infty$ or $-\infty$. Therefore it disappears.

$$\int_{-\infty}^{0} \frac{2\sigma^3}{\sqrt{2\pi}} d\left(e^{-\frac{x^2}{2\sigma^2}}\right) = \frac{2\sigma^3}{\sqrt{2\pi}} \left[e^{-\frac{x^2}{2\sigma^2}}\right]_{-\infty}^{0} = \frac{2\sigma^3}{\sqrt{2\pi}}$$

$$\int_{0}^{\infty} \frac{2\sigma^3}{\sqrt{2\pi}} d\left(e^{-\frac{x^2}{2\sigma^2}}\right) = \frac{2\sigma^3}{\sqrt{2\pi}} \left[e^{-\frac{x^2}{2\sigma^2}}\right]_{0}^{\infty} = \frac{-2\sigma^3}{\sqrt{2\pi}}$$

Therefore
$$\mu_3 = \frac{2\sigma^3}{\sqrt{2\pi}} + \frac{-2\sigma^3}{\sqrt{2\pi}} = 0$$

The fourth moment of the curve is

$$\mu_4 = \frac{1}{N} \int_{-\infty}^{\infty} x^4 y \, dx = 2 \int_{0}^{\infty} \frac{x^4}{\sigma\sqrt{2\pi}} e^{-\frac{x^2}{2\sigma^2}} \, dx$$

The integration may be performed by parts, letting

$$u = \frac{-x^3\sigma}{\sqrt{2\pi}} \quad \text{and} \quad dv = \frac{-x}{\sigma^2} e^{-\frac{x^2}{2\sigma^2}} \, dx$$

whence
$$du = \frac{-3x^2\sigma}{\sqrt{2\pi}} \, dx \quad \text{and} \quad v = e^{-\frac{x^2}{2\sigma^2}}$$

Then

$$2\int_{0}^{\infty} \frac{x^4}{\sigma\sqrt{2\pi}} e^{-\frac{x^2}{2\sigma^2}} \, dx = 2\left[\frac{-x^3\sigma}{\sqrt{2\pi}} e^{-\frac{x^2}{2\sigma^2}}\right]_{0}^{\infty} + 3\sigma^2 \int_{0}^{\infty} \frac{2x^2}{\sigma\sqrt{2\pi}} e^{-\frac{x^2}{2\sigma^2}} \, dx$$

The expression in square brackets disappears, being identically zero when $x = 0$ and approaching zero as a limit when x approaches ∞. The integral on the right is μ_2, which has already been shown to be equal to σ^2.

Therefore
$$\mu_4 = 3\sigma^2\mu_2 = 3\sigma^4$$

also
$$\alpha_3 = \frac{\mu_3}{\mu_2^{3/2}} = \frac{0}{\sigma^3} = 0$$

and
$$\alpha_4 = \frac{\mu_4}{\mu_2^2} = \frac{3\sigma^4}{(\sigma^2)^2} = 3$$

APPENDIX C

SUPPLEMENTARY TECHNIQUES AND METHODS

The Computation of Mean and Standard Deviation by Cumulation or Successive Addition

The data used to illustrate this method are those of Tables XXII and XXIV, and the results may be compared with the values obtained there.

Arithmetic Pattern, with Origin at Midpoint of Lowest Interval

Class sort	x'	f	C_1 or first cumulation	C_2 or second cumulation
49–51	14	3		
46–48	13	2	3	
43–45	12	8	5	3
40–42	11	9	13	8
37–39	10	2	22	21
34–36	9	6	24	43
31–33	8	5	30	67
28–30	7	18	35	97
25–27	6	16	53	132
22–24	5	14	69	185
19–21	4	5	83	254
16–18	3	9	88	337
13–15	2	4	97	425
10–12	1	5	101	522
7–9	0	3	106	623
			$109 = N$	$729 = \Sigma fx'$
Total		$109 = N$	$729 = \Sigma fx'$	$3446 = \dfrac{\Sigma f(x')^2}{2} + \dfrac{\Sigma fx'}{2}$

$$\frac{\Sigma x'(x'+1)}{2} = \frac{\Sigma(x')^2}{2} + \frac{\Sigma x'}{2} = 3446 \qquad \overline{X} = 8 + 3(729)/109 = 28.06$$

$$\Sigma(x')^2 + \Sigma x' = 6892$$
$$\Sigma x' = 729 \qquad s^2 = 9\left[\frac{6163}{109} - \left(\frac{729}{109}\right)^2\right]$$
$$\Sigma(x')^2 = 6163 \qquad = 9(11.81) = 106.3$$
$$s = 3\sqrt{11.81} = 10.3$$

We shall consider first the routine to be followed when the origin is placed at the midpoint of the lowest step interval. To make the first cumulation, take the frequency in the step interval at the top of the distribution (which is 3) and record it in the C_1 column opposite the next lower interval. Add the two frequencies which are now on the same line $(2 + 3 = 5)$ and record in the next lower interval. Proceed in the same fashion for each successive interval until the frequency in the zero interval has been added in. The last entry is equal to N.

To make the second cumulation, proceed in the same fashion, but *do not add the last entry of C_1*. The last entry in the C_2 column will be the sum of the fx'. Note that 3, the frequency in the interval whose x' value is 14, has actually been added 14 times and that 2, the frequency corresponding to $x' = 13$, has been added 13 times, etc. This last entry in C_2 is the sum of all the C_1 terms except the last. The sum of all the C_2 terms, 3446, is equal to $\frac{1}{2}(\Sigma f(x')^2 + \Sigma fx')$, as may be seen from the algebraic pattern. The final steps in the computation are as shown.

When the origin is taken in the middle of the distribution, cumulation is from each end toward the middle, but not including f_0. In the illustration

$$f_7 + f_6 + f_5 + f_4 + f_3 + f_2 + f_1 = 35$$
$$f_0 = 18$$
$$f_{-7} + f_{-6} + f_{-5} + f_{-4} + f_{-3} + f_{-2} + f_{-1} = 56$$
$$N = \overline{109}$$

In the second cumulation

$$7f_7 + 6f_6 + 5f_5 + 4f_4 + 3f_3 + 2f_2 + f_1 = 132$$
$$7f_{-7} + 6f_{-6} + 5f_{-5} + 4f_{-4} + 3f_{-3} + 2f_{-2} + f_{-1} = 166$$

Therefore

$$7f_7 + \cdots 2f_2 + f_1 + 0 \cdot f_0 - f_{-1} \cdots - 7f_{-7} = 132 - 166 = -34$$

or

$$\sum_{x=-7}^{7} f_x x' = -34$$

In adding the terms of C_2 to obtain $\frac{1}{2}[\Sigma f(x')^2 + \Sigma fx']$, the last entry on the negative side must be omitted. Thus, in the illustration, omitting 166, the sum of the C_2 entries is 632. The reason for omitting this term can be seen in the algebraic pattern which follows. Those students to whom the algebra is not obvious may take this step for granted. Completion of the computation yields the same mean, standard deviation, and variance as previously obtained.

Algebraic Pattern, with Origin at Midpoint of Lowest Interval

x'	Frequency	C_1 or first cumulation	C_2 or Second Cumulation
7	f_7		f_7
6	f_6	f_7	$2f_7 + f_6$
5	f_5	$f_7 + f_6$	$3f_7 + 2f_6 + f_5$
4	f_4	$f_7 + f_6 + f_5$	$4f_7 + 3f_6 + 2f_5 + f_4$
3	f_3	$f_7 + f_6 + f_5 + f_4$	$5f_7 + 4f_6 + 3f_5 + 2f_4 + f_3$
2	f_2	$f_7 + f_6 + f_5 + f_4 + f_3$	$6f_7 + 5f_6 + 4f_5 + 3f_4 + 2f_3 + f_2$
1	f_1	$f_7 + f_6 + f_5 + f_4 + f_3 + f_2$	$7f_7 + 6f_6 + 5f_5 + 4f_4 + 3f_3 + 2f_2 + f_1 = \Sigma f x'$
0	f_0	$f_7 + f_6 + f_5 + f_4 + f_3 + f_2 + f_1 + f_0 = N$	

$$= 28f_7 + 21f_6 + 15f_5 + 10f_4 + 6f_3 + 3f_2 + f_1$$

$$= \frac{7 \cdot 8}{2}f_7 + \frac{6 \cdot 7}{2}f_6 + \frac{5 \cdot 6}{2}f_5 + \frac{4 \cdot 5}{2}f_4 + \frac{3 \cdot 4}{2}f_3 + \frac{2 \cdot 3}{2}f_2 + \frac{1 \cdot 2}{2}f_1 + \frac{0 \cdot 1}{2}f_0$$

$$= \sum_{x'=0}^{7} \frac{x'(x'+1)}{2} f_{x'}$$

318

Algebraic Pattern, with Origin Near Middle of Distribution

x'	Frequency	C_1 or first cumulation	C_2 or Second Cumulation
5	f_5	f_5	f_5
4	f_4	$f_5 + f_4$	$2f_5 + f_4$
3	f_3	$f_5 + f_4 + f_3$	$3f_5 + 2f_4 + f_3$
2	f_2	$f_5 + f_4 + f_3 + f_2$	$4f_5 + 3f_4 + 2f_3 + f_2$
1	f_1	$f_5 + f_4 + f_3 + f_2 + f_1$	$5f_5 + 4f_4 + 3f_3 + 2f_2 + f_1 = A$
0	f_0	$N = \left\{ f_0 \right.$	
-1	f_{-1}	$f_{-5} + f_{-4} + f_{-3} + f_{-2} + f_{-1}$	$5f_{-5} + 4f_{-4} + 3f_{-3} + 2f_{-2} + f_{-1} = B$
-2	f_{-2}	$f_{-5} + f_{-4} + f_{-3} + f_{-2}$	$4f_{-5} + 3f_{-4} + 2f_{-3} + f_{-2}$
-3	f_{-3}	$f_{-5} + f_{-4} + f_{-3}$	$3f_{-5} + 2f_{-4} + f_{-3}$
-4	f_{-4}	$f_{-5} + f_{-4}$	$2f_{-5} + f_{-4}$
-5	f_{-5}	f_{-5}	f_{-5}

$$\Sigma f x' = A - B$$

Sum of D and E is $\displaystyle\sum_{x'=-5}^{5} \frac{x'(x'+1)}{2} f_{x'}$

Sum of these terms is D

$$= 15f_5 + 10f_4 + 6f_3 + 3f_2 + f_1$$

$$= \frac{5\cdot 6}{2}f_5 + \frac{4\cdot 5}{2}f_4 + \frac{3\cdot 4}{2}f_3 + \frac{2\cdot 3}{2}f_2 + \frac{1\cdot 2}{2}f_1 + \frac{0\cdot 1}{2}f_0$$

Sum of these terms is E

$$= 10f_{-5} + 6f_{-4} + 3f_{-3} + f_{-2}$$

$$= \frac{(-5)(-4)}{2}f_{-5} + \frac{(-4)(-3)}{2}f_{-4} + \frac{(-3)(-2)}{2}f_{-3} + \frac{(-2)(-1)}{2}f_{-2} + \frac{(-1)(0)}{2}f_{-1}$$

319

Arithmetic Pattern, with Origin Near the Middle of the Distribution

Class Sort	x'	f	C_1 or First Cumulation	C_2 or Second Cumulation
49–51	7	3		
46–48	6	2	3	
43–45	5	8	5	3
40–42	4	9	13	8
37–39	3	2	22	21
34–36	2	6	24	43
31–33	1	5	30	67

$$28\text{–}30 \quad 0 \quad 18 \quad N = \begin{cases} 35 = \displaystyle\sum_{x'=1}^{7} f_{x'} & 97 \\[2mm] 18 = f_0 & 132 = \displaystyle\sum_{x'=1}^{7} f_{x'}x' \\[2mm] 56 = \displaystyle\sum_{x'=-7}^{-1} f_{x'} & \boxed{166} = \displaystyle\sum_{x'=-7}^{-1} f_{x'}x' \end{cases}$$

Class Sort	x'	f	C_1 or First Cumulation	C_2 or Second Cumulation
				110
25–27	−1	16	40	70
22–24	−2	14	26	44
19–21	−3	5	21	23
16–18	−4	9	12	11
13–15	−5	4	8	3
10–12	−6	5	3	
7–9	−7	3		
				632

$$N = 35 + 18 + 56 = \quad 109$$
$$\tfrac{1}{2}[\Sigma(x')^2 + \Sigma x'] = \quad 632$$
$$\Sigma(x')^2 + \Sigma x' = 1264$$
$$\Sigma x' = 132 - 166 = -34$$
$$\Sigma(x')^2 = 1298$$
$$\overline{X} = 29 + 3\left(\frac{-34}{109}\right) = 28.06$$
$$s^2 = 9[\tfrac{1298}{109} - (\tfrac{34}{109})^2] = 9(11.81) = 106.29$$

THE COMPUTATION OF MEAN AND STANDARD DEVIATION BY "FOLDING" THE DISTRIBUTION

A convenient computational short cut is illustrated in the accompanying Arithmetic Pattern. To obtain the mean, each frequency in a negative interval, that is, an interval with negative value of x', is subtracted from the frequency in the corresponding positive interval, and the result recorded in the column headed $f_+ - f_-$. To obtain the standard deviation these frequencies are added instead of subtracted, and the sum recorded in the column headed $f_+ + f_-$. Multiplication by x' and by $(x')^2$ is carried out as indicated. The sum of the entries in the column headed $x'(f_+ - f_-)$ is $\Sigma fx'$, and the sum of the entries in the column headed $(x')^2(f_+ + f_-)$ is $\Sigma f(x')^2$.

Arithmetic Pattern for Computing Mean and Standard Deviation by "Folding" the Distribution

Class Sort	f	x'	$f_+ - f_-$	$x'(f_+ - f_-)$	$f_+ + f_-$	$x'(f_+ + f_-)$	$(x')^2(f_+ + f_-)$
49–51	3	7	0		6	42	294
46–48	2	6	−3	−18	7	42	252
43–45	8	5	4	20	12	60	300
40–42	9	4	0		18	72	288
37–39	2	3	−3	−9	7	21	63
34–36	6	2	−8	−16	20	40	80
31–33	5	1	−11	−11	21	21	21
28–30	18	0		0		0	0
25–27	16	−1					
22–24	14	−2					
19–21	5	−3					
16–18	9	−4					
13–15	4	−5					
10–12	5	−6					
7– 9	3	−7					
Total	109			$20 - 54 = -34$			1298

$$\overline{X} = 29 - \tfrac{34}{109}(3) = 28.06$$
$$s^2 = 9[\tfrac{1298}{109} - (\tfrac{34}{109})^2] = 106.3 \qquad s = \sqrt{106.3} = 10.3$$

The Durost-Walker Correlation Chart *

The Durost-Walker Correlation Chart is designed to facilitate the computation of a Pearson product-moment coefficient of correlation. It embodies the following advantages:

* Published by World Book Company, Yonkers-on-Hudson, New York, and Chicago, Illinois. Copyright, 1938, by World Book Company. Copyright in Great Britain. *All rights reserved.*

1. It can be used either for hand or for machine computation.
2. Checks on the arithmetical processes involved occur at frequent intervals in the course of the computation, thereby making possible the rapid detection of errors.
3. Two independent derivations of the coefficient are possible, thus furnishing a valuable check even to the final computation.
4. The correlation ratios may be obtained with little additional work beyond that involved in the calculation of the coefficient.
5. The operations are indicated both in standard statistical notation and in a simplified alphabetical notation, so that the chart may be used by individuals who have had no training in statistics. *It should be noted that the symbols printed on the chart differ slightly from those employed in this text.*

Directions for Use

1. Enter the appropriate information in the spaces provided in the upper right-hand corner of the chart, above the heavy black line. Determine the width of the intervals which are to be used in grouping the X and Y scores, and record these values after "i_X" and "i_Y" respectively. After "X_0" "Y_0" write the midpoints of the lowest intervals of the X and Y distributions. (Step 1)

2. In the uppermost row, marked "X," enter the upper and lower limits of the successive intervals of the distribution of the X scores, starting with the lowest interval at the left-hand corner. Similarly, in the column at the left-hand side of the chart enter the limits of the intervals of the Y distribution, starting with the lowest interval in the box immediately above the one marked "Y." (Step 2)

3. Record a small tally mark in the appropriate cell in the scatter diagram for each pair of scores. After the tabulating is complete, the computer may, if he desires, place a numeral in each cell to indicate the number of tallies there; e.g., ⊞⑨ . Some computers find it easier to work from these numerals than directly from the tallies. These numerals should be encircled so as to be readily distinguishable from other numbers which will be entered in the cells. This step has not been shown in the illustrations in order to avoid overcrowding the diagrams.

Add the tally marks or numerals in each row, and record their sums in the column headed "F_Y." Add the tallies or numerals in each column, and record their sums in the "F_X" row. (Step 3)

4. Cumulate the values in the "F_Y" column from top to bottom, and record the cumulated values in the "C_1 to N" column, entering the first value one box below the highest interval in which any tallies occur, as shown in Figure I. Continue the cumulation to the bottom of the column, even though there be several intervals in which no frequencies occur. The final value, recorded in the box *immediately above* "N," equals the number of cases. Then, in the "C_2 to ΣY" column, cumulate the values in the "C_1 to N" column, again starting one box below the highest one in which there is any entry in the "C_1 to N" column, as in Figure I. Continue the cumulation to the end of the column. The final entry in this column is ΣY. Find the *sum* of the values in this column and record it as S_Y. (Step 4)

Similarly, cumulate the values in the "F_X" row, from **right to left,** entering these values in the "C_1 to N" row, the last value again equaling N. Re-cumulate in the "C_2 to ΣX" row, in each case starting one box to the left of the highest interval in which any entry occurs in the previous row, as shown in Figure I. Continue the cumulation to the end of the row, even if there be several intervals in which no frequencies occur. The final value in the "C_2 to ΣX" row is ΣX, and the *sum* of the values in this row is recorded as S_X. (Step 4)

5. Add the tally marks in the cells along the central diagonal, lower left to upper right, and record their sum in the "0" cell of the "$Y - X$" column. Add the tallies in each diagonal *above* the central one, find the corresponding $Y - X$ value at the left of the scatter diagram, and record their sums in the "$F_{Y-X(+)}$" column. Similarly add the tallies in each diagonal *below* the central one, find the corresponding $Y - X$ value at the right of the scatter diagram, and record the sums in the "$F_{Y-X(-)}$" column. The sum of the entries in the "F_{Y-X}" columns, including the entry in the "0" cell, must equal N. Cumulate and re-cumulate the values in the "F_{Y-X}" columns, recording the cumulated values in the "$C_{1(+)}$" and "$C_{2(+)}$" and "$C_{1(-)}$" and "$C_{2(-)}$" columns, proceeding as in the previous cumulations and recording the values as shown in Figure I. NOTE: The entry in the "S_{Y-X}" box is the sum of the values in the "$C_{2(-)}$" column, **exclusive of the entry in the lowest, or "$\Sigma Y - X$," box.**

In the spaces immediately below, fill in the indicated values, solving for $\Sigma(Y - X)$ and S_{Y-X}. (Step 5)

6. To obtain 1st ΣXY, cumulate the tallies within each *column* in the scatter diagram, as shown in Figure II, always starting one box below the highest one in which any tallies appear, and recording the cumulated values in red or some other distinctive color, in the lower right-hand corner of each cell. (These values are shown in heavy black type in

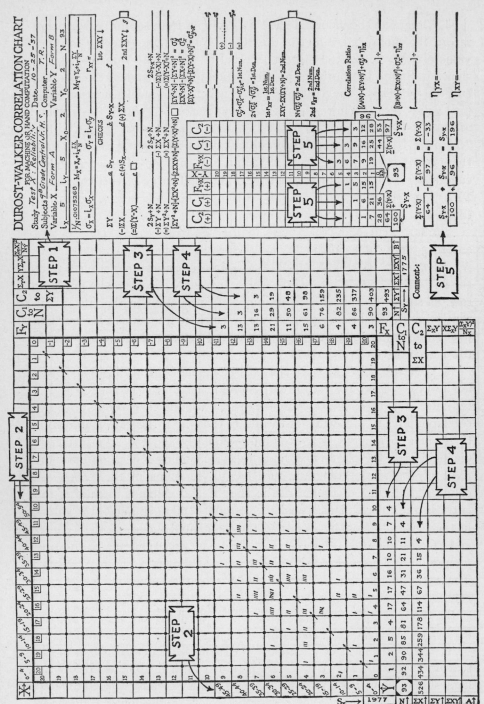

Fig. I. Correlation Chart, showing operations complete through Step 5.

324

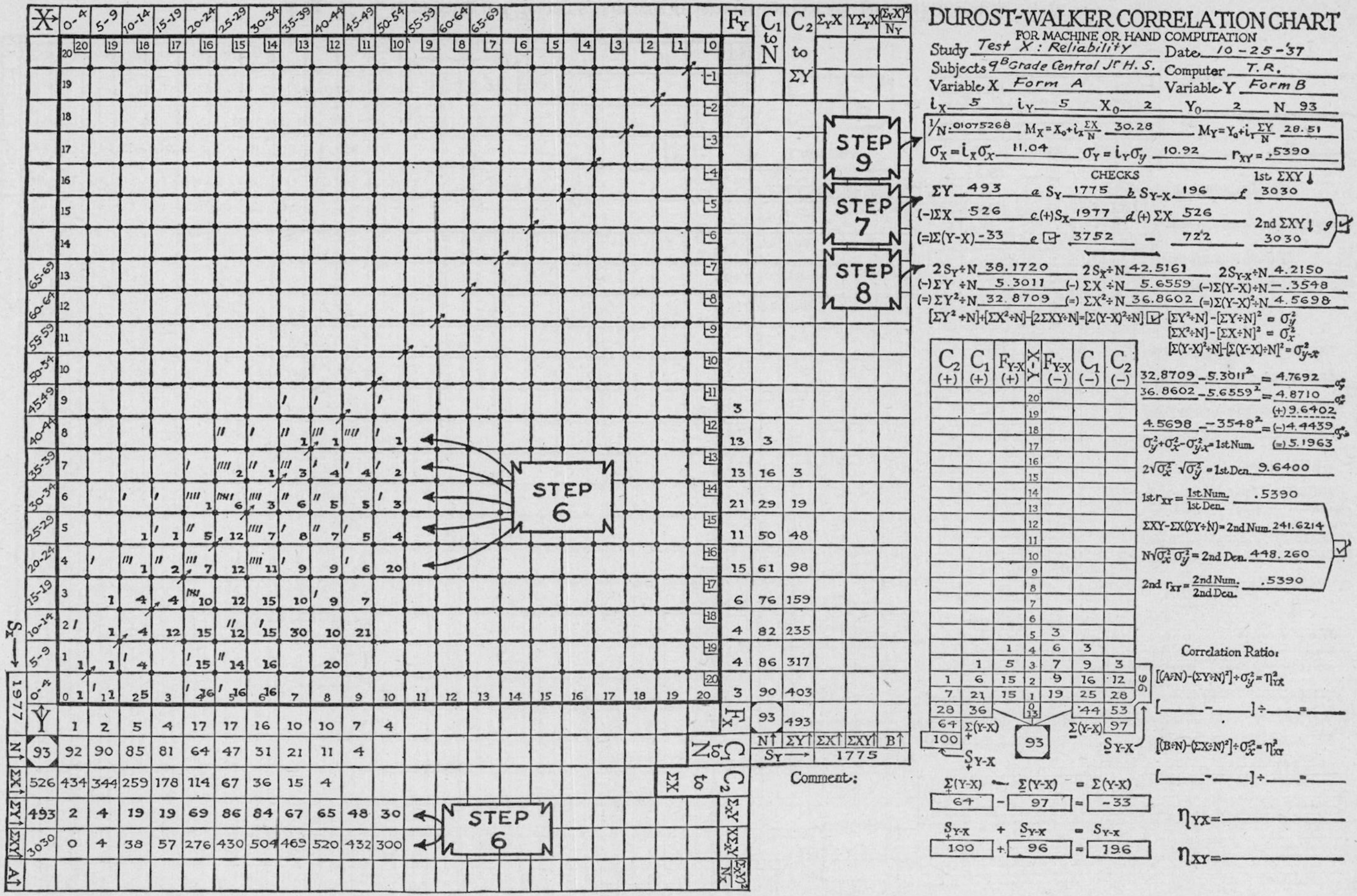

DUROST-WALKER CORRELATION CHART
FOR MACHINE OR HAND COMPUTATION
Study Test X: Reliability
Date 10-25-'37
Subjects 9B Grade Central Jr H. S.
Computer T. R.
Variable X Form A
Variable Y Form B
STEP 9
STEP 7
STEP 8
STEP 6
CHECKS
Correlation Ratio:
Comment:

Fig. II. Correlation Chart, showing operations complete through Step 9.

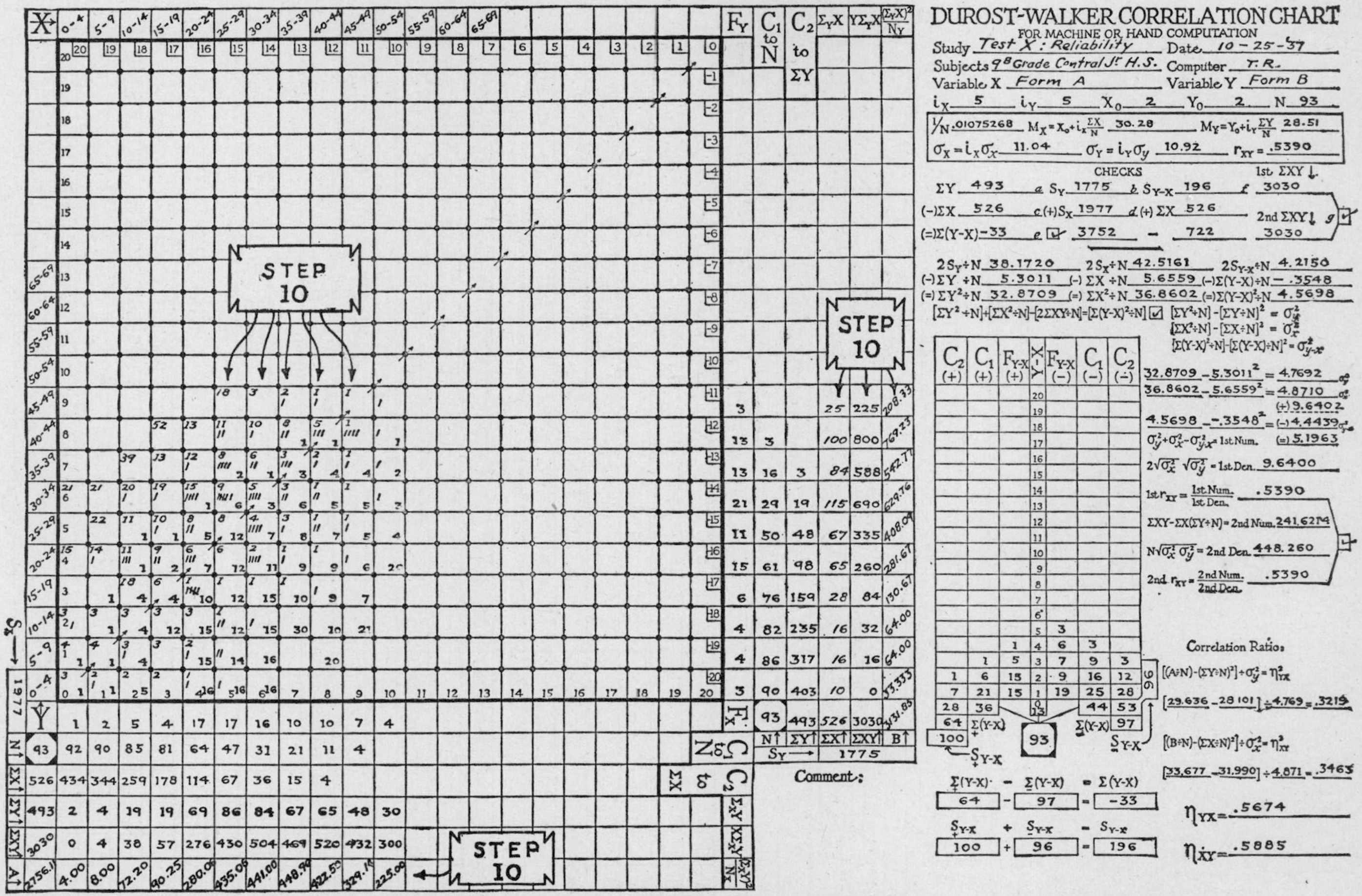

Fig. III. Correlation Chart, showing operations complete through Step 10.

WORK SHEET

N	93		$\frac{1}{N}$	.01075268
a	ΣY	493	h	$\Sigma Y/N$ 5.30107
b	S_Y	1775	h^2	$(\Sigma Y/N)^2$ 28.10134
$2b$	$2S_Y$	3550	i	$2S_Y/N$ 38.17201
c	ΣX	526	j	$\Sigma X/N$ 5.65591
d	S_X	1977	j^2	$(\Sigma X/N)^2$ 31.98932
$2d$	$2S_X$	3954	k	$2S_X/N$ 42.51610
e	$\Sigma(Y-X)$	-33	l	$\Sigma(Y-X)/N$ $-.35484$
f	S_{Y-X}	196	l^2	$[\Sigma(Y-X)/N]^2$ .12591
$2f$	$2S_{Y-X}$	392	m	$2S_{Y-X}/N$ 4.21505
g	ΣXY	3030		
$2g$	$2\Sigma XY$	6060	n	$2\Sigma XY/N$ 65.16124

$i-h=o$ 32.87094 $k-j=p$ 36.86019

$m-l=q$ 4.56989 $o+p-n=q$ 4.56989

$\sigma_y^2=o-h^2$ 4.76960 $\sigma_x^2=p-j^2$ 4.87177

$\sigma_{y-x}^2=q-l^2$ 4.44398

$\sigma_y^2+\sigma_x^2-\sigma_{y-x}^2=$ 1st Num. 5.19739

$2\sqrt{\sigma_x^2}\sqrt{\sigma_y^2}=$ 1st Den. 9.6415

1st r_{XY} .5390

$g-c(h)=$ 2nd Num. 241.6372

$N\sqrt{\sigma_y^2 \sigma_x^2}=$ 2nd Den. 448.2972

2nd r_{XY} .5390

Correlation Ratio

$A\div N=s$ 29.636 $B\div N=t$ 33.677

$\frac{s-h^2}{\sigma_y^2}=\eta_{yx}^2$ .3218 $\eta_{YX}=$ .5673

$\frac{t-j^2}{\sigma_x^2}=\eta_{XY}^2$ .3465 $\eta_{XY}=$ .5886

Figure II.) Continue the cumulation to the bottom of the column, even if no tallies occur in the few lowest cells.

When the cumulation in any column has been completed, the final value should equal the entry for that column which appears in the "F_X" row, unless tallies occur in the lowest or "0" interval; in this case the final cumulated value plus the number of tallies in the lowest interval should equal the "F_X" entry.*

Next, find the sum of the cumulated values you have written in each column and enter in the "$\Sigma_X Y$" row. As a check add the numbers in this row and verify its agreement with ΣY previously found. Multiply each of the values in this row by the corresponding "X" value which is printed in the *bottom* row of the scatter diagram, and enter these products in the "$X\Sigma_X Y$" row. The sum of the values in this row is 1st ΣXY. (Step 6) Record this value in the upper right-hand corner of the chart.

7. In the other spaces at the upper right of the chart, record the appropriate values, ΣY, ΣX, S_Y, S_X, etc. If the difference between ΣY and ΣX equals the already obtained $\Sigma(Y - X)$, place a check mark in the box to the right of the space provided for this value. (Step 7)

If they do not agree, an error has been made in at least one of the preceding steps, and this error must be found and corrected before proceeding.

Perform the other operations indicated until 2nd ΣXY is obtained. This value must check with 1st ΣXY.

8. In the back of the original chart a section marked "Work Sheet" is printed. This is reproduced here on p. 327. Enter in the first column the proper values. If a calculating machine such as the Monroe or Marchant is being used, set the reciprocal of N in the keyboard, and most of the values in the second column can be readily obtained by multiplication; the others may be read from a table of squares.

The remaining operations necessary for arriving at "r" are clearly indicated. Two independent derivations of the coefficient are possible, thus furnishing a valuable check even to the final computation. The values obtained may, if desired, be entered in the spaces provided at the right of the chart. (Step 8)

9. M_X, M_Y, σ_X, and σ_Y should be computed as indicated in the upper right-hand corner of the chart, and the values recorded in the appropriate places. (Step 9)

---

* It will readily be seen that if no frequencies occur in the few lowest intervals, a shorter cumulating method, yielding identical results, may be employed. Instead of repeating the highest cumulated value in each of the vacant cells, multiply it by the "Y" value which appears at the left of the scatter diagram in the same row, and record the product in the box immediately below the one in which this highest cumulated value first appears. This is the method which has been employed in the accompanying figures.

10. If the Correlation Ratio is desired, it may be obtained in the following manner:

To obtain η_{YX}, square each of the values in the "$\Sigma_X Y$" row and divide by the corresponding value which appears in the "F_X" row in the same column—i.e., the sum of the tallies in the column. Enter the results in the $\dfrac{(\Sigma_X Y)^2}{N_X}$ row. Find the sum of these values and record in the box immediately to the right of "$A \uparrow$." Transfer this value to the Work Sheet, and perform the other operations indicated to obtain η_{YX}.

In order to find η_{XY}, it is necessary to make an additional cumulation of the tallies in each row in the scatter diagram similar to the one already made for each column. Cumulate from right to left, as shown in Figure III, and record the sums for each row in the proper box in the "$\Sigma_Y X$" column. Square each of the entries in this column, and divide by the corresponding entry in the "F_Y" column, recording the results in the $\dfrac{(\Sigma_Y X)^2}{N_Y}$ column. Find the sum of these values and record immediately above "$B \uparrow$." Transfer this value to the Work Sheet, and solve as indicated for η_{XY}. (Step 10)

THE GEOMETRIC AND HARMONIC MEANS

These are very ancient terms. Sir Thomas Heath, in his *History of Greek Mathematics*, says: "We are told that in Pythagoras's time there were three means, the arithmetic, the geometric and the subcontrary, and that the name of the third (subcontrary) was changed by Archytas and Hippasus to 'harmonic.' A fragment of Archytas's work *On Music* actually defines the three: we have the arithmetic mean when, of three terms, the first exceeds the second by the same amount as the second exceeds the third; and the geometric mean when, of three terms, the first is to the second as the second is to the third; and the '*subcontrary* which we call the *harmonic*' when the three terms are such that 'by whatever part of itself the first exceeds the second, the second exceeds the third by the same part of the third.'"

Generalized Mean. We shall first show the formulas for the arithmetic, the harmonic, and the geometric mean, and the relation between them, and then shall discuss the types of situation calling for the harmonic mean and geometric mean. For N scores, $X_1, X_2 \cdots X_N$, the three means are defined as follows:

Arithmetic Mean:

$$\overline{X} = \frac{1}{N}(X_1 + X_2 + \cdots + X_N) = \frac{\Sigma X}{N}$$

Harmonic Mean:

$$\frac{1}{H} = \frac{1}{N}\left(\frac{1}{X_1} + \frac{1}{X_2} + \cdots + \frac{1}{X_N}\right) = \frac{\Sigma\frac{1}{X}}{N}$$

or
$$H = \frac{N}{\dfrac{1}{X_1} + \dfrac{1}{X_2} + \cdots + \dfrac{1}{X_N}} = \frac{N}{\Sigma\dfrac{1}{X}}$$

Geometric Mean:

$$\log G = \frac{1}{N}(\log X_1 + \log X_2 + \cdots + \log X_N) = \frac{\Sigma \log X}{N}$$

or
$$G = (X_1 \cdot X_2 \cdots X_N)^{\frac{1}{N}}$$

These can be generalized by the formula $M_p = \left[\dfrac{\Sigma X^p}{N}\right]^{\frac{1}{p}}$ where p is

an integer. When $p = 1$, this becomes $M_1 = \dfrac{\Sigma X}{N}$ which is the arith-

metic mean. When $p = -1$, it becomes $M_{-1} = \left[\dfrac{\Sigma X^{-1}}{N}\right]^{-1} = \dfrac{N}{\Sigma\dfrac{1}{X}}$

which is the harmonic mean. When $p = 0$, it reduces to an indeterminate
function whose limit, as $p \to 0$, is the geometric mean.

$$M_0 = \left[\frac{\Sigma X^0}{N}\right]^{\frac{1}{0}}$$

Since $X^0 = 1$, $\Sigma X^0 = N$, the expression in square brackets is $\dfrac{N}{N} = 1$,

and 1^∞ is indeterminate. To obtain its limit we may proceed as follows,
remembering that p is the variable under consideration.

$$\log M_p = \frac{\log\left(\dfrac{\Sigma X^p}{N}\right)}{p}$$

As $\log \dfrac{\Sigma X^0}{N} = \log \dfrac{N}{N} = 0$, we have now a fraction of the form $\dfrac{0}{0}$, and its
limit may be found by differentiating the numerator for a new numerator
and differentiating the denominator for a new denominator.

$$\text{Limit}_{p \to 0} \log M_p = \text{Limit}_{p \to 0} \frac{\dfrac{d}{dp}\left(\log \dfrac{\Sigma X^p}{N}\right)}{1} = \text{Limit}_{p \to 0} \frac{1}{\Sigma X^p}\Sigma X^p \log X$$

$$= \frac{1}{N}\Sigma \log X$$

Therefore $\log M_0 = \frac{1}{N} \Sigma \log X$

or $M_0 = [X_1 \cdot X_2 \cdots X_N]^{\frac{1}{N}}$ which is the geometric mean.

If every score is a positive number larger than unity, it can be proved that $H < G < \overline{X}$ except in the limiting case where all the N scores are exactly alike, and then the three means are equal to each other.

Proof that $H < G < \overline{X}$ may be found in the following:

Croxton and Cowden, *Applied General Statistics* (Prentice-Hall), p. 830. The proof given here entails no advanced mathematics.

Levy, Paul, *Calcul des Probabilities* (Gauthier-Villars et Cie, Paris, 1925), pp. 157–159.

Darmois, G., *Statistique Mathématique* (Gaston Doin et Cie, Editeurs, Paris), pp. 31–33.

The proofs given by Levy and Darmois are based on the formula for a generalized mean and are somewhat more difficult.

The Harmonic Mean. Certain problems concerning time, rate, and distance, or time, rate, and work, require the use of the harmonic rather than the arithmetic mean for averaging rates. Certain others require the use of the arithmetic mean, the appropriate procedure being easily ascertained by attention to the underlying logic of the situation.

This type of problem was of great practical concern in earlier days when the water supply of a town depended upon public fountains and it was important to know whether the pipes through which the water flowed were large enough to deliver an adequate supply. As an illustration, we may quote a problem from a work called the *Lilavati* (= "the beautiful") written in India in 1150 by Bhaskara: "Say quickly, friend, in what portion of a day will four fountains being let loose together, fill a cistern if, when separately opened they would fill it in one day, half a day, the third part of a day, and the sixth part of a day respectively."

The earliest instance of such a problem which has come to the writer's attention is in the Greek Anthology, and is of somewhat uncertain date, several centuries B.C. Variants of such problems, often very amusing, appear in most of the medieval arithmetics.

A modern illustration is provided by a recent paragraph in one of the metropolitan papers offering advice to motorists on how to get more mileage from a gallon of gasoline. The writer warned the motorists against what he called a common error in the computation of mileage. If one drives 10 miles at 20 miles per gallon and 90 miles at 10 miles per gallon, the average number of miles per gallon is not $\frac{1}{2}(10 + 20) = 15$

and is not $\frac{1}{100}(10 \times 20 + 90 \times 10) = 11$, but is $\dfrac{10 + 90}{\frac{10}{20} + \frac{90}{10}} = 10.5$. This correct result is the weighted harmonic mean of the two rates. The correctness of this solution is clear to anyone who analyzes the situation, whether he ever heard of the harmonic mean or not.

Driving   10 miles at 20 miles per gallon requires $\frac{10}{20} = 0.5$ gallons

"   90   "   " 10   "   "   "   " $\frac{90}{10} = 9.0$ "

"   100   "   " x "   "   "   " $\dfrac{100}{x} = 0.5 + 9.0$ gallons

Therefore $x = \dfrac{100}{\frac{10}{20} + \frac{90}{10}} = \frac{100}{9.5} = 10.5$

The harmonic mean is the reciprocal of the mean of the reciprocals of the values to be averaged. In other words, the reciprocal of the harmonic mean is the mean of the reciprocals of the values. If H be used to designate the harmonic mean, $\dfrac{1}{H} = \dfrac{1}{N}\left(\dfrac{1}{X_1} + \dfrac{1}{X_2} + \cdots + \dfrac{1}{X_N}\right) = \dfrac{1}{N}\Sigma\dfrac{1}{X}$

or, for a grouped frequency distribution

$$\frac{1}{H} = \frac{1}{N}\left(\frac{f_1}{X_1} + \frac{f_2}{X_2} + \cdots + \frac{f_k}{X_k}\right) = \frac{1}{N}\Sigma\frac{f}{X}$$

or $$H = \frac{N}{\dfrac{f_1}{X_1} + \dfrac{f_2}{X_2} + \cdots + \dfrac{f_k}{X_k}} = \frac{N}{\Sigma\dfrac{f}{X}}$$

where k is the number of step intervals and N is the number of cases.

Not all problems relating to rates demand the use of the harmonic mean. The problem quoted above might have been so phrased that the arithmetic mean would have been the correct value to use, though this phrasing is not that to which we have been accustomed.

If a man drives 10 miles using 0.05 gallon of gasoline per mile

and   "   90   "   " 0.10   "   "   "   "   "

then he   "   100   "   " x "   "   "   "   "

and $100x = (10)(0.05) + (90)(0.10)$

and $x = \dfrac{1}{100}[(10)(0.05) + (90)(0.10)] = \dfrac{9.5}{100} = 0.095$

Therefore if he uses an average of 0.095 gallon per mile, he drives an average of $\dfrac{1}{0.095} = 10.5$ miles per gallon. The average number of gallons per mile is here the (weighted) arithmetic mean of the number of gallons per mile of the separate observations, while the average number of miles per gallon is the (weighted) harmonic mean of the number of miles per gallon of the separate observations.

In order to understand the conditions which determine whether the harmonic mean or the arithmetic mean is to be used, let us suppose we wish to obtain the average rate, r_0, of three rates, r_1, r_2, and r_3, when we have

$$d_1 = r_1 t_1$$
$$d_2 = r_2 t_2$$
$$d_3 = r_3 t_3$$

We must consider (1) the case in which the time varies and distance is constant, (2) the case in which distance varies and time is constant, and (3) the case in which both vary.

(1) Let $d_1 = d_2 = d_3 = d$

and let r_0 = average rate which is to be found.

Here we are holding distance constant, or if the problem were phrased in terms of work rather than distance, we are dealing with a situation in which the same amount of work is performed in different periods of time at different rates. Adding the three equations,

$$3d = r_1 t_1 + r_2 t_2 + r_3 t_3$$

The total time required to travel $3d$ is $t_1 + t_2 + t_3$

Therefore $$3d = r_0(t_1 + t_2 + t_3)$$

Hence $$r_0 = \frac{3d}{t_1 + t_2 + t_3} = \frac{3d}{\dfrac{d}{r_1} + \dfrac{d}{r_2} + \dfrac{d}{r_3}} = \frac{3}{\dfrac{1}{r_1} + \dfrac{1}{r_2} + \dfrac{1}{r_3}}$$

When the amount accomplished (or distance traveled) is constant, and time varies, the average rate is the harmonic mean of the individual rates.

(2) Let $t_1 = t_2 = t_3 = t$

and r_0 = average rate which is to be found.

Then $$d_1 + d_2 + d_3 = r_0(t_1 + t_2 + t_3) = 3r_0 t$$

Hence $$r_0 = \frac{d_1 + d_2 + d_3}{3t} = \frac{r_1 t + r_2 t + r_3 t}{3t} = \frac{r_1 + r_2 + r_3}{3}$$

When the amount accomplished (or distance traveled) is variable and time is constant, the average rate is the arithmetic mean of the individual rates.

(3) *When neither time nor distance is constant, there is no way of expressing an average rate in terms of the observed individual rates.*

The Geometric Mean. When some variable is changing over a period of time at a relatively *constant rate*, the geometric mean may be used to obtain an average of several observations. When a variable is changing by a relatively *constant amount* in successive equal periods of time, the arithmetic mean is used to obtain the average of several observations. A familiar example of the distinction between constant rate of change and constant amount of change is provided by the increase in a given sum of money when invested at compound and at simple interest, as illustrated in the adjacent schedule.

| | Amount at Beginning of Year | |
	Simple Interest	Compound Interest
1st year	$1000	$1000.00
2nd year	1030	1030.00
3rd year	1060	1060.90
4th year	1090	1092.73
5th year	1120	1125.51
6th year	1150	1159.28

Suppose r to represent the rate of interest, n the number of years, and P the principal. Then the amount resulting from allowing simple interest to accumulate is $P(1 + nr)$, and the successive amounts form what is called an *arithmetic progression*. The amount resulting from allowing interest to be compounded annually is $P(1 + r)^n$, and the successive amounts form what is called a *geometric progression*. A treatment of arithmetic and geometric progressions will be found in almost any text in college algebra.

Data suggesting a constant rate of growth and hence requiring the geometric rather than the arithmetic mean are found in many growth studies in psychology and the biological sciences, in many studies dealing with population, school and college enrollments and institutional costs, rate of growth or decline in industry, and the like.

Suppose, for example, that measurements on a plant show its height in inches at the end of 2, 3, 4, etc., weeks to be as shown in the table on page 335. Its weekly increment in height, as shown in the third column, is not constant, but the weekly increment in its logarithm, as shown in the fifth column, is practically constant. The arithmetic mean would be 26.16, and this is obviously not a good estimate of the height of the plant at the middle of the series of observations, that is, at $4\frac{1}{2}$ weeks. The mean of the logarithms is 0.3889, and this is the logarithm of 24.48. A glance at the column of heights suggests that 24.48 is a reasonable

Weekly Change in Height of a Plant

Week	Height in Inches at End of Week	Increment of Height during Week	Log of Height	Increment of Log
2	14.30		0.1553	
3	17.73	3.43	.2487	.0934
4	22.03	4.30	.3430	.0943
5	27.27	5.24	.4357	.0927
6	33.82	6.55	.5292	.0935
7	41.83	8.01	.6215	.0923
Sum	156.98	27.53	2.3334	.4662
Mean	26.16	5.51	0.3889	.09324

estimate for the height of the plant at the middle of the period, that is, at $4\frac{1}{2}$ weeks. The constancy of the increase in the logarithm from week to week indicates a constant rate of increase in height.

Suppose now that we want to make an estimate of the plant's height at the end of the eighth week. We may obtain the mean increment in the logarithm, which is .09324. In $(8 - 4\frac{1}{2}) = 3\frac{1}{2}$ weeks, the logarithm would be expected to increase by $(3\frac{1}{2})$ $(.09324) = .32634$ above its mean value at the $4\frac{1}{2}$ week. The log height at 8 weeks is thus estimated as $0.3889 + (8 - 4\frac{1}{2})$ $(.09324) = 0.7152$, the antilog of which is 51.90, and this is the estimated height in inches.

The graphs on page 336 show these data plotted first on an ordinary grid and second on a semi-logarithmic grid. The first chart shows a curvilinear trend in height and shows that the height of the plant at $4\frac{1}{2}$ weeks was approximately 24.5 ($G = 24.48$ and $\overline{X} = 26.16$). In the second chart, the vertical axis is laid off on a logarithmic scale, and the linear relation which the points now exhibit indicates constancy of increase in the logarithm. Note that the height at $4\frac{1}{2}$ weeks appears to have been about $24\frac{1}{2}$ inches, and that the extrapolated height at 8 weeks is about 52 inches. (Our estimate = 51.9.)

Certain cautions must be observed. If any score is zero, the geometric mean is zero, and hence without meaning. If any scores are negative, the geometric mean has no meaning.

Care must be taken not to extrapolate beyond a point at which constant rate of change may reasonably be assumed. Experience leads one to know that this plant cannot go on growing forever at the same rate, but that soon the rate will begin to decrease and ultimately growth will cease altogether. It may be safe to estimate height for the eighth week on the assumption that the same rate of growth will be maintained, but

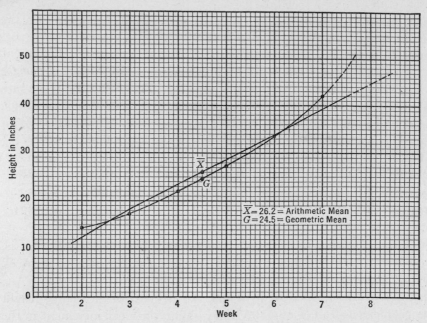

Weekly Observations on Height of Plant, Plotted on Ordinary Grid

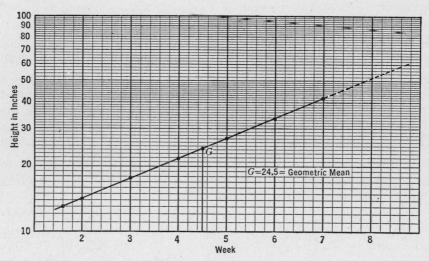

Weekly Observations on Height of Plant, Plotted on Semi-logarithmic Grid

most research workers would not venture to predict very far into the future except as previous studies had established a general growth pattern for the species.

A geometric mean should not be computed over so long a period that the rate of change cannot be assumed to be constant. The constancy of the rate of change may be judged crudely by plotting the data on semi-logarithmic paper and noting how well a straight line fits them, or by setting down their logs and examining the increments in the logs, as in the preceding table. (The procedure for studying the increments is called "differencing." The increments shown in the table are "first differences." When the original measures have a linear trend, their first differences are approximately equal and their "second differences" approximately zero, as for the log heights.)

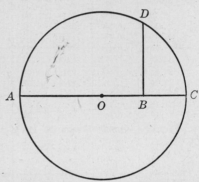

The very ancient term "geometric mean" is probably due to the fact that the Greeks knew how to obtain the geometric mean of any two positive numbers from a geometric diagram. Let the two numbers be represented by the line segments AB and BC. Let a circle be drawn with AC as diameter, and let a perpendicular BD be drawn to AC at B. Then BD is the geometric mean of AB and BC (more commonly called the mean proportional between AB and BC).

$$\frac{AB}{BD} = \frac{BD}{BC} \quad \text{or} \quad \overline{BD}^2 = \overline{AB} \cdot \overline{BC}$$

The correlation coefficient is the geometric mean of the two regression coefficients.

Problems calling for either the geometric mean or the harmonic mean are not often encountered, but when one of these means is needed, no other can be substituted for it. A particularly interesting interpretation exercise showing situations involving one or the other of these means is to be found in Wert's *Educational Statistics* (McGraw-Hill), pp. 76–80.

APPENDIX D

ORDINATES AND AREAS OF THE NORMAL CURVE *
(In terms of σ units)

$\frac{x}{\sigma}$	Area	Ordinate	$\frac{x}{\sigma}$	Area	Ordinate	$\frac{x}{\sigma}$	Area	Ordinate
00	.0000	.3989	.50	.1915	.3521	1.00	.3413	.2420
.01	.0040	.3989	.51	.1950	.3503	1.01	.3438	.2396
.02	.0080	.3989	.52	.1985	.3485	1.02	.3461	.2371
.03	.0120	.3988	.53	.2019	.3467	1.03	.3485	.2347
.04	.0160	.3986	.54	.2054	.3448	1.04	.3508	.2323
.05	.0199	.3984	.55	.2088	.3429	1.05	.3531	.2299
.06	.0239	.3982	.56	.2123	.3410	1.06	.3554	.2275
.07	.0279	.3980	.57	.2157	.3391	1.07	.3577	.2251
.08	.0319	.3977	.58	.2190	.3372	1.08	.3599	.2227
.09	.0359	.3973	.59	.2224	.3352	1.09	.3621	.2203
.10	.0398	.3970	.60	.2257	.3332	1.10	.3643	.2179
.11	.0438	.3965	.61	.2291	.3312	1.11	.3665	.2155
.12	.0478	.3961	.62	.2324	.3292	1.12	.3686	.2131
.13	.0517	.3956	.63	.2357	.3271	1.13	.3708	.2107
.14	.0557	.3951	.64	.2389	.3251	1.14	.3729	.2083
.15	.0596	.3945	.65	.2422	.3230	1.15	.3749	.2059
.16	.0636	.3939	.66	.2454	.3209	1.16	.3770	.2036
.17	.0675	.3932	.67	.2486	.3187	1.17	.3790	.2012
.18	.0714	.3925	.68	.2517	.3166	1.18	.3810	.1989
.19	.0753	.3918	.69	.2549	.3144	1.19	.3830	.1965
.20	.0793	.3910	.70	.2580	.3123	1.20	.3849	.1942
.21	.0832	.3902	.71	.2611	.3101	1.21	.3869	.1919
.22	.0871	.3894	.72	.2642	.3079	1.22	.3888	.1895
.23	.0910	.3885	.73	.2673	.3056	1.23	.3907	.1872
.24	.0948	.3876	.74	.2703	.3034	1.24	.3925	.1849
.25	.0987	.3867	.75	.2734	.3011	1.25	.3944	.1826
.26	.1026	.3857	.76	.2764	.2989	1.26	.3962	.1804
.27	.1064	.3847	.77	.2794	.2966	1.27	.3980	.1781
.28	.1103	.3836	.78	.2823	.2943	1.28	.3997	.1758
.29	.1141	.3825	.79	.2852	.2920	1.29	.4015	.1736
.30	.1179	.3814	.80	.2881	.2897	1.30	.4032	.1714
.31	.1217	.3802	.81	.2910	.2874	1.31	.4049	.1691
.32	.1255	.3790	.82	.2939	.2850	1.32	.4066	.1669
.33	.1293	.3778	.83	.2967	.2827	1.33	.4082	.1647
.34	.1331	.3765	.84	.2995	.2803	1.34	.4099	.1626
.35	.1368	.3752	.85	.3023	.2780	1.35	.4115	.1604
.36	.1406	.3739	.86	.3051	.2756	1.36	.4131	.1582
.37	.1443	.3725	.87	.3078	.2732	1.37	.4147	.1561
.38	.1480	.3712	.88	.3106	.2709	1.38	.4162	.1539
.39	.1517	.3697	.89	.3133	.2685	1.39	.4177	.1518
.40	.1554	.3683	.90	.3159	.2661	1.40	.4192	.1497
.41	.1591	.3668	.91	.3186	.2637	1.41	.4207	.1476
.42	.1628	.3653	.92	.3212	.2613	1.42	.4222	.1456
.43	.1664	.3637	.93	.3238	.2589	1.43	.4236	.1435
.44	.1700	.3621	.94	.3264	.2565	1.44	.4251	.1415
.45	.1736	.3605	.95	.3289	.2541	1.45	.4265	.1394
.46	.1772	.3589	.96	.3315	.2516	1.46	.4279	.1374
.47	.1808	.3572	.97	.3340	.2492	1.47	.4292	.1354
.48	.1844	.3555	.98	.3365	.2468	1.48	.4306	.1334
.49	.1879	.3538	.99	.3389	.2444	1.49	.4319	.1315
.50	.1915	.3521	1.00	.3413	.2420	1.50	.4332	.1295

* This table is reproduced from J. E. Wert, *Educational Statistics*, by courtesy of McGraw Hill Book Co.

ORDINATES AND AREAS OF THE NORMAL CURVE.—(*Concluded*)
(In terms of σ units)

$\frac{x}{\sigma}$	Area	Ordinate	$\frac{x}{\sigma}$	Area	Ordinate	$\frac{x}{\sigma}$	Area	Ordinate
1.50	.4332	.1295	2.00	.4772	.0540	2.50	.4938	.0175
1.51	.4345	.1276	2.01	.4778	.0529	2.51	.4940	.0171
1.52	.4357	.1257	2.02	.4783	.0519	2.52	.4941	.0167
1.53	.4370	.1238	2.03	.4788	.0508	2.53	.4943	.0163
1.54	.4382	.1219	2.04	.4793	.0498	2.54	.4945	.0158
1.55	.4394	.1200	2.05	.4798	.0488	2.55	.4946	.0154
1.56	.4406	.1182	2.06	.4803	.0478	2.56	.4948	.0151
1.57	.4418	.1163	2.07	.4808	.0468	2.57	.4949	.0147
1.58	.4429	.1145	2.08	.4812	.0459	2.58	.4951	.0143
1.59	.4441	.1127	2.09	.4817	.0449	2.59	.4952	.0139
1.60	.4452	.1109	2.10	.4821	.0440	2.60	.4953	.0136
1.61	.4463	.1092	2.11	.4826	.0431	2.61	.4955	.0132
1.62	.4474	.1074	2.12	.4830	.0422	2.62	.4956	.0129
1.63	.4484	.1057	2.13	.4834	.0413	2.63	.4957	.0126
1.64	.4495	.1040	2.14	.4838	.0404	2.64	.4959	.0122
1.65	.4505	.1023	2.15	.4842	.0395	2.65	.4960	.0119
1.66	.4515	.1006	2.16	.4846	.0387	2.66	.4961	.0116
1.67	.4525	.0989	2.17	.4850	.0379	2.67	.4962	.0113
1.68	.4535	.0973	2.18	.4854	.0371	2.68	.4963	.0110
1.69	.4545	.0957	2.19	.4857	.0363	2.69	.4964	.0107
1.70	.4554	.0940	2.20	.4861	.0355	2.70	.4965	.0104
1.71	.4564	.0925	2.21	.4864	.0347	2.71	.4966	.0101
1.72	.4573	.0909	2.22	.4868	.0339	2.72	.4967	.0099
1.73	.4582	.0893	2.23	.4871	.0332	2.73	.4968	.0096
1.74	.4591	.0878	2.24	.4875	.0325	2.74	.4969	.0093
1.75	.4599	.0863	2.25	.4878	.0317	2.75	.4970	.0091
1.76	.4608	.0848	2.26	.4881	.0310	2.76	.4971	.0088
1.77	.4616	.0833	2.27	.4884	.0303	2.77	.4972	.0086
1.78	.4625	.0818	2.28	.4887	.0297	2.78	.4973	.0084
1.79	.4633	.0804	2.29	.4890	.0290	2.79	.4974	.0081
1.80	.4641	.0790	2.30	.4893	.0283	2.80	.4974	.0079
1.81	.4649	.0775	2.31	.4896	.0277	2.81	.4975	.0077
1.82	.4656	.0761	2.32	.4898	.0270	2.82	.4976	.0075
1.83	.4664	.0748	2.33	.4901	.0264	2.83	.4977	.0073
1.84	.4671	.0734	2.34	.4904	.0258	2.84	.4977	.0071
1.85	.4678	.0721	2.35	.4906	.0252	2.85	.4978	.0069
1.86	.4686	.0707	2.36	.4909	.0246	2.86	.4979	.0067
1.87	.4693	.0694	2.37	.4911	.0241	2.87	.4979	.0065
1.88	.4699	.0681	2.38	.4913	.0235	2.88	.4980	.0063
1.89	.4706	.0669	2.39	.4916	.0229	2.89	.4981	.0061
1.90	.4713	.0656	2.40	.4918	.0224	2.90	.4981	.0060
1.91	.4719	.0644	2.41	.4920	.0219	2.91	.4982	.0058
1.92	.4726	.0632	2.42	.4922	.0213	2.92	.4982	.0056
1.93	.4732	.0620	2.43	.4925	.0208	2.93	.4983	.0055
1.94	.4738	.0608	2.44	.4927	.0203	2.94	.4984	.0053
1.95	.4744	.0596	2.45	.4929	.0198	2.95	.4984	.0051
1.96	.4750	.0584	2.46	.4931	.0194	2.96	.4985	.0050
1.97	.4756	.0573	2.47	.4932	.0189	2.97	.4985	.0048
1.98	.4761	.0562	2.48	.4934	.0184	2.98	.4986	.0047
1.99	.4767	.0551	2.49	.4936	.0180	2.99	.4986	.0046
2.00	.4772	.0540	2.50	.4938	.0175	3.00	.4987	.0044

APPENDIX D

FOUR–PLACE SQUARES OF NUMBERS

N	0	1	2	3	4	5	6	7	8	9
1.0	1.000	1.020	1.040	1.061	1.082	1.103	1.124	1.145	1.166	1.188
1.1	1.210	1.232	1.254	1.277	1.300	1.323	1.346	1.369	1.392	1.416
1.2	1.440	1.464	1.488	1.513	1.538	1.563	1.588	1.613	1.638	1.664
1.3	1.690	1.716	1.742	1.769	1.796	1.823	1.850	1.877	1.904	1.932
1.4	1.960	1.988	2.016	2.045	2.074	2.103	2.132	2.161	2.190	2.220
1.5	2.250	2.280	2.310	2.341	2.372	2.403	2.434	2.465	2.496	2.528
1.6	2.560	2.592	2.624	2.657	2.690	2.723	2.756	2.789	2.822	2.856
1.7	2.890	2.924	2.958	2.993	3.028	3.063	3.098	3.133	3.168	3.204
1.8	3.240	3.276	3.312	3.349	3.386	3.423	3.460	3.497	3.534	3.572
1.9	3.610	3.648	3.686	3.725	3.764	3.803	3.842	3.881	3.920	3.960
2.0	4.000	4.040	4.080	4.121	4.162	4.203	4.244	4.285	4.326	4.368
2.1	4.410	4.452	4.494	4.537	4.580	4.623	4.666	4.709	4.752	4.796
2.2	4.840	4.884	4.928	4.973	5.018	5.063	5.108	5.153	5.198	5.244
2.3	5.290	5.336	5.382	5.429	5.476	5.523	5.570	5.617	5.664	5.712
2.4	5.760	5.808	5.856	5.905	5.954	6.003	6.052	6.101	6.150	6.200
2.5	6.250	6.300	6.350	6.401	6.452	6.503	6.554	6.605	6.656	6.708
2.6	6.760	6.812	6.864	6.917	6.970	7.023	7.076	7.129	7.182	7.236
2.7	7.290	7.344	7.398	7.453	7.508	7.563	7.618	7.673	7.728	7.784
2.8	7.840	7.896	7.952	8.009	8.066	8.123	8.180	8.237	8.294	8.352
2.9	8.410	8.468	8.526	8.585	8.644	8.703	8.762	8.821	8.880	8.940
3.0	9.000	9.060	9.120	9.181	9.242	9.303	9.364	9.425	9.486	9.548
3.1	9.610	9.672	9.734	9.797	9.860	9.923	9.986	10.05	10.11	10.18
3.2	10.24	10.30	19.37	10.43	10.50	10.56	10.63	10.69	10.76	10.82
3.3	10.89	10.96	11.02	11.09	11.16	11.22	11.29	11.36	11.42	11.49
3.4	11.56	11.63	11.70	11.76	11.83	11.90	11.97	12.04	12.11	12.18
3.5	12.25	12.32	12.39	12.46	12.53	12.60	12.67	12.74	12.82	12.89
3.6	12.96	13.03	13.10	13.18	13.25	13.32	13.40	13.47	13.54	13.62
3.7	13.69	13.76	13.84	13.91	13.99	14.06	14.14	14.21	14.29	14.36
3.8	14.44	14.52	14.59	14.67	14.75	14.82	14.90	14.98	15.05	15.13
3.9	15.21	15.29	15.37	15.44	15.52	15.60	15.68	15.76	15.84	15.92
4.0	16.00	16.08	16.16	16.24	16.32	16.40	16.48	16.56	16.65	16.73
4.1	16.81	16.89	16.97	17.06	17.14	17.22	17.31	17.39	17.47	17.56
4.2	17.64	17.72	17.81	17.89	17.98	18.06	18.15	18.23	18.32	18.40
4.3	18.49	18.58	18.66	18.75	18.84	18.92	19.01	19.10	19.18	19.27
4.4	19.36	19.45	19.54	19.62	19.71	19.80	19.89	19.98	20.07	20.16
4.5	20.25	20.34	20.43	20.52	20.61	20.70	20.79	20.88	20.98	21.07
4.6	21.16	21.25	21.34	21.44	21.53	21.62	21.72	21.81	21.90	22.00
4.7	22.09	22.18	22.28	22.37	22.47	22.56	22.66	22.75	22.85	22.94
4.8	23.04	23.14	23.23	23.33	23.43	23.52	23.62	23.72	23.81	23.91
4.9	24.01	24.11	24.21	24.30	24.40	24.50	24.60	24.70	24.80	24.90
5.0	25.00	25.10	25.20	25.30	25.40	25.50	25.60	25.70	25.81	25.91
5.1	26.01	26.11	26.21	26.32	26.42	26.52	26.63	26.73	26.83	26.94
5.2	27.04	27.14	27.25	27.35	27.46	27.56	27.67	27.77	27.88	27.98
5.3	28.09	28.20	28 30	28.41	28.52	28.62	28.73	28.84	28.94	29.05
5.4	29.16	29.27	29.38	29.48	29.59	29.70	29.81	29.92	30.03	30.14
N	0	1	2	3	4	5	6	7	8	9

FOUR–PLACE SQUARES OF NUMBERS (*Continued*)

N	0	1	2	3	4	5	6	7	8	9
5.5	30.25	30.36	30.47	30.58	30.69	30.80	30.91	31.02	31.14	31.25
5.6	31.36	31.47	31.58	31.70	31.81	31.92	32.04	32.15	32.26	32.38
5.7	32.49	32.60	32.72	32.83	32.95	33.06	33.18	33.29	33.41	33.52
5.8	33.64	33.76	33.87	33.99	34.11	34.22	34.34	34.46	34.57	34.69
5.9	34.81	34.93	35.05	35.16	35.28	35.40	35.52	35.64	35.76	35.88
6.0	36.00	36.12	36.24	36.36	36.48	36.60	36.72	36.84	36.97	37.09
6.1	37.21	37.33	37.45	37.58	37.70	37.82	37.95	38.07	38.19	38.32
6.2	38.44	38.56	38.69	38.81	38.94	39.06	39.19	39.31	39.44	39.56
6.3	39.69	39.82	39.94	40.07	40.20	40.32	40.45	40.58	40.70	40.83
6.4	40.96	41.09	41.22	41.34	41.47	41.60	41.73	41.86	41.99	42.12
6.5	42.25	42.38	42.51	42.64	42.77	42.90	43.03	43.16	43.30	43.43
6.6	43.56	43.69	43.82	43.96	44.09	44.22	44.36	44.49	44.62	44.76
6.7	44.89	45.02	45.16	45.29	45.43	45.56	45.70	45.83	45.97	46.10
6.8	46.24	46.38	46.51	46.65	46.79	46.92	47.06	47.20	47.33	47.47
6.9	47.61	47.75	47.89	48.02	48.16	48.30	48.44	48.58	48.72	48.86
7.0	49.00	49.14	49.28	49.42	49.56	49.70	49.84	49.98	50.13	50.27
7.1	50.41	50.55	50.69	50.84	50.98	51.12	51.27	51.41	51.55	51.70
7.2	51.84	51.98	52.13	52.27	52.42	52.56	52.71	52.85	53.00	53.14
7.3	53.29	53.44	53.58	53.73	53.88	54.02	54.17	54.32	54.46	54.61
7.4	54.76	54.91	55.06	55.20	55.35	55.50	55.65	55.80	55.95	56.10
7.5	56.25	56.40	56.55	56.70	56.85	57.00	57.15	57.30	57.46	57.61
7.6	57.76	57.91	58.06	58.22	58.37	58.52	58.68	58.83	58.98	59.14
7.7	59.29	59.44	59.60	59.75	59.91	60.06	60.22	60.37	60.53	60.68
7.8	60.84	61.00	61.15	61.31	61.47	61.62	61.78	61.94	62.09	62.25
7.9	62.41	62.57	62.73	62.88	63.04	63.20	63.36	63.52	63.68	63.84
8.0	64.00	64.16	64.32	64.48	64.64	64.80	64.96	65.12	65.29	65.45
8.1	65.61	65.77	65.93	66.10	66.26	66.42	66.59	66.75	66.91	67.08
8.2	67.24	67.40	67.57	67.73	67.90	68.06	68.23	68.39	68.56	68.72
8.3	68.89	69.06	69.22	69.39	69.56	69.72	69.89	70.06	70.22	70.39
8.4	70.56	70.73	70.90	71.06	71.23	71.40	71.57	71.74	71.91	72.08
8.5	72.25	72.42	72.59	72.76	72.93	73.10	73.27	73.44	73.62	73.79
8.6	73.96	74.13	74.30	74.48	74.65	74.82	75.00	75.17	75.34	75.52
8.7	75.69	75.86	76.04	76.21	76.39	76.56	76.74	76.91	77.08	77.26
8.8	77.44	77.62	77.79	77.97	78.15	78.32	78.50	78.68	78.85	79.03
8.9	79.21	79.39	79.57	79.74	79.92	80.10	80.28	80.46	80.64	80.82
9.0	81.00	81.18	81.36	81.54	81.72	81.90	82.08	82.26	82.45	82.63
9.1	82.81	82.99	83.17	83.36	83.54	83.72	83.91	84.09	84.27	84.46
9.2	84.64	84.82	85.01	85.19	85.38	85.56	85.75	85.93	86.12	86.30
9.3	86.49	86.68	86.86	87.05	87.24	87.42	87.61	87.80	87.98	88.17
9.4	88.36	88.55	88.74	88.92	89.11	89.30	89.49	89.68	89.87	90.06
9.5	90.25	90.44	90.63	90.82	91.01	91.20	91.39	91.58	91.78	91.97
9.6	92.16	92.35	92.54	92.74	92.93	93.12	93.32	93.51	93.70	93.90
9.7	94.09	94.28	94.48	94.67	94.87	95.06	95.26	95.45	95.65	95.84
9.8	96.04	96.24	96.43	96.63	96.83	97.02	97.22	97.42	97.61	97.81
9.9	98.01	98.21	98.41	98.60	98.80	99.00	99.20	99.40	99.60	99.80
N	0	1	2	3	4	5	6	7	8	9

POWERS—ROOTS—RECIPROCALS. 1–100

n	n^2	n^3	$\sqrt{n}$	$\sqrt[3]{n}$	$1/n$	n	n^2	n^3	$\sqrt{n}$	$\sqrt[3]{n}$	$1/n$
1	1	1	1.000	1.000	1.0000	51	2,601	132,651	7.141	3.708	.0196
2	4	8	1.414	1.260	.5000	52	2,704	140,608	7.211	3.733	.0192
3	9	27	1.732	1.442	.3333	53	2,809	148,877	7.280	3.756	.0189
4	16	64	2.000	1.587	.2500	54	2,916	157,464	7.348	3.780	.0185
5	25	125	2.236	1.710	.2000	55	3,025	166,375	7.416	3.803	.0182
6	36	216	2.449	1.817	.1667	56	3,136	175,616	7.483	3.826	.0179
7	49	343	2.646	1.913	.1429	57	3,249	185,193	7.550	3.849	.0175
8	64	512	2.828	2.000	.1250	58	3,364	195,112	7.616	3.871	.0172
9	81	729	3.000	2.080	.1111	59	3,481	205,379	7.681	3.893	.0169
10	100	1,000	3.162	2.154	.1000	60	3,600	216,000	7.746	3.915	.0167
11	121	1,331	3.317	2.224	.0909	61	3,721	226,981	7.810	3.936	.0164
12	144	1,728	3.464	2.289	.0833	62	3,844	238,328	7.874	3.958	.0161
13	169	2,197	3.606	2.351	.0769	63	3,969	250,047	7.937	3.979	.0159
14	196	2,744	3.742	2.410	.0714	64	4,096	262,144	8.000	4.000	.0156
15	225	3,375	3.873	2.466	.0667	65	4,225	274,625	8.062	4.021	.0154
16	256	4,096	4.000	2.520	.0625	66	4,356	287,496	8.124	4.041	.0152
17	289	4,913	4.123	2.571	.0588	67	4,489	300,763	8.185	4.062	.0149
18	324	5,832	4.243	2.621	.0556	68	4,624	314,432	8.246	4.082	.0147
19	361	6,859	4.359	2.668	.0526	69	4,761	328,509	8.307	4.102	.0145
20	400	8,000	4.472	2.714	.0500	70	4,900	343,000	8.367	4.121	.0143
21	441	9,261	4.583	2.759	.0476	71	5,041	357,911	8.426	4.141	.0141
22	484	10,648	4.690	2.802	.0455	72	5,184	373,248	8.485	4.160	.0139
23	529	12,167	4.796	2.844	.0435	73	5,329	389,017	8.544	4.179	.0137
24	576	13,824	4.899	2.884	.0417	74	5,476	405,224	8.602	4.198	.0135
25	625	15,625	5.000	2.924	.0400	75	5,625	421,875	8.660	4.217	.0133
26	676	17,576	5.099	2.962	.0385	76	5,776	438,976	8.718	4.236	.0132
27	729	19,683	5.196	3.000	.0370	77	5,929	456,533	8.775	4.254	.0130
28	784	21,952	5.292	3.037	.0357	78	6,084	474,552	8.832	4.273	.0128
29	841	24,389	5.385	3.072	.0345	79	6,241	493,039	8.888	4.291	.0127
30	900	27,000	5.477	3.107	.0333	80	6,400	512,000	8.944	4.309	.0125
31	961	29,791	5.568	3.141	.0323	81	6,561	531,441	9.000	4.327	.0123
32	1,024	32,768	5.657	3.175	.0312	82	6,724	551,368	9.055	4.344	.0122
33	1,089	35,937	5.745	3.208	.0303	83	6,889	571,787	9.110	4.362	.0120
34	1,156	39,304	5.831	3.240	.0294	84	7,056	592,704	9.165	4.380	.0119
35	1,225	42,875	5.916	3.271	.0286	85	7,225	614,125	9.220	4.397	.0118
36	1,296	46,656	6.000	3.302	.0278	86	7,396	636,056	9.274	4.414	.0116
37	1,369	50,653	6.083	3.332	.0270	87	7,569	658,503	9.327	4.431	.0115
38	1,444	54,872	6.164	3.362	.0263	88	7,744	681,472	9.381	4.448	.0114
39	1,521	59,319	6.245	3.391	.0256	89	7,921	704,969	9.434	4.465	.0112
40	1,600	64,000	6.325	3.420	.0250	90	8,100	729,000	9.487	4.481	.0111
41	1,681	68,921	6.403	3.448	.0244	91	8,281	753,571	9.539	4.498	.0110
42	1,764	74,088	6.481	3.476	.0238	92	8,464	778,688	9.592	4.514	.0109
43	1,849	79,507	6.557	3.503	.0233	93	8,649	804,357	9.644	4.531	.0108
44	1,936	85,184	6.633	3.530	.0227	94	8,836	830,584	9.695	4.547	.0106
45	2,025	91,125	6.708	3.557	.0222	95	9,025	857,375	9.747	4.563	.0105
46	2,116	97,336	6.782	3.583	.0217	96	9,216	884,736	9.798	4.579	.0104
47	2,209	103,823	6.856	3.609	.0213	97	9,409	912,673	9.849	4.595	.0103
48	2,304	110,592	6.928	3.634	.0208	98	9,604	941,192	9.899	4.610	.0102
49	2,401	117,649	7.000	3.659	.0204	99	9,801	970,299	9.950	4.626	.0101
50	2,500	125,000	7.071	3.684	.0200	100	10,000	1,000,000	10.000	4.642	.0100

APPENDIX E
LIST OF FORMULAS

Number of formula	Formula	Page

Number of formula	Formula	Page

GLOSSARY OF SYMBOLS

The symbols used in this text and also certain symbols used in other texts are listed below in alphabetical order, the position of the Greek characters being determined by the spelling of their English names. Symbols representing concepts outside the scope of this volume have been listed only when related in some way to symbols used here or when their omission seemed likely to be a source of confusion to the student reading other statistical literature.

Greek Alphabet

Greek		*English*		*Greek*		*English*
A	α	Alpha		N	ν	Nu
B	β	Beta		Ξ	ξ	Xi
Γ	γ	Gamma		O	o	Omicron
Δ	δ	Delta		Π	π	Pi
E	ϵ	Epsilon		P	ρ	Rho
Z	ζ	Zeta		Σ	σ	Sigma
H	η	Eta		T	τ	Tau
Θ	θ	Theta		Υ	υ	Upsilon
I	ι	Iota		Φ	ϕ	Phi
K	κ	Kappa		X	χ	Chi
Λ	λ	Lambda		Ψ	ψ	Psi
M	μ	Mu		Ω	ω	Omega

A — Used here for an arbitrary origin or reference point. There is no standard usage, and various symbols are employed by different writers, as, for example, M', $\overline{X}'$, or M_g (for "guessed mean"). The symbols X_0 and Y_0 are used on the Durost-Walker Correlation Chart for the reference points of the X- and Y-scales.

a — Used here for the amount by which the mean exceeds the arbitrary origin, $a = \overline{X} - A$. There is no standard usage. Some writers use c (for "correction"). Some use c for the correction in interval units and C for the correction in score units.

α_3 — A measure of the skewness in a frequency distribution. Standardized. See formula (37). Cf. β_1.

α_4 — A measure of the kurtosis in a frequency distribution. Standardized. See formula (39). Cf. β_2.

$A.D.$ — The average deviation or mean deviation, sometimes written $M.D.$ Neither concept nor symbol is used in this text.

b_{xy}
b_{yx} — The standard symbol for a regression coefficient, usually written with two subscripts of which the first names the variate predicted and the second names the variate on the basis of which prediction is made. Thus b_{xy}, the regression of coefficient of x on y, is the regression coefficient used in the equation to predict x from y, is the slope of the regression line $\tilde{x} = b_{xy}y$ to the vertical. See formulas (45) to (48), (52), (53), (55), and (57).

$b_{12 \cdot 34}$ — The regression coefficient for predicting X_1 from X_2 in a multiple regression equation in which the dependent variables are X_2, X_3, and X_4. Not considered in this text.

β_1 — A measure of skewness. Standardized. See formula (36). Cf. α_3.

β_2 — A measure of kurtosis. Standardized. See formula (38). Cf. α_4.

β_{xy}
β_{yx}
$\beta_{12 \cdot 34}$ — The standard symbol for a regression coefficient when each variable is expressed as a multiple of its standard deviation, subscripts being used in the same manner as for the regression coefficient b. It is employed more especially in multiple regression equations which are not considered in this text.

C — Used on the Durost-Walker Correlation Chart and in the description of the procedure for computing mean and standard deviation by successive addition in Appendix C to represent the process of cumulation. C_1 represents the first cumulation and C_2 the second. Not standardized.

c — Used in this text as a subscript to indicate statistics obtained from a combined group composed of two or more component groups. An *ad hoc* symbol, not standardized.

c — Used in some texts for the correction to be applied to an arbitrary origin in order to obtain the mean. The letter a is used in this text for this purpose.

χ^2 — Chi-square; a criterion for testing the discrepancy between a set of observed values and the corresponding theoretical values obtained on the basis of some hypothesis as to the population. Outside the scope of this text.

CR — See t.

D	A decile, written with subscript to indicate which decile, as D_1, D_3, etc.
D	A measure of variability equal to the difference between the 10th and the 90th percentiles. $D = P_{90} - P_{10}$.
D or d	The difference between the ranks assigned to the same individual on each of two traits, as in formula (76) for rank order correlation.
d	Used by some writers for the deviation of a score from an arbitrary origin. In this text x' and y' are used for what some other writers denote by d_x and d_y.
d_i	Used in this text for the difference between the mean of a component subgroup and the mean of the combined group of which the subgroup is part, as in formulas (27) and (30). $d_i = \overline{X}_i - \overline{X}_c$.
e	A very important mathematical constant which is the base of the system of natural logarithms, with value approximately 2.7182818. Symbol universal. Used in formulas (43) and (44) for the ordinate of a normal curve.
η	A correlation ratio. There are two correlation ratios which must be distinguished by the order of the subscripts used, η_{xy} being, in general, not equal to η_{yx}. The symbol has been used for many years to designate an observed correlation ratio in a sample, but the modern tendency to use English letters for all sample statistics and Greek letters for the corresponding population parameters is likely to cause a change. Some writers use E for the sample correlation ratio. Neither idea nor symbol is used in this test, though both occur on the Durost-Walker Correlation Chart.
EC	See t.
F	Used on the Durost-Walker Correlation Chart for a frequency. The change from lower case to capital letter was made for typographical reasons.
F	The variance ratio; a criterion used in testing the reliability of the difference between two independent estimates of a population variance. $F = \dfrac{\tilde{\sigma}_1{}^2}{\tilde{\sigma}_2{}^2}$. Neither concept nor symbol is discussed in this text, as they relate to more advanced work.
f	A frequency. Symbol almost universal.
f_x	A frequency in the distribution of the variate X.

f_y	A frequency in the distribution of the variate Y.
f_{xy}	A frequency in the bivariate distribution of X and Y, i.e., the number of cases whose X value lies in a particular interval on the X-scale and whose Y value lies in a particular interval on the Y-scale.
G	The geometric mean, often written $G.M.$
H	The harmonic mean, often written $H.M.$
h	Used in some texts for the width of a step-interval, but not so used here.
i	The width of a step-interval, as in formulas (6), (9), (9a), (13), and (15). While not standardized, the symbol is widely used.
i	Used as a variable subscript to indicate an unspecified individual or unspecified group to which some measure belongs. See the discussion of "Multiple Subscripts" in Chapter VI. Other letters commonly used for the same purpose are j, k, l, and r. Symbolism is widely used. See formulas (87), (89), (90), (93), (96).
I.Q.	Intelligence quotient.
I-shape	The form of frequency curve having a single mode somewhere near the middle of the range. Terminology is standard.
j	Used as a variable subscript, as in formulas (92) and (93). See i above.
J-shape	The form of frequency curve having a single mode at one end of the range.
k	Used here for the number of component subgroups into which a total group is divided. See formulas (28), (29), (30), (91), (92), (93).
k	The coefficient of alienation, $k = \sqrt{1 - r^2}$.
k	Used as a variable subscript in same manner as i and j.
M	Used in some texts as a symbol for the arithmetic mean, but not used here. M_x and M_y are used on the Durost-Walker Correlation Chart.
M'	Used in some texts as a symbol for an arbitrary origin, but not used here.
Md, Med, or Mdn	The median. Not standardized.
Mo	Used by some writers for the mode. There is no standard symbol for mode. Not used here.

$\breve{M}$	Used by some writers for the mode. There is no standard symbol for mode. Not used here.
μ	Used here for the mean of a population from which a sample has been drawn.
$\tilde{\mu}$	Used here for the estimate of the population mean based upon data obtained from a sample. See formulas (91), (92), and (93).
μ	A moment of a frequency distribution taken around the mean of that distribution, always written with a subscript to indicate the power to which deviations have been raised as μ_2, μ_3, etc. See formula (35).
μ'	A moment of a frequency distribution taken around some reference point other than the mean, always written with a subscript to indicate the power to which deviations have been raised as μ_2', μ_3', etc. See formulas (33) and (34).
N	The number of cases under consideration.
P	A percentile, written with subscript to indicate which percentile. Thus P_{12} is the twelfth percentile and P_{06} is the sixth.
$p.e.$ or $P.E.$	The probable error. In a normal distribution $p.e.$ $= 0.6745\sigma$.
π	A mathematical constant (3.1416) which is the ratio of the circumference of a circle to its diameter, occurring in formulas (43) and (44) for the ordinate of a normal curve. Symbol is universal.
Q	The semi-interquartile range. $Q = \frac{1}{2}(Q_U - Q_L)$ $= \frac{1}{2}(Q_3 - Q_1)$. The symbol is in general use.
Q_1	The first or lower quartile, which is the 25th percentile. The same as Q_L.
Q_2	The second quartile, or median.
Q_3	The third or upper quartile, which is the 75th percentile. The same as Q_U.
Q_L	The lower quartile, which is the 25th percentile.
Q_U	The upper quartile, which is the 75th percentile.
R	A widely used symbol for correlation between ranks. See formula (76). Some writers use ρ.
$R_{1\cdot234}$	A coefficient of multiple correlation; the correlation of X_1 with a linear combination of X_2, X_3, and X_4. Outside the scope of this text.
r	The standard symbol for a correlation coefficient, sub-

	scripts being used to name the variables correlated when lack of such subscripts could cause any ambiguity, as r_{xy}, r_{12}, r_{45}, etc.
r	Used in formulas (33), (34), and (35) as a general symbol for some unspecified integer.
$r_{12 \cdot 34}$	A coefficient of partial or net correlation. The correlation between X_1 and X_2 when the influence of X_3 and X_4 is eliminated. Outside the scope of this text.
ρ	The correlation coefficient in a population, as distinct from r, which is the correlation coefficient computed for an observed sample. The symbol is not universal, but its use is growing rapidly.
ρ	Used in some texts for correlation between ranks, but not so used here.
S	Used by many mathematical writers as a symbol for summation, but not so used here. See Σ.
S	Used on the Durost-Walker Correlation Chart to indicate the sum of the figures produced in the second cumulation. The subscripts X, Y, and $Y - X$ refer to the variables which have been cumulated. This is an *ad hoc* usage, not general.
S.D.	Used by some writers for the standard deviation. Not so used here.
S.E.	Used by some writers for the standard error, not so used here.
s	The standard deviation of an observed sample. The symbol σ was introduced for this purpose in 1892 and is still very widely used, but modern mathematical writers tend to apply Greek letters to population values, English letters to sample values. In this text σ is used for the standard deviation of a population, but on the Durost-Walker Correlation Chart it is used for the standard deviation of a sample. The confusion in present practice as to symbolism is well described in a footnote on page 69 of *Statistical Procedures and Their Mathematical Bases*, by Peters and Van Voorhis.
$s_{y \cdot x}$	(also $s_{x \cdot y}$, $s_{1 \cdot 2}$, etc.) The standard error of estimate of y from x; the standard deviation of the residuals in trait y when y is predicted from x. See formula (78). Many writers use $\sigma_{y \cdot x}$, $\sigma_{x \cdot y}$, $\sigma_{1 \cdot 2}$, etc. The pattern of subscripts and use of the dot to separate primary and sec-

ondary subscripts is very widely used. Some writers have used $S.D._{est}$, σ_{est}, and $S.E.$

$s_{y \cdot x}{}^2$ (also $s_{x \cdot y}{}^2$, $s_{1 \cdot 2}{}^2$, etc.) The residual variance in y when predicted from x, the variance of the Y scores around the line of regression $\tilde{y} = b_{yx}x$. See formula (77).

σ Used here and by most writers on mathematical statistics for the standard deviation of a population.

σ Used by some writers for the standard deviation of a sample. This usage is still widespread, but on the decrease. See s.

$\tilde{\sigma}$ The estimate of σ (the standard deviation of the population) based upon knowledge of s, as in formulas (81a) and (82a). The symbol is not widely used, but seems highly appropriate.

σ^2 The variance in a population.

$\tilde{\sigma}^2$ The estimate of σ^2 based upon knowledge of s^2, as in formulas (81) and (82).

$\sigma_{\bar{x}}$ The standard error of a mean, as in formula (80). Many texts use σ_M, some use $S.E._M$ or $S.E._{mean}$ or $S.E.$ of M.

$\tilde{\sigma}_{\bar{x}}$ The estimate of the standard error of a mean based on information obtained from a sample, as in formula (84). Most elementary texts use the same symbol for $\sigma_{\bar{x}}$ and $\tilde{\sigma}_{\bar{x}}$.

σ_s The standard error of a standard deviation. Some texts use σ_σ, and some use $S.E._\sigma$ or $S.E.$ of $S.D.$

$\tilde{\sigma}_s$ The estimate of the standard error of a standard deviation, as in formula (83a). Most elementary texts use the same symbol for σ_s and $\tilde{\sigma}_s$.

$\sigma_{\bar{x}_1 - \bar{x}_2}$ The standard error of a difference between means. Some texts use $\sigma_{M_1 - M_2}$, and some use σ_{dif}, and some $S.E.\ Dif.$, $S.E.D.$ or $S.D.D.$

$\tilde{\sigma}_{\bar{x}_1 - \bar{x}_2}$ The estimate of the standard error of the difference between two means based on information obtained from a sample. Most elementary texts use the same symbol for $\sigma_{\bar{x}_1 - \bar{x}_2}$ and $\tilde{\sigma}_{x_1 - x_2}$.

Sk A measure of skewness as in formulas (31) and (32). No very satisfactory symbol is in use.

Σ The sign of summation; a symbol indicating that certain quantities, represented by a symbol following the Σ, are to be added. Thus ΣX may be read "The sum of all the X's" or "Summation X." The limits of summation may be written above and below the Σ if their omission is likely to cause ambiguity. Thus $X_4 + X_5 + X_6 + X_7$ $+ X_8$ may be written $\sum_{i=4}^{8} X_i$. See pages 85 to 86. This usage is standard among mathematicians, a large capital S being sometimes used in the same way.

T A T-score; the symbol was introduced by McCall and has wide usage. See page 184.

t The ratio of any normally distributed variate to its estimated standard error. Among mathematical statisticians, t is the standard symbol for this purpose, but it is used in few of the more elementary texts, which employ instead a great variety of symbols. The term "critical ratio," invented by McGaughy, was originally applied to a particular value of t, but came later to be used for the variable t in general. Therefore some texts use the symbol $C.R.$ Likewise the term "Experimental Coefficient," invented by McCall, was originally applied to the particular value $t = 2.78$, and came later to be sometimes applied to the variable t in general. Therefore, some texts use the symbol $E.C.$ Some use the term "significance ratio."

U-shape   The form of frequency curve having two modes, one at or near each end of the range. Terminology is standard.

u Used in this text in formula (44) for the ordinate of a unit normal curve. Most texts use z, which has become almost standardized. Because students have already learned to use z as the symbol for x/σ, which is the abscissa of a unit normal curve, the use of the same letter for the ordinate also is too confusing to be recommended.

V The coefficient of variation, as in formula (16). The symbol is in fairly general use.

v Used by some writers for the variance, but not so used here.

X A gross score. (Similarly any other capital letter.)

$\bar{X}$ The mean. (Similarly any other letter with a bar over it indicates the mean of the variate named by that letter.) See formulas (17) and (19).

$\breve{X}$ The mode. See also Mo.

X_0 Used on the Durost-Walker Correlation Chart to represent the score corresponding to the arbitrary origin.

$\tilde{X}$ An estimate of X obtained from a regression equation based on some related variable.

x The deviation of a score from the mean of its distribution. $x = X - \overline{X}$. (Similarly for other letters.)

x' The deviation of a score from some reference point other than the mean of its distribution, no matter whether that deviation is expressed in original score units or in interval units, as a code. $x' = X - A$. (Similarly for other letters.)

$\tilde{x}$ An estimate of x obtained from a regression equation based on some related variable. (Similarly for other letters.)

Z Score transformed by the formula $Z = \dfrac{10(X - \overline{X})}{s} + 50$.

z A deviation from the mean of a distribution expressed as a multiple of the standard deviation. $z = \dfrac{x}{s} = \dfrac{X - \overline{X}}{s}$. Symbol is widely used.

z A function related to r and used as a transformation for r in testing the reliability of a correlation coefficient and of the difference between two correlation coefficients. See footnote on page 187. Symbol is standard among mathematical statisticians, but seldom used in elementary tests. Outside the scope of this text.

z Used by many writers for the ordinate of a unit normal curve. The symbol u has been used for this purpose in this text.

z A criterion for testing the significance of the difference between two independent variances, used in work in statistical inference, "Fisher's z." $z = \frac{1}{2} \log \dfrac{\tilde{\sigma}_1{}^2}{\tilde{\sigma}_2{}^2}$.

$z = \frac{1}{2} \log F$. $e^{2z} = F$. Symbol is standard among mathematical statisticians, but is not used in this text because the idea it represents is outside the scope of a beginning text. It is mentioned here only for purposes of record, and to distinguish the other uses of z from it.

∞ Infinity.

$|x|$ The absolute or numerical value of x. Similarly for any other letter or number.

$x^{\frac{1}{2}}$ or $\sqrt{x}$ The positive square root of x. $\sqrt{4} = 2$, not -2.

$-x^{\frac{1}{2}}$ or $-\sqrt{x}$ The negative square root of x. $-\sqrt{4} = -2$.

$\{\}, [], ()$ Symbols of aggregation, indicating that all the terms inclosed therein are to be treated as a unit. The bar of a fraction or the bar over the radicand in a root serves the same purpose.

INDEX

(*q* indicates a quotation; *n*, a note; *r*, a reference)

361